The Magical Bag of Mathematical Tricks

Leaving Cert. Higher Level Maths, Paper 1

Tony Kelly & Kieran Mills

Published by Kieran Mills

Published by Kieran Mills
Box 7433,
Dublin 16,
Ireland.
www.studentxpress.ie

0 9546 7390 5

Printed by Kilkenny People

Front Page Illustration of the magician by Becky Galligan & Conor Barry

Cover Design by Artworks Graphic Design

Typeset and Illustrations by Kieran Mills

Proofed by Patricia Saville & Christine McCartney

Contents

About this Book

This book covers Paper 1 of the Higher Level Leaving Certificate (LC) Maths Course. It can be used as a text book in school both in fifth year and sixth year or as a self-study aid at home. It can also be used as a revision book as it has numerous worked examples and hints to help you with the exam. Good luck with your revision and have fun.

LC Higher Level, Paper 1

Paper I has 8 questions. You must attempt 6 questions.

Questions 1 & 2: **Algebra**

Covered in the Algebra Section, page 1

Question 3: **Complex Numbers and Matrices**

Covered in Complex Numbers (page 91) and Matrices (page 141)

Questions 4 & 5: **Sequences, Series, Algebra and Proof by Induction**

Covered in Sequences (page 175), Series (page 217), Algebra (page 1) and Proofs (page 419)

Questions 6 & 7: **Differentiation and its Applications**

Covered in Differentiation (page 255) and Applications of Differentiation (page 309)

Question 8: **Integration**

Covered in Integration (page 353)

Each section is full of examples showing you how to solve problems. **Tricks** and **steps** for solving problems are included to simplify the process. There are loads of **exercises** for you to practice what you have learned. The answers to the exercises are provided at the end of each section. If you experience difficulties with these exercises go online to our website where experienced teachers at the **Maths Forum** are standing by to answer your queries and help you with your problems.

There are **Revision Questions** at the end of each section. These are 3 part questions similar to LC questions. The answers and hints on how to solve these questions are on the website.

www.studentxpress.ie

Algebra

1. ALGEBRAIC EXPRESSIONS

1.1 POLYNOMIAL OPERATIONS

Polynomials are expressions with many terms.
There are 3 types on the LC course.

1. **Linear (L)**: $3x - 7$
2. **Quadratic (Q)**: $-2x^2 + 7x - 3$
3. **Cubic (C)**: $x^3 - 2x^2 - 7x + 1$

[A] **Addition, Subtraction, Multiplication by scalar (constant)**
Trick: Multiply out the terms in a bracket by a scalar and then combine like terms.

Example 1: Simplify $3x^2 + 2x - 7(x^3 + 5x^2 - 4x + 1)$

SOLUTION

$3x^2 + 2x - 7(x^3 + 5x^2 - 4x + 1)$
$= 3x^2 + 2x - 7x^3 - 35x^2 + 28x - 7$
$= -7x^3 - 32x^2 + 30x - 7$

[B] **Multiplication of brackets**

Example 2: Simplify $(2x - 1)(4x^2 + 3x - 2)$

SOLUTION

$(2x - 1)(4x^2 + 3x - 2)$
$= 8x^3 + 6x^2 - 4x - 4x^2 - 3x + 2$
$= 8x^3 + 2x^2 - 7x + 2$

TRICK
Multiply each term in one bracket by each term in the other and then combine like terms.

Linear (L) × Linear (L) = Quadratic (Q)
Linear (L) × Quadratic (Q) = Cubic (C)
Linear (L) × Linear (L) × Linear (L) = Cubic (C)

When you multiply
Linear × Linear
F × F = F (F = First)
La × La = La (La = Last)

TRICK

When you multiply
Linear × Quadratic
F × F = F (F = First)
La × La = La (La = Last)

TRICK

When you multiply
Linear × Linear × Linear
F × F × F = F
La × La × La = La

Example: Simplify $(2x - 3)(4x + 1)$

SOLUTION

$(2x - 3)(4x + 1) = 8x^2 + \text{Stuff in } x - 3$

La × La = La

F × F = F

Example: Simplify $(2x - 3)(x^2 - 6x - 1)$

SOLUTION

$(2x - 3)(x^2 - 6x - 1) = 2x^3 + \text{Stuff in } x^2 + \text{Stuff in } x + 3$

La × La = La

F × F = F

Example: Simplify $(x - 1)(2x + 1)(x - 3)$

SOLUTION

$(x - 1)(2x + 1)(x - 3) = 2x^3 + \text{Stuff in } x^2 + \text{Stuff in } x + 3$

La × La × La = La

F × F × F = F

These tricks are very useful in factorisation.

[C] **Division**: The long division process

Example:

$$\begin{array}{r} 2 \\ 3\overline{)7} \\ \underline{6} \\ 1 \end{array}$$

$\Rightarrow \frac{7}{3} = 2R1 = 2 + \frac{1}{3} = 2\frac{1}{3}$

$\therefore \frac{7}{3} = 2\frac{1}{3}$

Trick: In general

$$\begin{array}{rl} Q & \text{— Quotient} \\ \text{Divisor — } D\overline{)P} & \text{— Polynomial} \\ \vdots & \\ \overline{R} & \text{— Remainder} \end{array}$$

TRICK

1. When you divide a **C** by an **L** the quotient is a quadratic.
2. When you divide a **C** by a **Q** the quotient is a linear.

$$\Rightarrow \frac{P}{D} = Q + \frac{R}{D}$$

$$\therefore P = QD + R$$

Example 3: Divide $2x^3 - 3x^2 + 5x - 7$ by $x - 7$

SOLUTION

$$\begin{array}{r} 2x^2 + 11x + 82 \\ x-7\overline{)\,2x^3 - 3x^2 + 5x - 7} \\ \underline{\mp 2x^3 \pm 14x^2} \\ 11x^2 + 5x - 7 \\ \underline{\mp 11x^2 \pm 77x} \\ 82x - 7 \\ \underline{\mp 82x \pm 574} \\ 567 \end{array}$$

$$\therefore \frac{2x^3 - 3x^2 + 5x - 7}{x - 7} = 2x^2 + 11x + 82 + \frac{567}{x - 7}$$

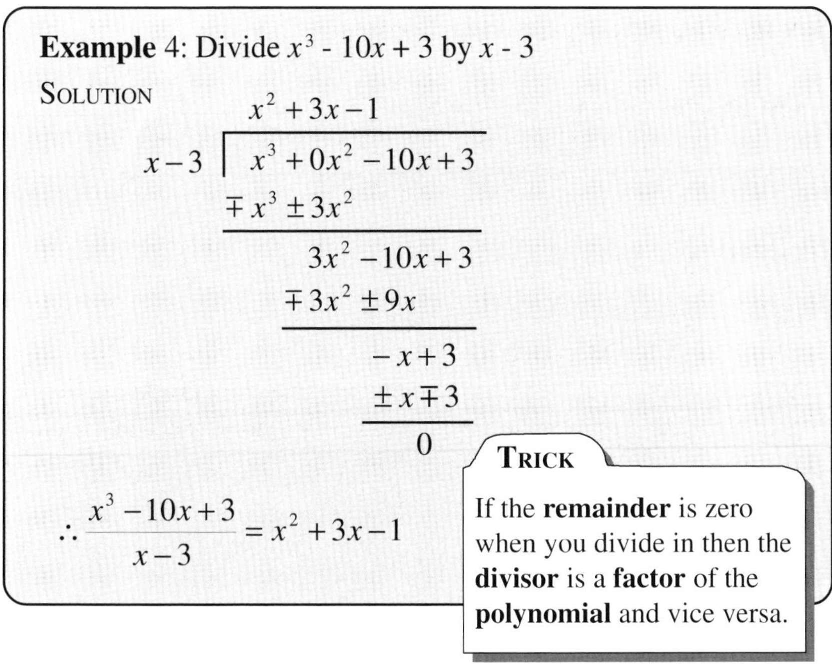

Example 4: Divide $x^3 - 10x + 3$ by $x - 3$

SOLUTION

$$
\begin{array}{r|l}
 & x^2 + 3x - 1 \\
\hline
x - 3 & x^3 + 0x^2 - 10x + 3 \\
 & \mp x^3 \pm 3x^2 \\
\hline
 & \quad 3x^2 - 10x + 3 \\
 & \quad \mp 3x^2 \pm 9x \\
\hline
 & \qquad -x + 3 \\
 & \qquad \pm x \mp 3 \\
\hline
 & \qquad\quad 0
\end{array}
$$

$$\therefore \frac{x^3 - 10x + 3}{x - 3} = x^2 + 3x - 1$$

TRICK

If the **remainder** is zero when you divide in then the **divisor** is a **factor** of the **polynomial** and vice versa.

[D] **Factors**: This is one of the most important algebraic techniques as it is essential for solving equations.

STEPS

1. Take out the highest common factor (HCF).
2. Look at what's left and apply one of the following methods:

- Grouping
- DOTS (Difference of 2 squares)
- SOTC (Sum of 2 cubes)
- DOTC (Difference of 2 cubes)
- Trinomial (Q = L × L)
- PS (Perfect square)
- No factors

NOTES: (F = First; S = Second)

1. **DOTS**: $F^2 - S^2 = (F - S)(F + S)$

2. **SOTC**: $F^3 + S^3 = (F + S)(F^2 - FS + S^2)$

3. **DOTC**: $F^3 - S^3 = (F - S)(F^2 + FS + S^2)$

4. **PS**: $F^2 \pm 2FS + S^2 = (F \pm S)^2$

Example 5: Factorise the following

1. $18y^3 - 8y$

SOLUTION

$18y^3 - 8y = 2y(9y^2 - 4) = 2y(3y - 2)(3y + 2)$

2. $3y^3 - y^2 - 2y$

SOLUTION

$3y^3 - y^2 - 2y = y(3y^2 - y - 2) = y(3y + 2)(y - 1)$

3. $x^2 - 6x + 9 - z^2$

SOLUTION

$x^2 - 6x + 9 - z^2 = (x^2 - 6x + 9) - z^2 = (x - 3)^2 - z^2$
$= (x - 3 - z)(x - 3 + z)$

4. $x^4 + xy^3 - x^3y - y^4$

SOLUTION

$x^4 + xy^3 - x^3y - y^4 = x^3(x - y) + y^3(x - y) = (x - y)(x^3 + y^3)$
$= (x - y)(x + y)(x^2 - xy + y^2)$

Factors are identities. This means 2 things:
1. They are true for all values of the variable. So you can plonk in any value(s) you like.
2. When you multiply out factors every term must line up with every term in the original expression.

Example 6: If $x - 3$ is a factor of $6x^3 - 17x^2 + kx + 6$ find k and the other factors.

SOLUTION
$6x^3 - 17x^2 + kx + 6 = (x - 3)(6x^2 + ax - 2)$
[F × F = F and La × La = La]
Multiply out:
$6x^3 - 17x^2 + kx + 6 = 6x^3 + x^2(-18 + a) + x(-3a - 2) + 6$
Lining up x^2: $a - 18 = -17 \therefore a = 1$
Lining up x: $-3a - 2 = k \Rightarrow k = -5$
$\therefore 6x^3 - 17x^2 + kx + 6 = (x - 3)(6x^2 + x - 2)$
$= (x - 3)(3x + 2)(2x - 1)$

Note: There is a quicker way to do this later (Factor Theorem)

Exercise 1 (Answers: page **81**)
Polynomial Operations

1. Simplify
(a) $(x - 3)^2$
(b) $(2x + 7)^2$
(c) $(x - 1)(x + 2)(x + 1)$
(d) $(4x - 1)(3x - 5)$
(e) $(5x - 2)(5x + 2)$

2. Division
(a) $2x^3 - 5x + 3 \div x - 1$
(b) $5x^2 - 16x + 3 \div 5x - 1$
(c) $x^3 + 2x^2 + 2x + 15 \div x^2 - x + 5$
(d) $4x^3 - 7x^2 - 6x + 9 \div x - 1$
(e) $8x^3 - 1 \div 2x - 1$
(f) $2x^3 - 5x^2 \div x + 5$

3. Factors
Factorise completely
(a) $27x^2 + y^3x^5$
(b) $8x^2 - 14x + 3$
(c) $x^4 - y^4$
(d) $x^6 - y^6$
(e) $x^3 - 2 + x - 2x^2$
(f) $9x^2 - 6xy + y^2$
(g) $ax^3 - a$
(h) $40x^2 + 52x + 12$
(i) $x^4 + 2x^2 + 1$
(j) $a^2 - 2ab + b^2 - a + b$

1.2 FRACTIONAL EXPRESSIONS

[A] OPERATIONS

1. **Addition and Subtraction**: These are the most difficult operations in fractions.

TRICK
You must use a common denominator. **Look out for the lowest common denominator (LCD).**

Example 7: Simplify $\frac{3}{x-5}+\frac{2}{5-x}$

SOLUTION

$$\frac{3}{x-5}+\frac{2}{5-x}=\frac{3}{x-5}-\frac{2}{x-5}=\frac{3-2}{x-5}=\frac{1}{x-5}$$

Example 8: Simplify $\frac{4}{x^2-1}-\frac{7}{2x^2-3x-5}$

SOLUTION

$$\frac{4}{x^2-1}-\frac{7}{2x^2-3x-5}=\frac{4}{(x-1)(x+1)}-\frac{7}{(2x-5)(x+1)}$$

$$=\frac{4(2x-5)-7(x-1)}{(2x-5)(x+1)(x-1)}=\frac{x-13}{(2x-5)(x+1)(x-1)}$$

2. **Multiplication**: Multiply tops and multiply bottoms and/or cancel.

Example 9: Simplify $\frac{(a+b)^2}{(a+b)}\times\frac{b-a}{b^2-a^2}$

SOLUTION

$$\frac{(a+b)^2}{(a+b)}\times\frac{b-a}{b^2-a^2}=\frac{(a+b)\times(b-a)}{(b-a)\times(b+a)}=1$$

TRICK

Never cancel bits of a sum. $\frac{\not{a}+b}{\not{a}}$ is illegal but $\frac{\not{a}b}{\not{a}}=b$ is OK.

3. **Division**: Invert divisor fraction and multiply.

Example 10: Simplify $\frac{xy}{x^2-y^2} \div \frac{x^2y^3}{x+y}$

SOLUTION

$$\frac{xy}{x^2-y^2} \div \frac{x^2y^3}{x+y} = \frac{xy}{x^2-y^2} \times \frac{x+y}{x^2y^3}$$

$$= \frac{xy}{(x-y)(x+y)} \times \frac{(x+y)}{x^2y^3} = \frac{1}{(x-y)xy^2}$$

[B] **Double Decker Fractions**: These are fractional expressions divided by fractional expressions. To handle them you need a trick.

TRICK

A fraction does not change value if you multiply top and bottom by the same number.

Example: $\frac{1}{2} = \frac{1}{2} \times \frac{3}{3} = \frac{3}{6}$

TRICK

To simplify a double decker fraction multiply above and below by the LCD of all fractions.

Example 11: Simplify $\frac{\frac{1}{2}+\frac{4}{3}}{\frac{2}{5}-\frac{1}{4}}$

SOLUTION

$$\frac{\frac{1}{2}+\frac{4}{3}}{\frac{2}{5}-\frac{1}{4}} \cdot \frac{60}{60} = \frac{30+80}{24-15} = \frac{110}{9}$$

Example 12: Simplify $\dfrac{\frac{1}{x}+\frac{1}{y}}{\frac{1}{y^2}-\frac{1}{x^2}}$

SOLUTION

$$\frac{\frac{1}{x}+\frac{1}{y}}{\frac{1}{y^2}-\frac{1}{x^2}}\cdot\frac{x^2y^2}{x^2y^2}=\frac{xy^2+x^2y}{x^2-y^2}=\frac{xy(y+x)}{(x-y)(x+y)}=\frac{xy}{x-y}$$

Exercise 2 (Answers: page **81**)

Fractional Expressions

1. Simplify

(a) $\dfrac{y}{x}-\dfrac{(x+y)^2}{xy}+\dfrac{x}{y}$

(b) $\dfrac{a^2-b^2}{ab+a^2}\times\dfrac{ab}{a-b}$

(c) $\dfrac{4}{p-2}+\dfrac{2p}{2-p}$

(d) $\dfrac{\alpha}{\beta}-\dfrac{\beta}{\alpha}$

(e) $\dfrac{x}{2}-\dfrac{1}{x}$

(f) $\dfrac{1}{x}+\dfrac{1}{y}+\dfrac{1}{z}$

(g) $\dfrac{x^2}{x^2+2x+1}+\dfrac{x-1}{3x+3}-\dfrac{1}{6}$

(h) $\dfrac{x}{x-1}-\dfrac{x}{x-2}$

(i) $\left(\dfrac{x^3-y^3}{y^3}\times\dfrac{y}{x-y}\right)\div\dfrac{x^2+xy+y^2}{y^2}$

(j) $\left(\dfrac{x}{x^2-16}-\dfrac{1}{x+4}\right)\div\dfrac{4}{x+4}$

(k) $\dfrac{1}{x+3}+\dfrac{9x}{x^3+27}$

(l) $\dfrac{x^4-16}{x^2-x-6}\div\dfrac{2x^2-5x+2}{2x^2-7x+3}$

2. Simplify

(a) $\dfrac{\frac{1}{a+h}-\frac{1}{a}}{h}$

(b) $\dfrac{at-at^2}{\frac{a}{t}-\frac{a}{t^2}}$

(c) $\dfrac{a-b}{\frac{1}{a}-\frac{1}{b}}$

(d) $\dfrac{\dfrac{(a+b)^2}{a+b+2} - \dfrac{a^2}{a+2}}{b}$

(e) $\dfrac{3+\frac{2}{x}-\frac{5}{x^2}}{1+\frac{2}{x}-\frac{3}{x^2}}$

(f) $\dfrac{\frac{5}{x}-\frac{12}{xy}+\frac{4}{xy^2}}{\frac{2}{x}-\frac{8}{xy^2}}$

1.3 EXPONENTIAL (POWER) EXPRESSIONS

Operations

POWER RULES

1. $a^m.a^n = a^{m+n}$
2. $\dfrac{a^m}{a^n} = a^{m-n}$
3. $a^0 = 1$ [**Trick**: (Anything)^0 = 1]
4. $a^{-n} = \dfrac{1}{a^n}$

[**Trick**: This is how to deal with negative powers.]

5. $(a^m)^n = a^{mn}$
6. $(a^m b^n)^p = a^{mp} b^{np}$
7. $\left(\dfrac{a^m}{b^n}\right)^p = \dfrac{a^{mp}}{b^{np}}$
8. $\left(\dfrac{a^m}{b^n}\right)^{-p} = \left(\dfrac{b^n}{a^m}\right)^p$ [Flipping]

Don'ts: Never say $(a \pm b)^n = a^n \pm b^n$

Dos: $(ab)^n = a^n b^n$ and $\left(\frac{a}{b}\right)^n = \frac{a^n}{b^n}$

Danger!: Never move bits (terms) of an expression up or down.

$\frac{3}{(a+b)^{-1}} = 3(a+b)$ is OK

but $\frac{3}{a+b^{-1}} = \frac{3b}{a}$ is not OK

TRICK

You can get rid of negative powers in 2 ways:
1. Moving an expression up or down
2. Multiplying above and below by the opposite positive power.

Example 13: $\frac{x^{-1}}{2} = \frac{1}{2x}$

Example 14: $\frac{2}{x^{-2}y^{-3}} = 2x^2y^3$

Example 15: $\frac{3u^{-1}}{v^{-2}} = \frac{3v^2}{u}$

Example 16: $\frac{(a+b)^{-2}}{(3a-2b)^{-4}} = \frac{(3a-2b)^4}{(a+b)^2}$

Example 17:

$$\frac{(x+1)^{-2}+2}{(x+1)^2} = \frac{\left\{(x+1)^{-2}+2\right\}}{(x+1)^2}.\frac{(x+1)^2}{(x+1)^2} = \frac{1+2(x+1)^2}{(x+1)^4}$$

$$= \frac{1+2x^2+4x+2}{(x+1)^4} = \frac{2x^2+4x+3}{(x+1)^4}$$

Trick: Don't multiply out brackets on the bottom unless they are simple. Leave them as factors.

$$\frac{(x-3)}{(x-1)(x-2)} \text{ is fine but } \frac{x-1}{(\sqrt{x}-1)(\sqrt{x}+1)} = \frac{x-1}{x-1} = 1$$

Example 18: $\dfrac{x^{-1}+x}{3} = \dfrac{(x^{-1}+x)}{3} \cdot \dfrac{x}{x} = \dfrac{1+x^2}{3x}$

Example 19: $\sqrt{\dfrac{e^{-2x}(e^{x+1})^2}{(e^{x-2})^{\frac{1}{2}}}} = \left[\dfrac{e^{2x+2}}{e^{2x}e^{\frac{1}{2}x-1}}\right]^{\frac{1}{2}} = \left[\dfrac{e^{2x+2}}{e^{\frac{5}{2}x-1}}\right]^{\frac{1}{2}}$

$= (e^{-\frac{1}{2}x+3})^{\frac{1}{2}} = e^{-\frac{1}{4}x+\frac{3}{2}}$

Example 20: $\left(\dfrac{x^2+1}{x^2-1}\right)^{-\frac{1}{2}} = \left(\dfrac{x^2-1}{x^2+1}\right)^{\frac{1}{2}}$ Flip

Example 21: $\dfrac{u^{-1}+v^{-2}}{u^{-2}v^{-1}} = (u^{-1}+v^{-2})u^2v^1 = uv+u^2v^{-1}$

$= \dfrac{uv+u^2v^{-1}}{1} \cdot \dfrac{v}{v} = \dfrac{uv^2+u^2}{v} = \dfrac{u(v^2+u)}{v}$

OR

$\dfrac{u^{-1}+v^{-2}}{u^{-2}v^{-1}} = \dfrac{u^{-1}+v^{-2}}{u^{-2}v^{-1}} \cdot \dfrac{u^2v^2}{u^2v^2}$

$= \dfrac{uv^2+u^2}{v} = \dfrac{u(v^2+u)}{v}$

Exercise 3 (Answers: page **82**)
Exponents

1. Simplify giving your answer with positive exponents only:

(a) $\dfrac{32n^5m^{-8}}{16n^2m^{-3}}$

(b) $\dfrac{u+v}{u^{-1}+v^{-1}}$

(c) $(a^2+b^2)^{-1}$

(d) $\dfrac{x^{-1}-x^{-2}}{x^2+1}$

(e) $\left(\dfrac{u^3v^2w^{-1}}{uv^{-3}w^{-2}}\right)^{-3}$

(f) $\dfrac{xy^{-2}-x^{-2}y^1}{x^3}$

(g) $\left(\dfrac{a^{-1}}{b^{-1}+a^{-1}}\right)^{-2}$

(h) $\dfrac{15(a-2b)^{-2}}{3(2b-a)^{-3}}$

(i) $\dfrac{x^{-2}-y^{-3}}{x^{-2}+y^{-3}}$

2. Simplify giving your answer with positive exponents only:

(a) $(x^{-\frac{3}{2}})^6$

(b) $\dfrac{x^{\frac{1}{2}}.x^{-\frac{1}{3}}}{x^{-2}}$

(c) $\dfrac{(x^{\frac{1}{2}})^3}{(x^{-2})^{\frac{2}{3}}}$

(d) $\left(\dfrac{x^3y^{-2}z^{\frac{1}{2}}}{x^{\frac{1}{2}}y^2z^{\frac{1}{4}}}\right)^3$

(e) $\left(\dfrac{16x^{-2}}{y^4}\right)^{-\frac{1}{2}}$

(f) $\left(\dfrac{3^x}{y^4}\right)^2$

(g) $\left(\dfrac{2^x}{3^{x^2}}\right)^{\frac{1}{2}}$

(h) $\left(\dfrac{e^{x^2}}{e^{3x^2}}\right)^{\frac{1}{3}}$

(i) $\left(\dfrac{e^x e^{3x}}{e^{5x}}\right)^{-2}$

(j) $\left(\dfrac{x^{-\frac{1}{3}}x^{\frac{1}{2}}}{x^{\frac{2}{3}}y^{-\frac{1}{2}}}\right)^2$

1.4 SURDS (IRRATIONALS)

[A] Properties of surds

1. $\sqrt{ab}=\sqrt{a}.\sqrt{b}$

2. $\sqrt{\dfrac{a}{b}}=\dfrac{\sqrt{a}}{\sqrt{b}}$

Don't ever say $\sqrt{a+b}=\sqrt{a}+\sqrt{b}$

[B] **Operations**

1. **Addition and Subtraction**: You can only add and subtract like terms.

Example 22: $\sqrt{3}+2\sqrt{3}=3\sqrt{3}$

2. **Factoring out of surds**: Hit the factor with the root as it comes out.

Example 23: $\sqrt{4-x}=\sqrt{4(1-\frac{x}{4})}=2\sqrt{1-\frac{x}{4}}$

Example 24: $\sqrt{28}=\sqrt{4\times 7}=2\sqrt{7}$

3. **Multiplying into surds**: The number is squared as it goes in.

Example 25: $2\sqrt{7}=\sqrt{4\times 7}=\sqrt{28}$

Example 26: $x\sqrt{1-\frac{4}{x}}=\sqrt{x^2(1-\frac{4}{x})}=\sqrt{x^2-4x}$

4. **Multiplication**: Multiply term by term.

Example 27:
$(\sqrt{2}+\sqrt{3})(\sqrt{2}+3\sqrt{3})=2+\sqrt{6}+3\sqrt{6}+9=11+4\sqrt{6}$

5. **Rationalising numerator or denominator**

This means getting rid of surds in the numerator or denominator.

(a) **Numerator**: Multiply above and below by the **conjugate** of the top. To get the conjugate, just change the sign between the number and the surd (or between a surd and a surd).

Example 28: $\dfrac{3-\sqrt{2}}{4}=\dfrac{3-\sqrt{2}}{4}\cdot\dfrac{3+\sqrt{2}}{3+\sqrt{2}}=\dfrac{7}{4(3+\sqrt{2})}$

Example 29:

$$\sqrt{a+h}-\sqrt{a}=\frac{\sqrt{a+h}-\sqrt{a}}{1}\cdot\frac{\sqrt{a+h}+\sqrt{a}}{\sqrt{a+h}+\sqrt{a}}=\frac{h}{\sqrt{a+h}+\sqrt{a}}$$

Note: You will need this in Differentiation from first principles.

(b) **Denominator**: Multiply above and below by the conjugate of the bottom.

Example 30: $\frac{2}{\sqrt{3}-1}=\frac{2}{\sqrt{3}-1}\cdot\frac{\sqrt{3}+1}{\sqrt{3}+1}=\frac{2(\sqrt{3}+1)}{2}=\sqrt{3}+1$

Note: You will need this in trigonometry a lot.

Exercise 4 (Answers: page **82**)
Surd Expressions

1. Simplify (rationalising the denominator if necessary):

(a) $(\sqrt{2})^3$

(b) $\sqrt{2^6}$

(c) $\sqrt{2}\sqrt{3}\sqrt{4}$

(d) $\frac{\sqrt{2}}{\sqrt{6}}$

(e) $\sqrt{5}+\sqrt{45}+\sqrt{80}$

(f) $\frac{\sqrt{32}}{\sqrt{2}}$

(g) $(\sqrt{2}-\sqrt{3})^2$

(h) $(\sqrt{2}-\sqrt{3})(\sqrt{2}+\sqrt{3})$

(i) $\frac{2-\sqrt{2}}{1-\sqrt{2}}$

(j) $\sqrt{3}+\sqrt{27}+\sqrt{12}$

2. Rationalise the denominator:

(a) $\frac{3}{\sqrt{7}}$

(b) $\dfrac{2\sqrt{5}}{\sqrt{17}}$

(c) $\dfrac{3\sqrt{10}}{\sqrt{19}}$

(d) $\dfrac{4\sqrt{c}}{\sqrt{d}}$

(e) $\dfrac{2}{1-\sqrt{2}}$

(f) $\dfrac{2+\sqrt{3}}{\sqrt{3}-7}$

(g) $\dfrac{3}{4\sqrt{3}-\sqrt{2}}$

(h) $\dfrac{2+\sqrt{5}}{4-3\sqrt{2}}$

(i) $\dfrac{c-\sqrt{d}}{c+\sqrt{d}}$

(j) $\dfrac{y^2}{\sqrt{y^2+9}-3}$

(k) $\dfrac{5\sqrt{x}}{3-2\sqrt{x}}$

3. Rationalise the numerator:

(a) $\dfrac{\sqrt{a}-\sqrt{b}}{a-b}$

(b) $\dfrac{\sqrt{x}-\sqrt{y}}{\sqrt{x}+\sqrt{y}}$

(c) $\dfrac{\sqrt{3+x}+\sqrt{3}}{x}$

1.5 LOGS

[A] **Definition**: $\log_a x$ is the power to which you put a in order to get x.

$$\log_2 16 = 4 \text{ because } 16 = 2^4$$

Trick: Get out of logs by hooshing, i.e. hoosh a under the y and rub out the log.

$$\log_a x = y \Leftrightarrow x = a^y$$

Log Statement — *Hooshing* — Power Statement

You must be able to get out of logs to evaluate tough logs and to solve log equations.

Example 31: Evaluate $\log_4 8$.

SOLUTION

$\log_4 8 = x \Rightarrow 8 = 4^x \Rightarrow 2^3 = 2^{2x}$

$\therefore 3 = 2x \Rightarrow x = \frac{3}{2}$

Example 32: Evaluate $\log_{\frac{1}{3}} 9$

SOLUTION

$\log_{\frac{1}{3}} 9 = x \Rightarrow 9 = (\frac{1}{3})^x \Rightarrow 3^2 = 3^{-x}$

$\therefore x = -2$

[B] **Properties of logs**: These enable us to manipulate logs.

LOG RULES

1. $\log_a M + \log_a N = \log_a (MN)$

Example: $\log_2 16 + \log_2 4 = \log_2 64 \Leftrightarrow 4 + 2 = 6$

2. $\log_a M - \log_a N = \log_a \left(\frac{M}{N} \right)$

Example: $\log_2 16 - \log_2 4 = \log_2 4 \Leftrightarrow 4 - 2 = 2$

3. $N \log_a M = \log_a (M^N)$

Example: $2\log_3 9 = \log_3 81 \Leftrightarrow 2 \times 2 = 4$

4. **Change of base (COB) Trick**: $\log_a M = \log_b M \times \log_a b$
Note: It's like a chain rule.

Example: $\log_2 16 = \log_4 16 \times \log_2 4 \Leftrightarrow 4 = 2 \times 2$

5. $\log_a 1 = 0$ because $1 = a^0$

Trick: $\log_a 1 = 0$ is always 0.

6. **Trick**: $\log_a a = 1$ because $a = a^1$

7. **Drop Trick**: $\log_a b = \frac{1}{\log_b a}$

Example: $\log_2 8 = \frac{1}{\log_8 2} \Leftrightarrow 3 = \frac{1}{\frac{1}{3}}$

You must know log properties and log tricks to solve log equations and to differentiate logs.

Exercise 5 (Answers: page **83**)

Logs

1. Write the following as logs:

(a) $3^{-2} = \frac{1}{9}$
(b) $4^0 = 1$
(c) $625 = 25^2$
(d) $0.01 = 10^{-2}$
(e) $y = x^3$
(f) $y = 2^{2x}$
(g) $2^5 = 32$
(h) $36^{-\frac{1}{2}} = \frac{1}{6}$
(i) $r^s = t$
(j) $(-2)^4 = 16$

2. Write the following logs as exponentials:

(a) $\log_2 256 = 8$
(b) $5 = \log_3 243$
(c) $4 = \log_{10} 10000$
(d) $\log_5 1 = 0$
(e) $\frac{2}{3} = \log_{27} 9$
(f) $\log_3 27 = 3$
(g) $\log_{\frac{1}{2}} 4 = -2$
(h) $4 = \log_2 16$
(i) $\log_{\sqrt{2}} 16 = 8$
(j) $\log_{-3} 9 = 2$
(k) $\log_{625} 25 = \frac{1}{2}$

3. Evaluate the following either by your own cop on or by letting the log equal to x and changing to an exponential:

(a) $\log_4 16$
(b) $\log_2 8$
(c) $\log_4(\frac{1}{16})$
(d) $\log_{16} 8$
(e) $\log_{16} 2$
(f) $\log_4\left(\frac{1}{2}\right)$
(g) $\log_3 \sqrt{3}$
(h) $\log_{\frac{1}{3}} 9$
(i) $\log_{\sqrt{3}} 9$
(j) $\log_3 3^2$

---

4. Write as a single log:

(a) $2 \log_a 3$
(b) $3 \log_7 4 + \log_7 2$
(c) $\log_4 5 - \log_4 10$
(d) $\log_a 5 + 3 \log_a 2 - \log_a 4$
(e) $\log_2 x + 2 \log_2 y$
(f) $\log_3 7 + \frac{1}{2} \log_3 16$
(g) $\frac{1}{2} \log_a x + 2 \log_a y$
(h) $2 \log_7 x - 3 \log_7 y + 4 \log_7 z$
(i) $\frac{1}{2} \log_a x^2 + \frac{5}{2} \log_a y - \frac{1}{2} \log_a z$
(j) $\frac{1}{3}(4 \log_b x - 2 \log_b y)$
(k) $\log_{10} 20 - \log_{10} 2 + \log_{10} 100$
(l) $5 \log_2 y - 3 \log_2 y^2 + \frac{1}{2} \log_2 y^2$

5. Express as a string of logs:

(a) $\log_a (xy)$
(b) $\log_3 (x^2 y)$
(c) $\frac{1}{2}\log_5(\frac{x}{y^3})$
(d) $\frac{1}{2}\log_3 \sqrt{\frac{x}{y}}$
(e) $\log_4 \sqrt{x^3 y}$
(f) $\log_7 \sqrt{\frac{x^5}{y^2}}$
(g) $\log_2(\frac{1}{x^2})$
(h) $\log_b\left(\frac{x^2}{\sqrt{x^2-1}}\right)$
(i) $\log_3 \sqrt[5]{xy^2}$

6. Upside down switch

(a) $\log_2 4 = \frac{1}{\square}$
(b) $\log_2 8 = \frac{1}{\square}$
(c) $\log_2 16 = \frac{1}{\square}$
(d) $\log_{16} 8 = \frac{1}{\square}$
(e) $\frac{1}{\log_2 8} = \square$
(f) $\frac{1}{\log_b a} = \square$

7. Change of base:

(a) $\log_2 8 = \log_4 8 \times \square$
(b) $\log_2 16 = \log_4 16 \times \square$
(c) $\log_2 32 = \log_8 32 \times \square$
(d) $\log_3 16 = \log_2 16 \times \square$
(e) $\log_a 7 = \log_b 7 \times \square$
(f) $\log_4 9 = \log_3 9 \times \square$
(g) $\log_3 27 = \log_9 27 \times \square$
(h) $\log_{10} 100 = \log_{1000} 100 \times \square$
(i) $\log_a y = \log_b y \times \square$
(j) $\log_2 x = \log_e x \times \square$
(k) $\log_2 16 = \log_4 16 \times \square = \frac{\log_4 16}{\square}$
(l) $\log_4 16 = \log_8 16 \times \square = \frac{\log_8 16}{\square}$
(m) $\log_a y = \log_x y \times \square = \frac{\log_x y}{\square}$

8. Evaluate

(a) $\log_a 1$
(b) $\log_3 1$
(c) $\log_7 1$
(d) $\log_x 1$

1.6 SIMPLIFYING ALGEBRAIC EXPRESSIONS

STEPS

1. Get rid of negative powers by moving or multiplying above and below by positive power.
2. Get rid of double decker fractions by multiplying above and below by CD of all fractions.
3. Factorise (Look for HCF first of course).
4. Multiply out brackets if possible (last resort).

Example 33: Simplify $\dfrac{\frac{1}{3}x^{-2}+\frac{2}{5}x}{x^2}$

SOLUTION

$$\frac{(\frac{1}{3}x^{-2}+\frac{2}{5}x)}{x^2}\cdot\frac{15x^2}{15x^2}=\frac{5+6x^3}{15x^4}$$

(15 is the CD and x^2 is the positive power)

Example 34: Simplify $\dfrac{(x^2-1)^{\frac{1}{2}}+\frac{1}{2}(x^2-1)^{\frac{3}{2}}}{\frac{3}{4}(x^2-1)^2}$

SOLUTION

$$\frac{(x^2-1)^{\frac{1}{2}}+\frac{1}{2}(x^2-1)^{\frac{3}{2}}}{\frac{3}{4}(x^2-1)^2}\cdot\frac{4}{4}=\frac{4(x^2-1)^{\frac{1}{2}}+2(x^2-1)^{\frac{3}{2}}}{3(x^2-1)^2}$$

$$=\frac{2(x^2-1)^{\frac{1}{2}}\left\{2+(x^2-1)\right\}}{3(x^2-1)^2}=\frac{2(x^2+1)}{3(x^2-1)^{\frac{3}{2}}}$$

Example 35: Simplify $\left(\dfrac{x^3-y^3}{y^3}\cdot\dfrac{y}{x-y}\right)\div\left(\dfrac{x^2+xy+y^2}{y^2}\right)$

SOLUTION

Don't multiply out brackets.

$$\frac{x^3-y^3}{y^3}\cdot\frac{y}{x-y}\times\frac{y^2}{x^2+xy+y^2}$$

$$=\frac{(x-y)(x^2+xy+y^2)y}{y^3(x-y)}\times\frac{y^2}{x^2+xy+y^2}=1$$

Exercise 6 (Answers: page **85**)

Simplifying Algebraic Expressions

Simplify giving your answer with positive exponents only and fully factorised form.

1. $\dfrac{x^{-\frac{1}{2}}+3x^2}{x^1}$
2. $\dfrac{(x-1)^{-\frac{1}{2}}+2(x-1)^{\frac{1}{2}}}{(x-1)}$
3. $\dfrac{\frac{2}{3}(2x-1)^{-\frac{1}{3}}+\frac{1}{6}(2x+1)^{\frac{2}{3}}}{(2x+1)}$
4. $\dfrac{(x+2)^{\frac{2}{3}}-\frac{2}{3}x(x+2)^{-\frac{1}{3}}}{(x+2)^{\frac{5}{3}}}$
5. $\dfrac{(x-2)^3(x+1)^2-(x-2)^2(x+1)}{3(x-2)^2(x+1)}$
6. $\dfrac{(x-1)^{\frac{1}{2}}-4(x+1)(x-1)^{\frac{3}{2}}}{(x-1)^{\frac{5}{2}}}$
7. $\dfrac{x^{-1}+x^{-2}}{x}$
8. $\dfrac{\frac{1}{2}x^{-2}+x^2}{3x^3}$
9. $\dfrac{\frac{1}{2}(x-1)^{-\frac{1}{2}}+\frac{3}{2}(x-1)^{\frac{1}{2}}}{(x-1)^{\frac{5}{2}}}$
10. $\dfrac{x^{-2}+\frac{1}{2}x^2}{3x^2}$

1.7 IDENTITIES (ID)

[A] **What are they?**: These are mathematical statements which are true for all values of their variable(s).
They are just different ways of writing some mathematical object.
You know lots of them:

$$\tfrac{1}{x} = x^{-1}$$
$$(2x - 1)^2 = 4x^2 - 4x + 1$$
$$(x + y)^3 = x^3 + 3x^2y + 3xy^2 + y^3$$

Note: Factors are identities.
So: $x^2 - 5x + 6 = (x - 3)(x - 2)$ is an ID

[B] **Handling ID's**
There are 2 ways
Trick 1: Plonk in any values (choose wisely).
Trick 2: Line up coefficients.
Sometimes trick 1 is better than trick 2 and vice versa. You can of course use a mixture of both tricks.

Example 36: If $x - 1 = p(x + 2) + q(x - 3)$ for all x, find p and $q \in R$.
SOLUTION
$x - 1 = p(x + 2) + q(x - 3)$
Choosing $x = -2$: $-3 = -5q \therefore q = \tfrac{3}{5}$
Choosing $x = 3$: $2 = 5p \therefore p = \tfrac{2}{5}$

Example 37: If $2x^2 + 8x + 5 = 2(x + A)^2 + B$ for all x, find A, B.
SOLUTION
$2x^2 + 8x + 5 = 2(x + A)^2 + B$
$2x^2 + 8x + 5 = 2x^2 + 4Ax + (2A^2 + B)$
Lining up x terms: $4A = 8 \Rightarrow A = 2$
Lining up constant terms: $2A^2 + B = 5 \Rightarrow 8 + B = 5 \Rightarrow B = -3$

Example 38: If $\dfrac{5}{(x-1)(2x+1)} = \dfrac{A}{x-1} + \dfrac{B}{2x+1}$ for all x, find A, B.

SOLUTION

$$\frac{5}{(x-1)(2x+1)} = \frac{A}{x-1} + \frac{B}{2x+1} \Rightarrow 5 = A(2x+1) + B(x-1)$$

Choosing $x = 1$: $5 = 3A \Rightarrow A = \frac{5}{3}$

Choosing $x = -\frac{1}{2}$: $5 = -\frac{3}{2}B \Rightarrow B = -\frac{10}{3}$

Exercise 7 (Answers: page **85**)

Identities

1. If $\dfrac{x^3-1}{x-1} = Ax^2 + Bx + C$ for all x, find A, B, C.
2. If $\dfrac{2x+3}{x(x-1)} = \dfrac{A}{x} + \dfrac{B}{x-1}$ for all x find A, B.
3. If $2x^2 + 12x + 5 = 2(x + A)^2 + B$ for all x find A, B.
4. If $\dfrac{5}{(x-1)(x+1)} = \dfrac{A}{x-1} + \dfrac{B}{x+1}$ for all x, find A, B.
5. Find a, b if $(2x + a)^2 = 4x^2 + 20x + b$ for all x.
6. If $\dfrac{4x-13}{2x^2+x-6} = \dfrac{A}{x+2} + \dfrac{B}{2x-3}$ for all x find A, B.
7. Find A and B if $2(x - 1)^2 = A(x^2 + 1) + Bx$ for all x.
8. If $x^4 + 40x - 96 = (x^2 - ax + 12)(x^2 + 2x - b)$ for all x find a and b.
9. If $(lx + my)^3 = 8x^3 - 12x^2y + pxy^2 - y^3$ for all x, y find l, m, p.

1.8 FACTORIALS

You will meet factorials in many places on the course.

[A] **Definition**: $n! = n(n - 1)(n - 2) \ldots. 2.1,\ n \in \{1, 2, 3, \ldots.\}$
$n!$ is pronounced n factorial or factorial n.

Trick: To evaluate the factorial of a number you start with the number and keep on multiplying by a number 1 less than the previous one until you reach 1.

Example: $5! = 5.4.3.2.1 = 120$

Example: $(r + 2)! = (r + 2)(r + 1)(r)(r - 1).....1$

Example: $(2l + 5)! = (2l + 5)(2l + 4)......1$

NOTES

1. The calculator evaluates factorials for you.
2. You can only find the factorial of a whole positive number and zero.

$(-1)!$ does not exist.

$(\frac{1}{2})!$ does not exist.

3. $0! = 1$ (see later)

[B] **Tricks with factorials**

1. The division trick is the most important.

Example: $\dfrac{7!}{6!} = \dfrac{7.6.5.4.3.2.1}{6.5.4.3.2.1} = 7$

Example: $\dfrac{20!}{18!} = 20 \times 19 = 380$

Example: $\dfrac{(n-2)!}{(n-3)!} = \dfrac{(n-2)(n-3).....1}{(n-3).....1} = (n-2)$

Division trick: To divide a factorial

1. If the bigger one is on top, the answer is on the top and if the bigger one is on the bottom, the answer is on the bottom.
2. Find the difference between them. The difference is r.
3. Multiply r brackets starting with the bigger one and decreasing by 1 each time.

Example 39: $\frac{101!}{103!}$ (Bottom is bigger by $2 = r$)

SOLUTION

$$\therefore \frac{101!}{103!} = \frac{1}{103 \times 102} = \frac{1}{10506}$$

Example 40: $\frac{(n+1)!}{(n-2)!}$ (Top is bigger by $3 = r$)

SOLUTION

$$\therefore \frac{(n+1)!}{(n-2)!} = (n+1)(n)(n-1)$$

Example 41: $\frac{(n-m-1)!}{(n-m-3)!}$ (Top is bigger by $2 = r$)

SOLUTION

$$\therefore \frac{(n-m-1)!}{(n-m-3)!} = (n-m-1)(n-m-2)$$

2. **Multiplication trick**

$7 \times 6! = 7.6.5.4.3.2.1 = 7!$

$n \times (n - 1)! = n!$

3. **Fractions trick**

Trick: The CD is the bigger of the 2 factorials.

Example 42: Simplify $\frac{1}{(n+1)!} + \frac{1}{(n+2)!}$

SOLUTION

$$\frac{1}{(n+1)!} + \frac{1}{(n+2)!} = \frac{(n+2)+1}{(n+2)!} = \frac{n+3}{(n+2)!}$$

4. **Addition trick**

Trick: To add factorials take out the HCF.

Example: $20! + 21! = 20!(1 + 21) = 22.20!$

Example: $n! + (n+1)! = n!\{1 + (n+1)\} = (n+2)n!$

Exercise 8 (Answers: page **85**)

Factorials

1. Evaluate

(a) $4!$ (b) $7!$ (c) $2!$

(d) $1!$ (e) $\frac{12!}{8!}$ (f) $\frac{100!}{98!}$

(g) $\frac{14!}{11!3!}$ (h) $\frac{10!}{(5!)^2}$ (i) $\frac{12!}{13!}$

(j) $\frac{100!}{99!}$

2. Show

(a) $7.6! = 7!$

(b) $9.8! = 9!$

(c) $23! + 24! = 25.23!$

(d) $71! - 70! = 70.70!$

(e) $6! - 3.5! - 15.4! = 0$

3. Simplify

(a) $n! + (n - 1)!$

(b) $\frac{1}{n!}+\frac{1}{(n+1)!}$

(c) $\frac{(n+1)n!}{(n+1)!}$

(d) $\frac{(n-2)!}{(n+2)!}$

(e) $\frac{(n-r)!}{(n-r-1)!}$

(f) $\frac{1}{n!}-\frac{1}{(n+1)!}$

4. Solve

(a) $\frac{n!}{(n-1)!}=7$

(b) $\frac{n!}{(n-2)!}=2$

(c) $\frac{(2n+1)!}{(2n-1)!}=110$

(d) $\frac{(n+1)!}{(n-1)!}=12$

1.9 BINOMIAL COEFFICIENTS

[A] **Definition**: $^{n}C_{r}=\frac{n!}{r!(n-r)!}=\frac{\text{(Fac Top)}}{\text{(Fac Bot)}\times\text{(Fac Top} - \text{Bot)}}$

$n, r \in \{0,1,2,3,....\}$ with $n \geq r \geq 0$.

Example: $^{5}C_{3}=\frac{5!}{3!2!}=\frac{5.4.3.2.1}{3.2.1.2.1}=10$

NOTES: 1. The calculator evaluates Binomial Coefficients

2. **Trick**: The quick way $\binom{n}{r}$

$$^{n}C_{r}=\binom{n}{r}=\frac{\text{Multiply } r \text{ factors starting at } n \text{ and decreasing by 1}}{\text{Multiply } r \text{ factors starting at } r \text{ and decreasing by 1 down to 1}}$$

Guide Number

Example: $^{n}C_{r}=\binom{5}{3}={}^{5}C_{3}=\frac{5.4.3}{3.2.1}=10$

3 numbers

3 numbers

Guide Number

[B] **Tricks**

1. $^{n}C_{r} = {}^{n}C_{n-r}$

PROOF

LHS	*RHS*
$^{n}C_{r}$	$^{n}C_{n-r}$
$= \dfrac{n!}{r!(n-r)!}$	$= \dfrac{n!}{(n-r)!r!}$

Examples

$$^{7}C_{4} = {}^{7}C_{3} = \binom{7}{3} = \frac{7.6.5}{3.2.1} = 35$$

$$^{101}C_{99} = {}^{101}C_{2} = \binom{101}{2} = \frac{101.100}{2}$$

$= 5,050$

2. $^{n}C_{0} = {}^{n}C_{n} = \dfrac{n(n-1).......1}{n(n-1).......1} = 1 = \dbinom{n}{0} = \dbinom{n}{n}$

Note: $^{n}C_{0} = 1 = \dfrac{n!}{0!n!} = \dfrac{1}{0!} = 1 \Rightarrow 0! = 1$

Example: $^{5}C_{0} = {}^{6}C_{0} = \dbinom{5}{5} = \dbinom{6}{0} = \dbinom{100}{100} = 1$

3. $^{n}C_{1} = \dbinom{n}{1} = \dfrac{n}{1} = n$

Example: $^{5}C_{1} = \dbinom{5}{1} = 5$

Example 43: Prove $\dbinom{n}{r} + \dbinom{n}{r+1} = \dbinom{n+1}{r+1}$

SOLUTION

LHS

$$\binom{n}{r} + \binom{n}{r+1} = \frac{n!}{r!(n-r)!} + \frac{n!}{(r+1)!(n-r-1)!}$$

$$= \frac{n!(r+1) + n!(n-r)}{(r+1)!(n-r)!} = \frac{n!(n-r+r+1)}{(r+1)!(n-r)!}$$

$$= \frac{(n+1)!}{(r+1)!(n-r)!}$$

RHS

$$\binom{n+1}{r+1}$$

$$= \frac{(n+1)!}{(r+1)!(n-r)!}$$

Exercise 9 (Answers: page 86)

(Answers: page **86**)

Binomial Coefficients

1. Evaluate

(a) $\binom{11}{7}$ (b) $\binom{20}{3}$

(c) $\binom{101}{100}$ (d) $\binom{100}{98}$

(e) $\binom{10}{8}$ (f) $\binom{15}{11}$

(g) $\binom{18}{0}$ (h) $\binom{17}{1}$

(i) $\binom{5}{5}$ (j) $\binom{10}{2}$

2. Show $\binom{8}{2}+\binom{8}{3}=\binom{9}{3}$

3. Prove

(i) $\binom{n}{r}=\binom{n}{n-r}$

(ii) $\binom{k}{k}=\binom{k+1}{k+1}=1$

(iii) $\binom{r+2}{3}-\binom{r}{3}=r^2$

(iv) $\binom{n}{r}=\frac{n-r+1}{r}.\binom{n}{r-1}$

(v) $\binom{n}{3}+\binom{n+1}{3}+\binom{n+2}{3}=\frac{n(n^2+1)}{2}$

4. Solve

(a) $\binom{n+2}{2}=3$

(b) $\binom{n}{r}=\binom{100}{57}$

(c) $\binom{n-1}{2}=10$

(d) $\binom{2n-1}{2}=21$

2. EQUATIONS

2.1 FACTOR THEOREM (FT): This is the basic method of solution of polynomial equations. These are equations of the form $a_0x^n + a_1x^{n-1} + a_2x^{n-2} + ... + a_n = 0$ where $n \in N$. However, we have to deal with:

Linears (L): $ax + b = 0$, e.g. $2x - 5 = 0$
Quadratics (Q): $ax^2 + bx + c = 0$, e.g. $5x^2 - 2x - 1 = 0$
Cubics (C): $ax^3 + bx^2 + cx + d = 0$, e.g. $2x^3 - 3x^2 + 5x - 1 = 0$
The Factor Theorem states:

> If $(x - k)$ is a factor of $f(x)$ then k is a root of $f(x) = 0$, i.e. $f(k) = 0$ and vice versa.

It's obvious, isn't it?

Example: $f(x) = (x - 3)(x - 2)(x + 1)$
$f(x)$ has 3 factors which means $f(3) = 0$, $f(2) = 0$ and $f(-1) = 0$.

TRICK
If you are told $(x - k)$ is a factor of $f(x)$ then k is a root, i.e. $f(k) = 0$

TRICK
If you are told or can guess that $f(k) = 0$, i.e. k is a root of $f(x) = 0$, then $(x - k)$ is a factor of $f(x)$.

Example: If a polynomial has $f(3) = 0$ this means $(x - 3)$ has to be a factor of $f(x)$, i.e $f(x) = (x - 3).g(x)$ where $g(x)$ is a polynomial one degree less than $f(x)$.

Example 1: If $x - 1$ is a factor of $2x^3 - cx^2 + 3x - 1$, find c.

SOLUTION
$x - 1$ is a factor means 1 is a root, i.e. $f(1) = 0$.
$f(x) = 2x^3 - cx^2 + 3x - 1$
$f(1) = 2 - c + 3 - 1 = 0 \Rightarrow c = 4$

TRICK
If you are told or can guess that $f(k) = 0$, i.e. that k is a root of $f(x) = 0$, then you can say $(x - k)$ is a factor of $f(x)$ and so $f(x) = (x - k).g(x)$ .... Identity

Example 2: If $f(1) = 0, f(2) = 0$ and $f(3) = 4$ find the cubic polynomial $f(x)$.

SOLUTION

$f(1) = 0 \Rightarrow x - 1$ is a factor of $f(x)$, i.e. L

$f(2) = 0 \Rightarrow x - 2$ is a factor of $f(x)$, i.e. L

$\therefore f(x) = (x - 1)(x - 2)(x - k)$, i.e. 3L

$f(3) = 2.1.(3 - k) = 4 \Rightarrow k = 1$

$\therefore f(x) = (x - 1)(x - 2)(x - 1) = x^3 - 4x^2 + 5x - 2$

So the FT can be summarised in the following:

$$f(k) = 0 \Leftrightarrow k \text{ is a root of } f(x) = 0$$
$$\Leftrightarrow \text{ Curve crosses X-axis at } k$$
$$\Leftrightarrow (x - k) \text{ is a factor } \Leftrightarrow f(x) = (x - k).g(x)$$

For a cubic, $g(x)$ would be a Q or 2L.
The proof of FT is required. (See page 420 in the **PROOFS** section.)

General tricks on polynomial equations

1. Always write down all the consequences of the FT.
$f(k) = 0 \Leftrightarrow k$ is a root of $f(x) = 0 \Leftrightarrow$ Curve crosses X-axis at k
$\Leftrightarrow (x - k)$ is a factor $\Leftrightarrow f(x) = (x - k).g(x)$

2. Roots = Solutions = Places where curve crosses X-axis.

α, β, γ are roots

$\Rightarrow f(\alpha) = f(\beta) = f(\gamma)$

$\Rightarrow (x - \alpha), (x - \beta), (x - \gamma)$ are factors

$\Rightarrow f(x) = (x - \alpha)(x - \beta)(x - \gamma)$

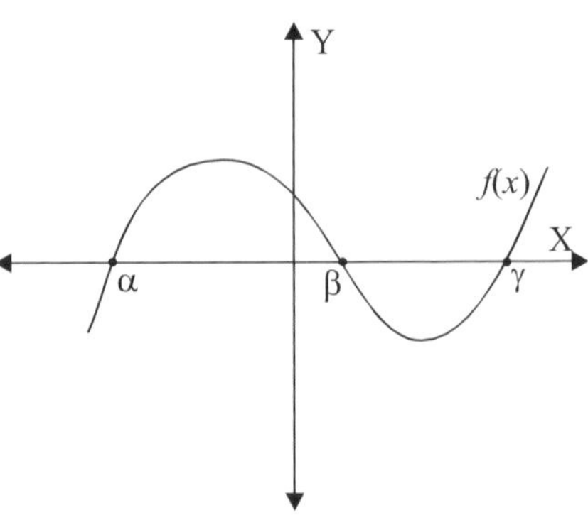

3. Roots satisfy the original equation. So you can plonk them into it.

Exercise 10 (Answers: page **86**)

Factor Theorem

1. Test to see if
(i) $x - 3$ is a factor of $x^2 - 2x - 3$
(ii) $x - 4$ is a factor of $4x^3 - x^2 + 5x - 6$
(iii) $2x - 1$ is a factor of $5x^3 - 6x + 5$

2. (i) $x - 1$ is a factor of $x^3 + 2x^2 - 3ax + 4$, find a.
(ii) $x + 2$ is a factor of $kx^2 - 2x - 3$, find k.
(iii) $2x - 1$ is a factor of $4x^2 - 6x - 9k$, find k.
(iv) $x + 1$ is a factor of $2x^3 - 4x^2 + 3ax - 7$, find a.
(v) $x + 1$ and $x - 2$ are both factors of $ax^3 - 6x^2 - bx + 6$, find a, b.

3. (i) For a quadratic $g(x)$, $g(-2) = 0$ and $g(1) = 0$, find the quadratic.
(ii) For a cubic $f(x)$, $f(-2) = 0$, $f(3) = 0$ and $f(-1) = 0$, find the cubic.
(iii) For the quadratic $g(x)$, $g(1) = -2$ and $g(3) = 0$, find it.
(iv) For the cubic $f(x)$, if $f(1) = -3$ and $f(2) = 0$ and $f(-1) = 0$, find the cubic.

4. Find k if
(i) $x^3 + x^2 + kx + 8$ is divisible by $x - 1$
(ii) $x^3 + kx^2 - 2x + 1$ is divisible by $x + 2$
(iii) $2x^3 - 3x^2 - kx + 7$ is divisible by $2x - 1$
(iv) $2x^3 - 5x^2 + 3x - k$ is divisible by $x - 2$

5. Find a and b if
(i) $x^3 + ax^2 - 9x + b$ is divisible by $x - 1$ and $x + 3$.
(ii) $x^3 + ax^2 + 2x + b$ is divisible by $x + 1$ and $x - 2$.

6. Divide $f(x) = ax^3 + bx^2 + cx + d$ by $x - k$ and hence show that the remainder is $ak^3 + bk^2 + ck + d$. Deduce if $f(k) = 0$ then $f(x)$ is divisible by $x - k$.

2.2 LINEAR EQUATIONS

These are equations of the form $y = f(x) = ax + b = 0$.

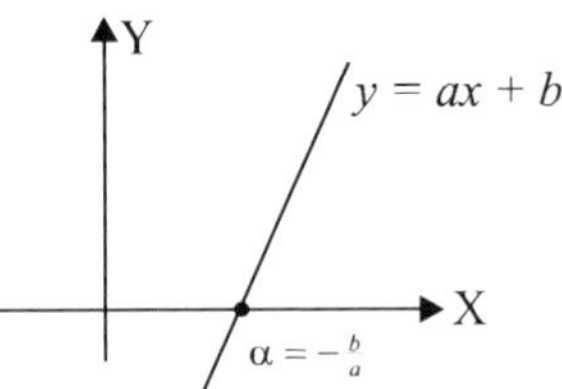

Method of solution: Do it

$ax + b = 0 \Rightarrow x = -\frac{b}{a} = \alpha$ .... one root

Graph of linear function $y = f(x) = ax + b$

It crosses the X-axis, $y = 0$, at only one place: $x = \alpha = -\frac{b}{a}$

Exercise 11 (Answers: page **86**)

Linear Equations

Solve the following:

1. $2x + 3(x - 2) = 5$

2. $\frac{x-1}{7} - \frac{3(x+2)}{5} = -1$

3. $\frac{2}{x} + \frac{3}{x} = 4$

4. $\frac{5}{x} - \frac{4}{2x-1} = \frac{3}{x(2x-1)}$

5. $-\frac{2}{a} - \frac{4}{3} = \frac{7}{a} - \frac{3}{2}$

6. $\frac{3x}{2} - \frac{4(x+3)}{8} = \frac{2}{9}$

2.3 QUADRATIC EQUATIONS

These are equations of the form $y = f(x) = ax^2 + bx + c = 0$

[A] **Method of Solution**

1. Factorisation ... Doesn't always work (Fast)
2. Completing the square (CS) .... Always works (Slow)
3. Magic Formula ..... Always works (Fast)

$$x = \frac{-b \pm \sqrt{b^2 - 4ac}}{2a}$$

Example 3: Solve $2x^2 - 7x - 9 = 0$

SOLUTION

1. **Factorisation**

$2x^2 - 7x - 9 = 0 \Rightarrow (2x - 9)(x + 1) = 0$

$\Rightarrow x = \frac{9}{2}, -1$

2. **CS**

$2x^2 - 7x - 9 = 0$

$\Rightarrow (x^2 - \frac{7}{2}x) - \frac{9}{2} = 0$ (Make the coefficient of x^2 one by dividing by 2)

$\Rightarrow (x - \frac{7}{4})^2 - \frac{9}{2} - \frac{49}{16} = 0$

$\Rightarrow (x - \frac{7}{4})^2 = \frac{121}{16} \Rightarrow x - \frac{7}{4} = \pm\frac{11}{4}$

$\Rightarrow x = +\frac{7}{4} \pm \frac{11}{4}$

$\Rightarrow x = \frac{9}{2}, -1$

3. **Magic**

$2x^2 - 7x - 9 = 0$

$a = 2, b = -7, c = -9$

$$\Rightarrow x = \frac{7 \pm \sqrt{49 + 72}}{4} = \frac{7 \pm \sqrt{121}}{4} = \frac{7 \pm 11}{4}$$

$\Rightarrow x = \frac{9}{2}, -1$

Note: CS is needed for integration and the magic formula is a summary of CS.

Example 4: Solve the quadratic
$(p + r - t)x^2 + 2rx + (t + r - p) = 0$

SOLUTION

$(p + r - t)x^2 + 2rx + (t + r - p) = 0$

$a = (p + r - t) = [r + (p - t)]$

$b = 2r$

$c = (t + r - p) = [r - (p - t)]$

$$x = \frac{-2r \pm \sqrt{4r^2 - 4[r+(p-t)][r-(p-t)]}}{2(p+r-t)}$$

$$= \frac{-2r \pm \sqrt{4r^2 - 4r^2 + 4(p-t)^2}}{2(p+r-t)} = \frac{-2r \pm \sqrt{4(p-t)^2}}{2(p+r-t)}$$

$$= \frac{-2r \pm 2(p-t)}{2(p+r-t)}$$

$$x = \frac{-2r + 2p - 2t}{2(p+r-t)} = \frac{2(p-r-t)}{2(p+r-t)} = \frac{p-r-t}{p+r-t}$$

$$\text{or } x = \frac{-2r - 2p + 2t}{2(p+r-t)} = \frac{-2(p+r-t)}{2(p+r-t)} = -1$$

[B] **Properties of roots** α, β

Sum: $S = \alpha + \beta = -\frac{b}{a} = \frac{-\text{2nd}}{\text{1st}}$

Product: $P = \alpha\beta = \frac{c}{a} = \frac{\text{3rd}}{\text{1st}}$

NOTES

1. The roots α, β satisfy their own equation of course.
2. $\alpha^2 + \beta^2 = (\alpha + \beta)^2 - 2\alpha\beta$

   $\alpha^3 + \beta^3 = (\alpha + \beta)(\alpha^2 - \alpha\beta + \beta^2)$

   $\alpha^4 + \beta^4 = (\alpha^2 + \beta^2)^2 - 2\alpha^2\beta^2$

3. The roots satisfy their own equation. If you are told that something is a root of $ax^2 + bx + c = 0$ then you can plonk it in. So if k is a root of $ax^2 + bx + c = 0 \Rightarrow ak^2 + bk + c = 0$.

There are 5 basic types of problem: T1, T2, T3, T4 and T5.

T1: FUNCTIONS OF THE ROOTS

Example 5: If α, β are the roots of $x^2 - 3x - 1 = 0$ find
1. $\alpha+\beta$, 2. $\alpha\beta$, 3. $\alpha^2+\beta^2$, 4. $\frac{1}{\alpha}+\frac{1}{\beta}$, 5. $\alpha^3+\beta^3$, 6. $\alpha^4+\beta^4$, 7. $(\alpha-\beta)^2$, 8. $\alpha-\beta$, 9. $\alpha^2-\beta^2$, 10. $\alpha^4\beta^5+\alpha^5\beta^4$

SOLUTION

1. $\alpha+\beta=3$ 2. $\alpha\beta=-1$

3. $\alpha^2+\beta^2=(\alpha+\beta)^2-2\alpha\beta=9+2=11$

4. $\frac{1}{\alpha}+\frac{1}{\beta}=\frac{\beta+\alpha}{\alpha\beta}=\frac{3}{-1}=-3$

5. $\alpha^3+\beta^3=(\alpha+\beta)(\alpha^2-\alpha\beta+\beta^2)=(3)(11+1)=36$

6. $\alpha^4+\beta^4=(\alpha^2+\beta^2)^2-2\alpha^2\beta^2=(11)^2-2(1)=119$

7. $(\alpha-\beta)^2=\alpha^2+\beta^2-2\alpha\beta=11+2=13$

8. $\alpha-\beta=\pm\sqrt{13}$

9. $\alpha^2-\beta^2=(\alpha-\beta)(\alpha+\beta)=\pm3\sqrt{13}$

10. $\alpha^4\beta^5+\alpha^5\beta^4=\alpha^4\beta^4(\alpha+\beta)=1(3)=3$

T2: RELATIONSHIP BETWEEN ROOTS

If you are told

1. Roots are equal: α, α or $b^2 = 4ac$ (see later)
2. Roots add to zero: α, $-\alpha$
3. Roots add to 2: α, $2-\alpha$
4. One root is twice the other: α, 2α
5. Product of roots is 3: α, $\frac{3}{\alpha}$
6. One root is 3 bigger than the other: α, $\alpha+3$
7. Roots are reciprocals of each other: α, $\frac{1}{\alpha}$
8. Roots are in the ratio 4:3: 4α, 3α

Example 6: If the roots of $x^2 - ax + b = 0$ are in the ratio 4:3 show that $12a^2 = 49b$.

SOLUTION

$x^2 - ax + b = 0$

Roots: 4α, 3α

S: $7\alpha = a \Rightarrow \alpha = (\frac{a}{7})$

P: $12\alpha^2 = b \Rightarrow 12(\frac{a}{7})^2 = b \quad \therefore \; 12a^2 = 49b$

T3: 2 DIFFERENT QUADRATICS

Split page in two and treat separately until the end.

Example 7: If the roots of $x^2 - 7x + 3 = 0$ are α and β find p and q if the roots of $x^2 + px + q = 0$ are $\alpha + 2$, $\beta + 2$.

SOLUTION

First

$x^2 - 7x + 3 = 0$

α, β

$S = \alpha + \beta = 7$

$P = \alpha\beta = 3$

Second

$x^2 + px + q = 0$

$\alpha + 2, \beta + 2$

$S = (\alpha + \beta) + 4 = -p \Rightarrow p = -11$

$P = \alpha\beta + 2\alpha + 2\beta + 4 = q$

$\Rightarrow q = 3 + 2(7) + 4$

$\therefore q = 21$

T4: FORMING A QUADRATIC EQUATION GIVEN ITS ROOTS

$$x^2 - Sx + P = 0.$$

Example 8: Form the quadratic equation with roots 3, $-\frac{1}{4}$.

SOLUTION

$x^2 - (3 - \frac{1}{4})x + (3)(-\frac{1}{4}) = 0$

$\Rightarrow x^2 - \frac{11}{4}x - \frac{3}{4} = 0$

$\Rightarrow 4x^2 - 11x - 3 = 0$

Example 9: Form the quadratic equation with roots m, $\frac{1}{m}$.

SOLUTION

$x^2-(m+\frac{1}{m})x+m.\frac{1}{m}=0 \Rightarrow x^2-(m+\frac{1}{m})x+1=0$

$\Rightarrow mx^2 - (m^2+1)x+m=0$

T5: NEW FROM OLD

Split the page in two and treat separately until the end.

Example 10: If α, β are the roots of $x^2 - 7x + 5 = 0$ form the equation with roots $\frac{1}{\alpha^2}$, $\frac{1}{\beta^2}$.

SOLUTION

Old	**New**
Roots: α, β	Roots: $\frac{1}{\alpha^2}$, $\frac{1}{\beta^2}$
Equation: $x^2 - 7x + 5 = 0$	Equation:
S: $\alpha+\beta=7$	$x^2-\left(\frac{1}{\alpha^2}+\frac{1}{\beta^2}\right)x+\frac{1}{\alpha^2}\frac{1}{\beta^2}=0$
P: $\alpha\beta=5$	$\Rightarrow x^2-\left(\frac{\alpha^2+\beta^2}{\alpha^2\beta^2}\right)x+\frac{1}{\alpha^2\beta^2}=0$
$\alpha^2+\beta^2=(\alpha+\beta)^2-2\alpha\beta$	$\Rightarrow x^2-\left(\frac{39}{25}\right)x+\frac{1}{25}=0$
$= 49 - 10 = 39$	$\therefore\ 25x^2 - 39x + 1 = 0$

[C] Nature of the roots and graphs of quadratics

The nature of the roots is determined by the expression under the square root sign in the magic formula. It is $b^2 - 4ac$ and is called the **DISCRIMINANT**.

1. $b^2 - 4ac > 0 \Rightarrow \alpha \neq \beta \Rightarrow$ 2 different real roots $\Rightarrow$ Curve crosses X-axis at 2 different places.

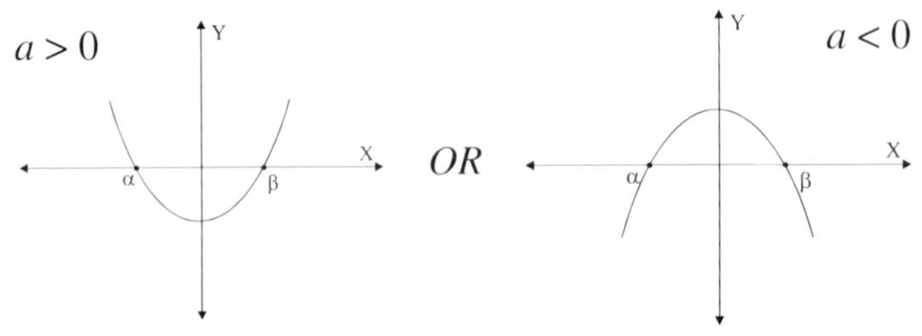

2. $b^2 - 4ac = 0 \Rightarrow \alpha = \beta \Rightarrow$ 2 same real roots $\Rightarrow$ Curve crosses X-axis at 1 place only.

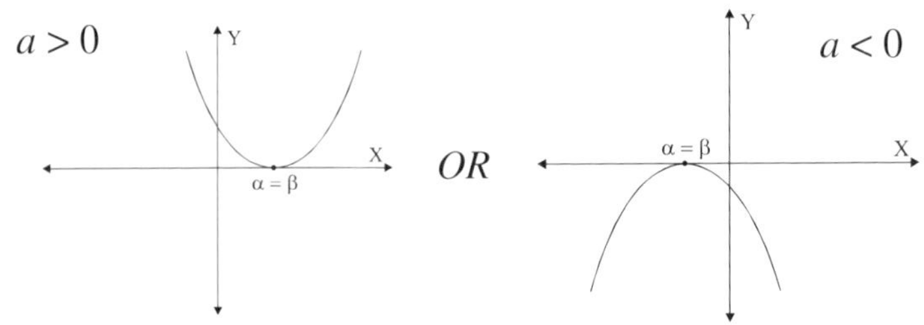

3. $b^2 - 4ac < 0 \Rightarrow \alpha, \beta$ not real $\Rightarrow$ no real roots (complex roots) $\Rightarrow$ Curve does not cross X-axis.

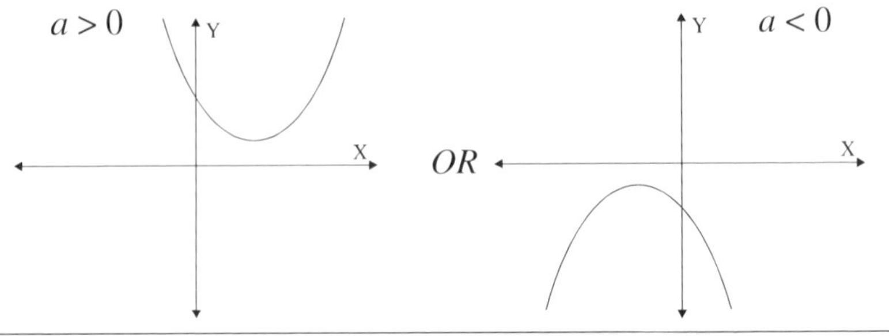

TRICK

Real roots: $b^2 \geq 4ac$
Equal roots: $b^2 = 4ac$
Complex roots: $b^2 < 4ac$

General shape of Graphs of quadratics: $ax^2 + bx + c = 0$
Concave up (CUP) ($a > 0$) ∪
OR
Concave down (CAP) ($a < 0$) ∩

Example 11: Find k if $x^2 - kx + 4 = 0$ has equal roots.

SOLUTION

Method 1: Equal roots α, α

S: $2\alpha = k$

P: $\alpha^2 = 4 \Rightarrow \alpha = \pm 2$

$\therefore k = \pm 4$

Method 2: Equal roots

$\Rightarrow b^2 = 4ac$

$\Rightarrow k^2 = 16$

$\therefore k = \pm 4$

Trick: Remember that a root can always be plonked into the original equation (Factor Theorem).

Example 12: If 3 is a root of $x^2 + kx - 15 = 0$, find k.

SOLUTION

Method 1.

Plonk 3 into

$x^2 + kx - 15 = 0$

$\Rightarrow 9 + 3k - 15 = 0$

$\therefore 3k = 6$

$\therefore k = 2$

OR

Method 2.

$x^2 + kx - 15 = 0$

Roots: α, 3

S: $3 + \alpha = -k$

P: $3\alpha = -15 \Rightarrow \alpha = -5$

$\therefore k = -3 - \alpha = -3 + 5 = 2$

Example 13: Find k if $x^2 - 7x + k = 0$ has reciprocal roots.

SOLUTION

$x^2 - 7x + k = 0$

Roots: α, $\frac{1}{\alpha}$

Sum: $\alpha + \frac{1}{\alpha} = 7$ Product: $\alpha \times \frac{1}{\alpha} = k = 1$

Example 14: Form the quadratic function from its graph.

SOLUTION

1. -1, 2 are roots

$\Rightarrow (x + 1), (x - 2)$ are factors

$\Rightarrow f(x) = y = (x + 1)(x - 2)$

$= x^2 - x - 2$

OR

2. -1, 2 are roots

$\Rightarrow$ S = 1, P = -2

$\Rightarrow f(x) = x^2 - 1x - 2$

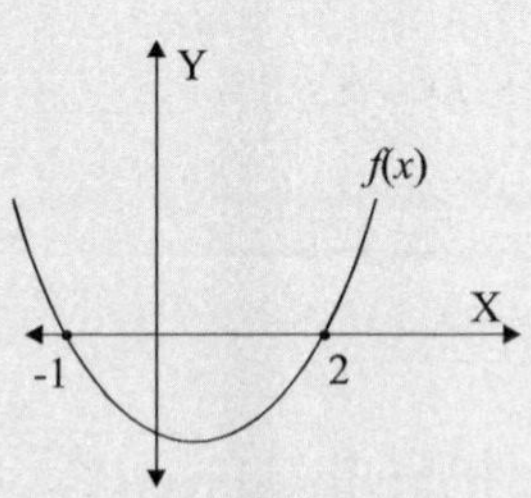

Example 15: Without solving, state the nature of the roots of $x^2 + 3x + 5 = 0$.

SOLUTION

$b^2 = 9$

$4ac = 20$

$\therefore b^2 - 4ac = -11 < 0$

$\Rightarrow$ Roots are unreal (complex)

Example 16: Without solving, state the nature of the roots of $2x^2 - 5x - 3 = 0$

SOLUTION

$b^2 = 25$

$4ac = -24$

$\therefore b^2 - 4ac = 49$

$\Rightarrow$ Roots are real and rational as 49 is a perfect square.

Exercise 12 (Answers: page **86**)

Quadratics

1. Solve
(i) $2x^2 + 7x - 4 = 0$
(ii) $x^2 - 2x - 9 = 0$
(iii) $8x^2 - 6x + 1 = 0$
(iv) $x^2 - 4x + 1 = 0$

2. If α, β are the roots of $x^2 - 7x - 3 = 0$ find the values of:
(i) $\alpha+\beta$ (ii) $\alpha\beta$
(iii) $\frac{1}{\alpha}+\frac{1}{\beta}$ (iv) $\alpha^2+\beta^2$
(v) $(\alpha+\beta)^2$ (vi) $\frac{1}{\alpha^2}+\frac{1}{\beta^2}$
(vii) $\alpha^3+\beta^3$ (viii) $(\alpha-\beta)^2$
(ix) $\alpha-\beta$ (x) $\alpha^2-\beta^2$
(xi) $\alpha^4+\beta^4$
(xii) $\alpha^5\beta^7+\alpha^7\beta^5$

3. If α, β are the roots of $2x^2 + 3x - 7 = 0$, find:
(i) $\alpha+\beta$ (ii) $\alpha\beta$
(iii) $\alpha^2+\beta^2$ (iv) $\alpha^3+\beta^3$
(v) $\frac{1}{\alpha}+\frac{1}{\beta}$ (vi) $\frac{1}{\alpha^2}+\frac{1}{\beta^2}$
(vii) $\alpha^4+\beta^4$ (viii) $(\alpha+\beta)^2$
(ix) $(\alpha-\beta)^2$ (x) $\alpha-\beta$
(xi) $\alpha^2-\beta^2$
(xii) $\alpha^5\beta^6+\alpha^6\beta^5$

4. Find the relationship between a, b, c for the quadratic $ax^2 + bx + c = 0$ if:
(i) one root is double the other,
(ii) one root is three times the other,
(iii) the roots are in the ratio 2:5,
(iv) one root is three-quarters of the other.

5. The roots of $2x^2 + 5x + 9 = 0$ are α and β. The roots of $px^2 - 3x + q = 0$ are $\alpha + 2$ and $\beta + 2$. Find p and q.

6. Form the equations with roots:
(i) 1, 3 (ii) $-\frac{1}{2}$, 2
(iii) $-\frac{1}{2}$, $\frac{1}{3}$ (iv) -2, -2
(v) $\sqrt{2}$, 1
(vi) $2-\sqrt{7}$, $2+\sqrt{7}$
(vii) $\sqrt{2}$, $\sqrt{3}$
(viii) $\frac{p}{q}$, $\frac{q}{p}$
(ix) p, $-p$ (x) α, β
(xi) $\frac{1}{3}$, -7 (xii) $1 - p$, $p - 2$

7. If α, β are the roots of $x^2 - 4x + 5 = 0$, form the equations with roots:

(i) $\frac{1}{\alpha}, \frac{1}{\beta}$ (ii) α^2, β^2

(iii) $\alpha + 2, \beta + 2$

(iv) $\frac{\alpha}{\beta}, \frac{\beta}{\alpha}$ (v) $1 - \frac{1}{\alpha}, 1 - \frac{1}{\beta}$

8. If α, β are the roots of $2x^2 + 5x + 1 = 0$, form the equations with roots:

(i) α^2, β^2 (ii) $\frac{1}{\alpha^2}, \frac{1}{\beta^2}$

(iii) $\alpha^3\beta, \beta^3\alpha$

(iv) $\alpha + 2\beta, \beta + 2\alpha$

(v) $\alpha + \frac{2}{\beta}, \beta + \frac{2}{\alpha}$

(vi) α^3, β^3

(vii) $\frac{\alpha^2}{\beta}, \frac{\beta^2}{\alpha}$

9. The roots of $x^2 + ax + a - 1 = 0$ are α and β. The roots of $x^2 + (a - 2)x + a + 2 = 0$ are $\alpha + 1, \beta + 1$. Find a and solve the equations.

10. Find k in the following:
(i) 3 is a root of $2x^2 - kx + 7 = 0$,
(ii) $-\frac{1}{2}$ is a root of $kx^2 - 3x - 9 = 0$,
(iii) the roots of $x^2 - kx + 4 = 0$ are equal,
(iv) the roots of $2x^2 - 3x + k = 0$ are reciprocals of each other,
(v) the roots of $3x^2 - k + 7 = 0$ add to zero.

11. State whether the roots of the following are either:
(a) real and rational, (b) real and irrational, (c) equal, (d) unreal
(i) $x^2 - 3x - 2 = 0$
(ii) $x^2 + 5x - 7 = 0$
(iii) $2x^2 + 4x + 3 = 0$
(iv) $4x^2 - x - 3 = 0$
(v) $x^2 + x - 2 = 0$
(vi) $4x^2 - 12x + 9 = 0$

12. One of the roots of $x^2 + ax + b^3 = 0$ is the square of the other. Show that $a + b + b^2 = 0$.

13. If one root of $x^2 + px + q = 0$ is twice the other show $2p^2 = 9q$. If one root of $x^2 + (2k + 4)x + (k^2 + 3k + 2) = 0$ is twice the other, find k, $k > 0$.

2.4 CUBIC EQUATIONS

These are equations of the form $y = f(x) = ax^3 + bx^2 + cx + d = 0$.

[A] **Method of solution**: Guess at a root using the factor theorem.
The basic method for solving a cubic equation is:

STEPS

1. Guess at a root (it must divide exactly into the constant term) = α.
2. Form a L factor from the root $(x - \alpha)$.
3. Factorise fully using division process or identity ($C = Q \times L$).

Example 17: Show that -2 is a root of $f(x) = x^3 - x^2 - 5x + 2$.
Hence solve the equation $x^3 - x^2 - 5x + 2 = 0$.

SOLUTION

$f(x) = x^3 - x^2 - 5x + 2$

$f(-2) = -8 - 4 + 10 + 2 = 0$ $\therefore$ -2 is a root.

$\therefore$ $(x + 2)$ is a factor.

$\therefore$ $x^3 - x^2 - 5x + 2 = (x + 2)(x^2 + kx + 1)$ ... ID

Multiply out: $x^3 - x^2 - 5x + 2 = x^3 + x^2(k + 2) + x(2k + 1) + 2$

Lining up x^2: $-1 = k + 2 \Rightarrow k = -3$

$\therefore$ $x^3 - x^2 - 5x + 2 = (x + 2)(x^2 - 3x + 1) = 0$

$\Rightarrow x = -2,\ x = \dfrac{3 \pm \sqrt{9-4}}{2}$ (Magic)

Roots: -2, $\dfrac{3 \pm \sqrt{5}}{2}$

Example 18: Solve $x^3 - 7x^2 + 10x + 6 = 0$.

SOLUTION

Step 1: Guess $f(x) = x^3 - 7x^2 + 10x + 6$

(Root must divide into 6 - try 1, 2, 3)

$f(1) = 1 - 7 + 10 + 6 = 10$

$f(2) = 8 - 28 + 20 + 6 = 6$

$f(3) = 27 - 63 + 30 + 6 = 0$ (Breakthrough)

$\therefore$ 3 is a root.

Step 2: $\therefore$ $(x - 3)$ is a L factor.

Step 3: $x^3 - 7x^2 + 10x + 6 = (x - 3)(x^2 + kx - 2)$

$\Rightarrow x^3 - 7x^2 + 10x + 6 = x^3 + x^2(k - 3) + x(-2 - 3k) + 6$

Lining up x^2: $k - 3 = -7 \Rightarrow k = -4$

$\therefore$ $x^3 - 7x^2 + 10x + 6 = (x - 3)(x^2 - 4x - 2) = 0$

$$\Rightarrow x = 3,\ x = \frac{4 \pm \sqrt{16+8}}{2}$$

Roots: $3,\ 2 \pm \sqrt{6}$

[B] **Properties of Roots**

Properties of roots of $ax^3 + bx^2 + cx + d = 0$:

Sum of roots, S: $\alpha + \beta + \gamma = \frac{-b}{a} = \frac{-\text{2nd}}{\text{1st}}$

Sum of Product in Pairs, SPP: $\alpha\beta + \beta\gamma + \alpha\gamma = \frac{c}{a} = \frac{\text{3rd}}{\text{1st}}$

Product, P: $\alpha\beta\gamma = \frac{-d}{a} = \frac{-\text{4th}}{\text{1st}}$

Forming a cubic equation from its roots: $x^3 - Sx^2 + SPPx - P = 0$

The roots (solutions) satisfy their own equation of course.

[C] Graphs of Cubics

General Shape:

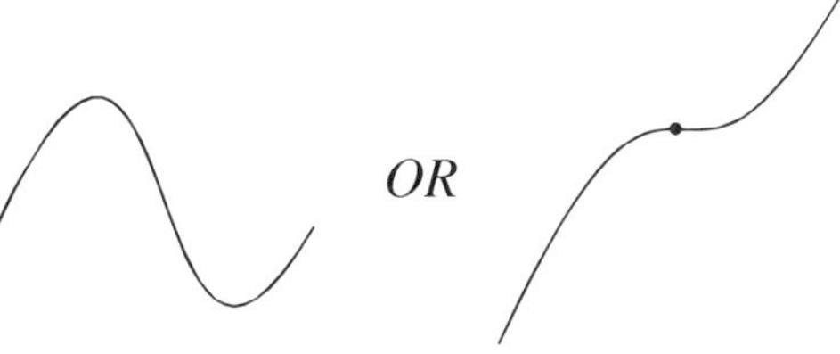

Where do you start a cubic graph?

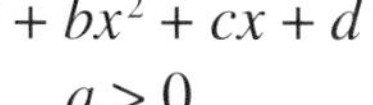

$y = ax^3 + bx^2 + cx + d$

$a > 0$

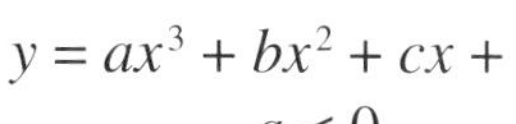

$y = ax^3 + bx^2 + cx + d$

$a < 0$

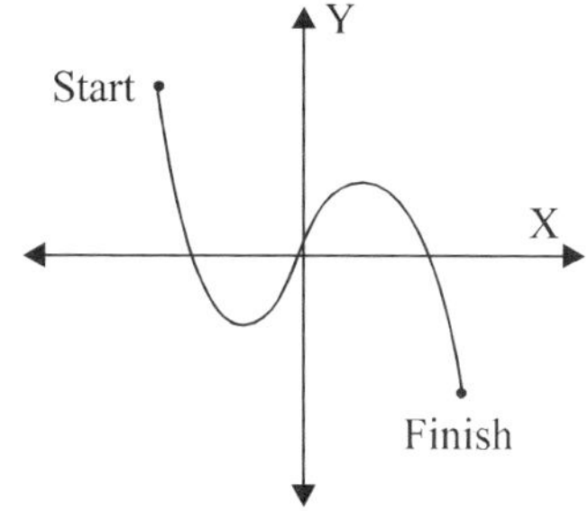

Types

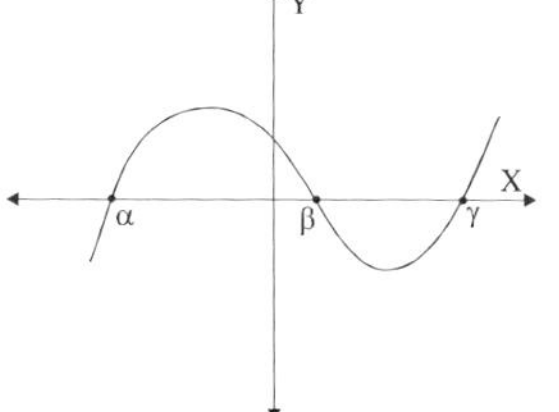

3 real, different roots

3 real roots, 2 the same

3 real roots, all the same

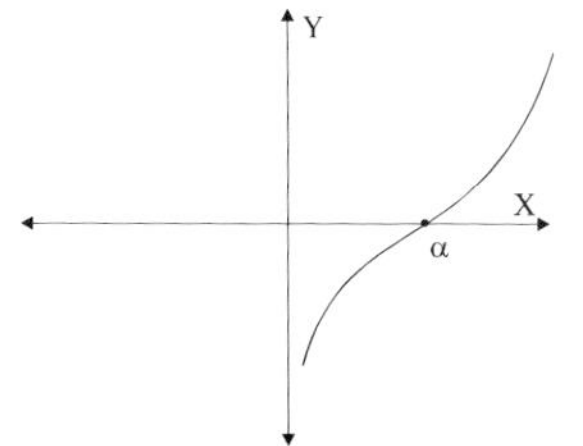

1 real root & 2 complex roots

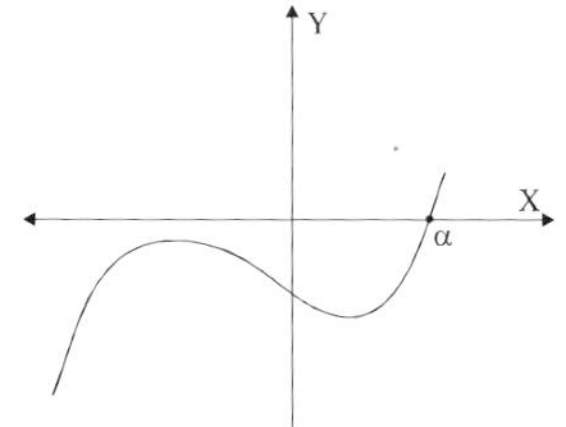

Example 19: If 1 is a root of $x^3 + 2x^2 - 3ax + 4 = 0$ find $a \in R$.

SOLUTION

$x^3 + 2x^2 - 3ax + 4 = 0$

1 is a root $\Rightarrow 1^3 + 2(1)^2 - 3a(1) + 4 = 0 \Rightarrow a = \frac{7}{3}$

Example 20: $y = f(x)$ is the graph of a cubic function. Find k and $f(x)$.

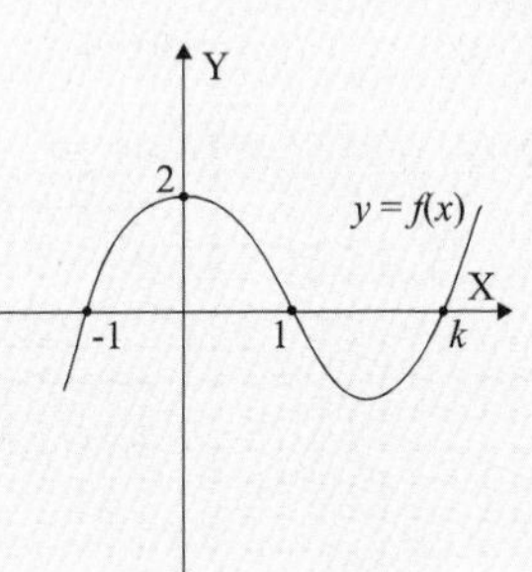

SOLUTION

-1, 1, k are roots

$\Rightarrow x + 1, x - 1, x - k$ are factors

$\therefore f(x) = (x + 1)(x - 1)(x - k) = y$

Now when $x = 0$, $y = 2$

$\Rightarrow 2 = (1)(-1)(-k) \Rightarrow k = 2$

$\therefore f(x) = (x + 1)(x - 1)(x - 2)$

$= x^3 - 2x^2 - x + 2$

Example 21: Form the cubic equation with roots

(a) 1, 2, 3 (b) 1, $2 - \sqrt{3}$, $2 + \sqrt{3}$.

SOLUTION

(a) $x^3 - \mathrm{S}x^2 + \mathrm{SPP}x - \mathrm{P} = 0$

$\Rightarrow x^3 - 6x^2 + 11x - 6 = 0$

(b) $x^3 - \mathrm{S}x^2 + \mathrm{SPP}x - \mathrm{P} = 0$

$\Rightarrow x^3 - 5x^2 + 5x - 1 = 0$

Example 22: If $x - k$ is a factor of $x^3 - c = f(x)$ show (i) $k^3 = c$, (ii) $x = k$ is the only real root of $f(x) = 0$.

SOLUTION

(i) $x - k$ is a factor $\Rightarrow k$ is a root

$\Rightarrow f(k) = k^3 - c = 0 \Rightarrow k^3 = c$

(ii) $f(x) = x^3 - k^3 = (x - k)(x^2 + kx + k^2) = 0$

$\Rightarrow x = k$ and $x^2 + kx + k^2 = 0 \Rightarrow b^2 - 4ac = k^2 - 4k^2 = -3k^2 < 0$.

No real solutions for the quadratic $\Rightarrow x = k$ is only real root.

Example 23: If $x^2 - px + 1$ is a factor of $ax^3 + bx + c$ show that $c^2 = a(a - b)$.

SOLUTION

$ax^3 + 0x^2 + bx + c = (x^2 - px + 1)(ax + c)$ .... ID

$\therefore\ ax^3 + 0x^2 + bx + c = ax^3 - apx^2 + cx^2 + ax - cpx + c$

$= ax^3 + x^2(c - ap) + x(a - cp) + c$

Lining up

1. x^2: $c - ap = 0 \Rightarrow c = ap \Rightarrow\ p = \frac{c}{a}$

2. x: $a - cp = b \Rightarrow a - c(\frac{c}{a}) = b \Rightarrow a^2 - c^2 = ab$

$\therefore\ a(a - b) = c^2$

Exercise 13 (Answers: page **87**)

Cubic Equations

1. Show by substitution that the given value of x is a root of the equation:
(a) $x = 2$ of $x^3 - 7x + 6 = 0$
(b) $x = 3$ of $x^3 - 4x^2 + 9 = 0$

2. Divide $y = f(x) = 2x^3 + x^2 - 2x - 6$ by $x - 3$.

3. From the roots given for the cubic equation:
(a) 1, 2, -3 (b) 0, 4, 4
(c) $\frac{1}{2}$, 2, $-\frac{1}{3}$ (d) $\frac{2}{3}$, $\sqrt{3}$, $-\sqrt{3}$

4. Show that
(i) $x - 2$ is a factor of $x^3 - 2x^2 - x + 2$ and hence solve the equation $x^3 - 2x^2 - x + 2 = 0$,
(ii) $x + 2$ is a factor of $6x^3 + 11x^2 - 3x - 2$ and hence solve the equation $6x^3 + 11x^2 - 3x - 2 = 0$,
(iii) $x + 3$ is a factor of $2x^3 + 9x^2 + 11x + 6$ and hence solve the equation $2x^3 + 9x^2 + 11x + 6 = 0$.

5. Solve the following cubics if:
(a) 4 is a root of $x^3 - 15x - 4 = 0$,
(b) -1 is a root of $4x^3 - 7x - 3 = 0$,
(c) $\frac{2}{3}$ is a root of $3x^3 + 16x^2 - 8 = 0$,
(d) -2 is a root of $x^3 + 5x^2 + 7x + 2 = 0$.

6. Find k if $x^3 - 2x^2 - 3x - k$ is divisible by $x - 2$ and hence solve $x^3 - 2x^2 + 3x - k = 0$.

7. Solve, given there is an integer root:
(a) $2x^3 - 3x^2 - 10x + 3 = 0$
(b) $2x^3 - x^2 - 2x + 1 = 0$
(c) $x^3 + x^2 - x + 2 = 0$
(d) $x^3 - x^2 - 3x + 2 = 0$
(e) $6x^3 + 5x^2 - 3x - 2 = 0$

8. If $(x - 1)^2$ is a factor of $ax^3 + bx^2 + 1$, find a and b.

9. If $(x - a)^2$ is a factor of $x^3 + 3rx + q$ show (i) $r = - a^2$, (ii) $q = 2a^3$.

10. If $(x + 1)$ is a factor of $x^3 + 5x^2 + kx - 12$ find k and the other two factors.

11. $P(x) = 6 + x - 4x^2 + x^3$. Show $3 - x$ is a factor of $P(x)$. Find the other factors.

12. If $x^2 + ax + b$ is a factor of $x^3 + qx^2 + rx + s$ show $r - b = a(q - a)$, $s = b(q - a)$.

13. $g(x)$ is a cubic polynomial with $g(-1) = 0$, $g(1) = 0$ and $g(2) = 5g(0)$. Find $g(x)$.

2.5 LITERAL EQUATIONS

[A] **The Idea**: These are equations involving more than one letter. You must be able to solve for one letter in terms of the others.

[B] **Difficulties**: 2 things cause difficulty:

1. **Fractions**

TRICK
Always get rid of fractions first by multiplying by the common denominator.

Example 24: If $\frac{1}{u}+\frac{1}{v}=\frac{1}{f}$ express v in terms of u and f.

SOLUTION

$\frac{1}{u}+\frac{1}{v}=\frac{1}{f}$ (Multiply across by uvf)

$\Rightarrow vf+uf=uv$ (Get v stuff on one side)

$\Rightarrow uf=uv-vf \Rightarrow uf=v(u-f)$

$\therefore \dfrac{uf}{u-f}=v$

2. **Square Roots**

Trick: Isolate it and then square both sides.

Example 25: If $A=r+\sqrt{r^2+h^2}$ find h.

SOLUTION

$A=r+\sqrt{r^2+h^2}$

$\Rightarrow (A-r)=\sqrt{r^2+h^2}$ (Isolate square root)

$\Rightarrow (A-r)^2=r^2+h^2$ (Square both sides)

$\Rightarrow (A-r)^2-r^2=h^2$

$\Rightarrow \sqrt{(A-r)^2-r^2}=h$

$\therefore h=\sqrt{A^2-2Ar}$

Exercise 14 (Answers: page **88**)

Literal Equations

Solve

1. $\frac{1}{R_1} + \frac{1}{R_2} = \frac{2}{R}$ for R_1

2. $T = 2\pi\sqrt{\frac{h^2 + k^2}{g}}$ for h

3. $\frac{f - f_1}{f + f_2} = 2$ for f_1

4. $s = 2\pi r^2 + 2\pi rh$ for h

5. $P = f\left(\frac{R^2 - r^2}{R^2 + r^2}\right)$ for r

6. $L = \frac{Wh}{d(W + p)}$ for W

7. $m^2 + \frac{Rm}{L} + \frac{1}{Lc} = 0$ for L

8. $E = I(R + r)$ for r

9. $\frac{1}{s} - \frac{1}{b} = (u - 1)\left(\frac{1}{R} + \frac{1}{r}\right)$ for u

10. $s = \frac{lr - a}{r - 1}$ for r

11. $P = r + \frac{n}{\sqrt{z}}$ for z

12. $pv^{\frac{3}{2}} = k(v - x)^{\frac{3}{2}}$ for v

2.6 MODULUS EQUATIONS

[A] **The Idea**: You will meet the idea of modulus (absolute value) in 3 different parts of the course: Algebra, vectors and complex numbers. It always means the same thing - the distance to the origin.

[B] **Notation**: $|x|$ = mod x = distance of the number x to the origin

Example: $|3| = 3$ and $|-3| = 3$

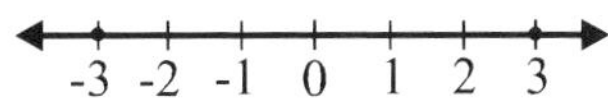

[C] **Methods of Solution**

$|x| = 5$ means find the number or numbers, x, whose distance from the origin is 5.

Obviously: $x = \pm 5$

Example 26: Solve $|2x - 1| = 7$.

SOLUTION

$|2x - 1| = 7 \Rightarrow (2x - 1) = \pm 7$

$2x - 1 = 7$	$2x - 1 = -7$
$\Rightarrow x = 4$	$\Rightarrow x = -3$

TRICK

To solve a mod equation simply remove the bars and put $\pm$ on one side or the other.

Example 27: $|3x + 1| = |2x - 1|$

SOLUTION

$|3x + 1| = |2x - 1|$

$\Rightarrow (3x + 1) = \pm(2x - 1)$

$3x + 1 = 2x - 1$	$3x + 1 = -2x + 1$
$\Rightarrow x = -2$	$\Rightarrow x = 0$

Example 28: Solve $\left|\sqrt{3m-2}\right| = m$.

SOLUTION

$\left|\sqrt{3m-2}\right| = m$

$\Rightarrow 3m - 2 = m^2$

$\Rightarrow m^2 - 3m + 2 = 0$

$\Rightarrow (m - 1)(m - 2) = 0$

$\Rightarrow m = 1, 2$

TRICK

If there is a square root in a mod equation square both sides. This automatically lifts the bars.

Exercise 15 (Answers: page **88**)

Modulus Equations

Solve

1. $|x| = 3$
2. $|x - 7| = 11$
3. $|2x + 4| = 5$
4. $|2x - 7| = |3x - 2|$
5. $|5x - 6| = 2$
6. $|7x + 4| = |x|$
7. $\left|\dfrac{7x-3}{2x+1}\right| = 4$
8. $|5x - 1| = |2x + 3|$
9. $|m-2| = 2m+1$
10. $\left|\sqrt{17-2m}\right| = m-1$

2.7 EXPONENT EQUATIONS (Variable power)

[A] **The Idea**: These are equations of the form: $a^{f(x)} = c$

[B] **Methods of Solution**

STEPS

1. Tidy up the algebra.
2. Try to express everything in the same base and read off the value of the variable from the powers *OR* take the common log of both sides if you can't get the same base.
3. **Hard**: Sums of exponential functions:

   (i) Isolate the common exponential function.

   (ii) Bracket it.

   (iii) Make a substitution by putting the object inside the bracket equal to a letter, say u.

   (iv) Solve the resulting quadratic.

   (v) Find all answers for the original variable.

Example 29: Solve $\frac{4^x}{2^{-x}} = \frac{8}{8^{2x}}$.

SOLUTION

$$\frac{4^x}{2^{-x}} = \frac{8}{8^{2x}} \Rightarrow 4^x.\,8^{2x} = 8.\,2^{-x} \Rightarrow 2^{2x}.\,2^{6x} = 2^3.\,2^{-x}$$

$$\Rightarrow 2^{8x} = 2^{3-x} \Rightarrow 8x = 3 - x \Rightarrow x = \tfrac{1}{3}$$

Example 30: Solve $\frac{7^x}{2^{2x}} = 11$.

SOLUTION

$$\frac{7^x}{2^{2x}} = 11 \Rightarrow \frac{7^x}{4^x} = 11 \Rightarrow \left(\frac{7}{4}\right)^x = 11$$

$$\Rightarrow x\log_{10}\left(\frac{7}{4}\right) = \log_{10}11 \Rightarrow x = \frac{\log_{10}11}{\log_{10}(\frac{7}{4})}$$

Example 31: Solve $2^{2x+8} + 1 = 32.\,2^x$.

SOLUTION

$$2^{2x+8} + 1 = 32.\,2^x \Rightarrow 2^8.\,2^{2x} - 32.\,2^x + 1 = 0$$

$$\Rightarrow 2^8.(2^x)^2 - 32.(2^x) + 1 = 0 \Rightarrow 256.(2^x)^2 - 32.(2^x) + 1 = 0$$

Let $u = 2^x \Rightarrow u^2 = (2^x)^2$

Rewriting $256u^2 - 32u + 1 = 0 \Rightarrow (16u - 1)(16u - 1) = 0$

$\therefore u = 2^x = \frac{1}{16} \Rightarrow 2^x = 2^{-4} \Rightarrow x = -4$

Exercise 16 (Answers: page 89)

Exponential Equations

1. **Simple** (*Common Base*)

Solve:

(a) $3^{x-1} = 3^{2x+1}$

(b) $3^{2x+1} = 9^{4x}$

(c) $4^{2x} = 2^{x}$

(d) $2^{2x-5} = 4^{3x}$

(e) $2^{\frac{3}{x}} = 32$

(f) $9^{\frac{x}{2}} = 81$

(g) $(25)^{x+1} = (125)^{2x}$

(h) $4^{2x} = \dfrac{64}{2^{x}}$

(i) $4^{-x} = \dfrac{1}{16.2^{-x}}$

(j) $9^{x^2} = 3^{x+1}$

2. **Simple** (*Uncommon base*)

Solve giving your answers in terms of $\log_{10}$:

(a) $3^{x} = 5$

(b) $4^{2x} = 5$

(c) $(0.1)^{x} = 9$

(d) $5 \times 3^{x} = 80$

(e) $3^{x}.3^{2x+1} = 10$

(f) $5^{x}.5^{3x-2} = 100$

(g) $\dfrac{5^{x}}{5^{-x}} = 7$

(h) $2^{\frac{3}{x}} = 16$

(i) $4^{\frac{3}{2x}} = \frac{1}{10}$

(j) $\dfrac{5^{3x}}{5^{-2x}} = 11$

3. **Harder Questions**

Solve:

(a) $2^{2x} - 5.2^{x+1} + 16 = 0$

Hint: Let $u = 2^{x}$

(b) $2.3^{x} - 2.3^{-x} = 3$

Hint: Let $u = 3^{x}$

(c) $5^{2x} - 26.5^{x+1} + 625 = 0$

(d) $3^{2x} - 12.3^{x} + 27 = 0$

(e) $4^{2x} - 12.4^{x} + 32 = 0$

(f) $2.2^{2x} - 7.2^{x} + 6 = 0$

(g) $4^{2x+1} - 36.4^{x} + 80 = 0$

(h) $3e^{x} - 7 + 2e^{-x} = 0$

(i) $2^{2x} - 5.2^{x} + 4 = 0$

(j) $2e^{x} - 2.e^{-x} = 3$

(k) $2^{x+1} + 7 - 4.2^{-x} = 0$

2.8 LOG EQUATIONS

[A] **The Idea**: These are equations obviously involving logs.

[B] **Steps for solution**

STEPS

1. Get all the logs in the same base.

Trick: There are 2 ways to do this:

(i) Change of base (COB): $\log_a M = \log_b M \times \log_a b$

(ii) Inverting (Drop): $\dfrac{1}{\log_b a} = \log_a b$

2. Get all the logs on one side.
3. Get out of logs (hoosh).
4. Solve the resulting equation.
5. Check your answer.

Example 32: Solve $\log_4\left(\dfrac{x-2}{3}\right) = 2$

SOLUTION

$\log_4\left(\dfrac{x-2}{3}\right) = 2 \Rightarrow \dfrac{x-2}{3} = 4^2 \Rightarrow x - 2 = 48$

$\therefore\ x = 50$

Example 33: Solve $\log_2(x-4)-\log_2 5=-\log_2(2x-5)$.

SOLUTION

$$\log_2(x-4)-\log_2 5=-\log_2(2x-5)$$

$$\Rightarrow \log_2(x-4)+\log_2(2x-5)-\log_2 5=0$$

$$\Rightarrow \log_2\left\{\frac{(x-4)(2x-5)}{5}\right\}=0 \Rightarrow \frac{2x^2-13x+20}{5}=2^0$$

$$\Rightarrow 2x^2-13x+20=5 \Rightarrow 2x^2-13x+15=0$$

$$\Rightarrow (2x-3)(x-5)=0 \therefore x=\tfrac{3}{2}, x=5$$

Check: $x=\frac{3}{2}$ doesn't work - it gives logs of negative numbers on the first line. $x=5$ is fine.

Example 34: Solve $\log_3 x+3\log_x 3=4$.

SOLUTION

$$\log_3 x+3\log_x 3=4$$

$$\Rightarrow \log_3 x+\frac{3}{\log_3 x}=4 \text{ (Invert trick to get same base)}$$

$$\Rightarrow (\log_3 x)^2-4\log_3 x+3=0 \Rightarrow (\log_3 x-1)(\log_3 x-3)=0$$

$\Rightarrow \log_3 x=1, \log_3 x=3 \Rightarrow x=3, x=27$ (**Check**: Both work)

Example 35: Solve $\log_2 x\times\log_4 x=\frac{9}{2}$.

SOLUTION

$$\log_2 x\times\log_4 x=\tfrac{9}{2}$$

$$\Rightarrow \log_2 x(\log_2 x\times\log_4 2)=\tfrac{9}{2} \text{ (Change of Base trick)}$$

$$\Rightarrow (\log_2 x)^2\times\tfrac{1}{2}=\tfrac{9}{2} \Rightarrow (\log_2 x)^2=9 \Rightarrow \log_2 x=\pm 3$$

$\Rightarrow x=2^3, 2^{-3} \Rightarrow x=8, \frac{1}{8}$ (**Check**: Both work)

Exercise 17 (Answers: page **89**)
Log Equations

1. Solve

(a) $\log_2 x = 3$

(b) $\log_3 x^2 = 2$

(c) $\log_{10} \sqrt{x} = 4$

(d) $\log_2 (x^2 - 5x + 2) = 3$

(e) $\log_7 (x - 1) = 2$

(f) $\log_{10}\left(\dfrac{x-2}{3}\right) = 2$

(g) $\log_3\left(\dfrac{6x^2+14x-4}{x}\right) = 2$

---

2. Solve

(a) $2 \log_x 64 = 3$

(b) $\log_x 2 + \log_x 32 = 2$

(c) $1 + \log_2 (3x + 1) = \log_2 (2x + 1)$

(d) $\log_2 (x - 4) - \log_2 12 = -\log_2 (x - 5)$

(e) $3 \log_2 x - 2 \log_2 x - \log_2 (x - 1) = \log_2 5$

(f) $2 \log_5 x = 2 \log_5 3 + \log_5 (x - 2)$

---

3. Solve

(a) $\log_5 x = 1 + \log_5 (\frac{3}{2x+1})$

(b) $\dfrac{6}{\log_x 4} + \dfrac{6}{\log_4 x} = 13$

(c) $\log_9 (\frac{x}{3}) = \log_9 x . \log_x 3$

(d) $2 \log_9 x = \frac{1}{2} + \log_9 (5x + 18)$

(e) $2 \log_4 x + 3 \log_x 4 = 7$

(f) $(\log_2 x)^2 - 5 \log_2 x + 6 = 0$

2.9 SURD EQUATIONS

[A] **The Idea**: These are equations involving square roots.

[B] **Methods of Solution**

STEPS

1. If there is one square root isolate it.
2. Square both sides.
3. If a square root still remains, square again.
4. Solve.
5. Check your answers (There may be 0 or 1 or 2 solutions).

Example 36: Solve $\sqrt{5x+9}+1=x$.

SOLUTION

$\sqrt{5x+9}+1=x \Rightarrow \sqrt{5x+9}=(x-1) \Rightarrow 5x+9=x^2-2x+1$

$\Rightarrow 0=x^2-7x-8 \Rightarrow 0=(x+1)(x-8)$

$\therefore x=-1, x=8$

Check:

$x=-1$: $\sqrt{4}+1=-1$ (Wrong)

$x=8$: $\sqrt{49}+1=8$ (Correct)

$\therefore x=8$

Example 37: Solve $\sqrt{5-2x}-\sqrt{x+6}=\sqrt{x+3}$.

SOLUTION

$\sqrt{5-2x}-\sqrt{x+6}=\sqrt{x+3}$

$\Rightarrow (5-2x)+(x+6)-2\sqrt{5-2x}\sqrt{x+6}=x+3$

$\Rightarrow 8-2x=2\sqrt{5-2x}\sqrt{x+6} \Rightarrow 4-x=\sqrt{5-2x}\sqrt{x+6}$

$\Rightarrow 16-8x+x^2=(5-2x)(x+6)$

$\Rightarrow 16-8x+x^2=30-7x-2x^2$

$\Rightarrow 3x^2-x-14=0 \Rightarrow (3x-7)(x+2)=0$

$\therefore x=\frac{7}{3}, -2$ (Only -2 works)

Exercise 18 (Answers: page **90**)

Surd Equations

Solve

1. $\sqrt{3x+4}=2+\sqrt{x}$
2. $\sqrt{7x-2}-\sqrt{x+1}=\sqrt{3}$
3. $\sqrt{3x}+3=\sqrt{7x-3}$

4. $1+\sqrt{x-4}=\sqrt{x+1}$

5. $\sqrt{x-5}+\sqrt{x+7}=6$

6. $\sqrt{3x-11}+\sqrt{3x}=\sqrt{12x-23}$

7. $\sqrt{4x^2-7x+1}=2x-\frac{9}{5}$

8. $10-\sqrt{25+9x}=3\sqrt{x}$

9. $\sqrt{x-1}+\sqrt{x}=\frac{2}{\sqrt{x}}$

(**Hint**: Move $\sqrt{x}$ to the right before squaring)

10. $\sqrt{1+x}+\sqrt{x}=\dfrac{2}{\sqrt{1+x}}$

(**Hint**: Move $\sqrt{1+x}$ to the right before squaring)

11. $\sqrt{x+5}+\sqrt{x}=\frac{10}{\sqrt{x}}$

12. $1+2\sqrt{x}=\sqrt{4x+\sqrt{16x+2}}$

13. $\sqrt{8x-7}-\sqrt{2x+3}=\sqrt{2x-6}$

14. $\dfrac{5}{\sqrt{x+1}-\sqrt{x-4}}=\sqrt{2x+9}$

(**Hint**: Rationalise the denominator)

15. $\dfrac{\sqrt{x+1}-\sqrt{x}}{\sqrt{x+1}+\sqrt{x}}=\dfrac{1}{3}$

(**Hint**: Rationalise the denominator)

2.10 SIMULTANEOUS EQUATIONS

There are 4 types of simultaneous equation to be treated.

[A] 2 linear in 2 unknowns,

[B] 1 quadratic and 1 linear in 2 unknowns,

[C] 3 linears in 3 unknowns,

[D] 2 log equations in 2 unknowns.

[A] **2 linears in 2 unknowns** (2 intersecting straight lines)

STEPS

1. Eliminate 1 letter.
2. Solve for the other.
3. Plonk into either of the original equations to get second unknown.

Example 38: Solve $\sqrt{3}x-\sqrt{2}y=2\sqrt{3}$;

$2\sqrt{2}x+\sqrt{3}y=\sqrt{2}$.

SOLUTION

$\sqrt{3}x-\sqrt{2}y=2\sqrt{3}$ .... (1)

$2\sqrt{2}x+\sqrt{3}y=\sqrt{2}$ .... (2)

$3x-\sqrt{6}y=6$ .... (1) $\times\sqrt{3}$

$4x+\sqrt{6}y=2$ .... (2) $\times\sqrt{2}$

$7x \qquad =8$

$\therefore x=\frac{8}{7}$

Plonking into (1): $8(\frac{\sqrt{3}}{7})-\sqrt{2}y=2\sqrt{3}\Rightarrow 8\sqrt{3}-7\sqrt{2}y=14\sqrt{3}$

$$\Rightarrow -6\sqrt{3}=7\sqrt{2}y\Rightarrow y=\frac{-6\sqrt{3}}{7\sqrt{2}}=-\frac{3\sqrt{6}}{7}$$

[B] **1 linear and 1 quadratic** (a line intersecting a curve)

STEPS

1. Look at the letters in the quadratic to decide which is the easier to eliminate.
2. Use the linear to isolate this letter.
3. Plonk into quadratic and solve for the other letter.
4. Plonk these values into linear to get all solutions.

Example 39: Solve $x^2 + 2xy = 5$; $2x + 3y = 4$.

SOLUTION

$x^2 + 2xy = 5$ ..... (Q)

$y = \frac{(4-2x)}{3}$ ...... (L)

$\therefore x^2 + \frac{2x(4-2x)}{3} = 5$

$\Rightarrow 3x^2 + 8x - 4x^2 = 15$

$\Rightarrow 0 = x^2 - 8x + 15$

$\Rightarrow 0 = (x - 3)(x - 5)$

$\therefore\ x = 3, 5$

Plonking into linear:

$x = 3 \Rightarrow\ y = -\frac{2}{3}$

$x = 5\ \Rightarrow y = -2$

Solutions: $(3, -\frac{2}{3})$, $(5, -2)$

[C] **3 linears in 3 unknowns** (3 intersecting planes)

STEPS

1. Eliminate one letter using 2 equations.
2. Eliminate the same letter using 2 others.
3. Solve the resulting equations as for 2 equations in 2 unknowns.
4. Work backwards to find all letters.

Example 40: Solve

$x - 2y + 3z = 4$ ..... (1)

$2x + y - 4z = 3$ ..... (2)

$3x - 4y + z = 2$ ..... (3)

SOLUTION

$x - 2y + 3z = 4$ ..... (1)

$4x + 2y - 8z = 6$ ..... (2) × 2

$5x - 5z = 10$ ..... (4)

$-2x + 4y - 6z = -8$ ..... (1) × -2

$3x - 4y + z = 2$ ..... (3)

$x - 5z = -6$ ..... (5)

$x - 5z = -6$ ..... (5)

$-5x + 5z = -10$ ..... (4) × -1

$-4x = -16$

$\therefore\ x = 4$

Plonking $x = 4$ into (5): $4 - 5z = -6 \Rightarrow z = 2$

Plonking $x = 4$, $z = 2$ into (1): $4 - 2y + 6 = 4 \Rightarrow y = 3$

Solution: (4, 3, 2)

[D] 2 log equations in 2 unknowns

STEPS

1. Eliminate logs with the same base.
2. Get out of logs by hooshing.
3. Plonk into one of the original equations.

Example 41: Solve

$$\log_2 x - \log_3 y = 4$$
$$3\log_2 x + \log_3 y = 0$$

SOLUTION

$$\log_2 x - \log_3 y = 4$$
$$3\log_2 x + \log_3 y = 0$$
$$4\log_2 x = 4$$

$4\log_2 x = 4 \Rightarrow \log_2 x = 1$

$\Rightarrow x = 2^1 = 2$

$\Rightarrow \log_2 2 - \log_3 y = 4$

$\Rightarrow \log_3 y = -3$

$\Rightarrow y = \frac{1}{27}$

Exercise 19 (Answers: page **90**)

Simultaneous Equations

1. **2 linear equations in 2 unknowns**

Solve

(a) $5x + 3y = 11$
$2x - y = 11$

(b) $8x - 9y = -6$
$3x - 5y = 1$

(c) $\frac{(x+2)}{3} + \frac{(y-3)}{2} = 6$

$\frac{(x-2)}{5} - \frac{(y+3)}{6} = -1$

2. **3 linear equations in 3 unknowns**

Solve

(a) $x - 2y - 3z = -1$
$2x + y + z = 6$
$x + 3y - 2z = 13$

(b) $5x + 2y - z = -7$
$x - 2y + 2z = 0$
$3y + z = 17$

(c) $\frac{1}{x} = \frac{2}{3}$

$\frac{1}{x+y} = \frac{2}{5}$

$\frac{1}{x+y+z} = 1$

(d) $\frac{1}{x} = 1\frac{1}{4}$

$\frac{1}{x} + \frac{1}{y} = 2\frac{1}{3}$

$\frac{1}{x} + \frac{1}{y} + \frac{1}{z} = 3\frac{1}{2}$

(e) $\frac{3}{x} + \frac{1}{y} + \frac{4}{z} = 7$

$\frac{1}{x} + \frac{2}{y} + \frac{1}{z} = \frac{1}{2}$

$\frac{4}{x} - \frac{5}{y} - \frac{2}{z} = 12$

(**Hint**: Let $u = \frac{1}{x}$, $v = \frac{1}{y}$, $w = \frac{1}{z}$)

(f) $2x + y + z + 7 = 0$
$x + 2y + z + 8 = 0$
$x + y + 2z + 9 = 0$

(g) $6x - 3y + 2z = 5a - 2b$
$4x + 2y - z = 3(2a + 3b)$
$5x - 7y + 3z = -4(a + 3b)$

(h) $\frac{(x-z)}{4} - \frac{(x-y)}{3} = 0$

$\frac{(x-2)}{5} + \frac{(y+3)}{7} = \frac{x+y}{6}$

$(\frac{x}{2} - \frac{y}{3}) = 1 + \frac{y}{6} - \frac{z}{5}$

3. **One linear, one quadratic**

Solve

(a) $x^2 + xy = -1$
$x - y + 3 = 0$

(b) $y = x^2 - 4x - 2$
$2x + y = 1$

(c) $x + 3y = 9$
$xy = 6$

(d) $3x - y = 2$
$y^2 - x^2 = 12$

(e) $4xy + y^2 + 35 = 0$
$2x + 3y = 5$

(f) $x^2 + 2xy = 5$
$2x + 3y = 4$

(g) $x^2 + y^2 + 6x - 2y = 6$
$3x - 2y = 1$

(h) $2ax - by = a^2$
$bxy = a^3$

(i) $x + 3y = 5$
$x^2 + y^2 = 25$

4. **Simultaneous Log Equations**

Solve

(a) $3\log_4 y + 2\log_5 x = 3$
$\log_5 x + \log_4 y = 1$

(b) $\log_3 x - \log_3 y = 4$
$\log_2 (x - 33y) = 4$

(c) $2\log_3 x + \log_3 y = 5$
$\log_3 x - 2\log_3 y = 5$

(d) $2\log_3 x + \log_2 y = 10$
$4\log_3 x - 3\log_2 y = 0$

3. INEQUALITIES ($>, <, \geq, \leq$)

3.1 MANIPULATING INEQUALITIES

It is so easy to make a mistake when manipulating inequalities as certain operations reverse the inequality sign.

DO'S AND DON'TS

Example: $8 > 4$

1. **Add 7**: $8 + 7 > 4 + 7$ (Correct)
2. **Subtract 7**: $8 - 7 > 4 - 7$ (Correct)
3. **Move**: $8 - 4 > 0$ (Correct) and
   $0 > 4 - 8$ (Correct)
4. **Multiply by 7**: $56 > 28$ (Correct)
5. **Divide by 4**: $2 > 1$ (Correct)
6. **Multiply by -7**: $-56 > -28$ (Wrong)
7. **Divide by -4**: $-2 > -1$ (Wrong)

TRICK

You can do all the same operations for inequalities as for equalities except two.

TRICK

Never multiply or divide an inequality by a negative number. Otherwise, do what you do for equalities.

3.2 SOLVING INEQUALITIES

There are 4 types

[A] Linear
[B] Quadratic
[C] Rational
[D] Modulus

[B], [C] and [D]: These are all done by the **region test**.

[A] **Linear**: $ax + b > 0$

STEPS

1. Get letters on the side in order to give a positive coefficient and numbers on the other side.
2. Solve for the letter.

Example 1: Solve $2x + 7 > 5x - 2$

SOLUTION

$2x + 7 > 5x - 2 \Rightarrow -3x > -9 \Rightarrow 9 > 3x \Rightarrow 3 > x$

[B] **Quadratics**: $ax^2 + bx + c \leq 0$

STEPS

1. Get all terms on one side and zero on the other side.
2. Solve the corresponding equation to get the roots α, β.
3. Use the roots in ascending order to form regions: $\leftarrow \alpha \leftrightarrow \beta \rightarrow$
4. Choose a nice number in each region to test the inequality using the test box.

Example 2: Solve $2x^2 - 7x \leq 3$

SOLUTION

$2x^2 - 7x \leq 3$

$\boxed{2x^2 - 7x - 3 \leq 0}$ ....Test Box

Solve $2x^2 - 7x - 3 = 0$ by magic $\Rightarrow x = \dfrac{7 \pm \sqrt{73}}{4}$

Region Test on $2x^2 - 7x - 3 \leq 0$

$\longleftarrow$	$\frac{7-\sqrt{73}}{4}$	$\longleftrightarrow$	$\frac{7+\sqrt{73}}{4}$	$\longrightarrow$
-1		0		5
$2(-1)^2 - 7(-1) - 3 \leq 0$		$2(0)^2 - 7(0) - 3 \leq 0$		$2(5)^2 - 7(5) - 3 \leq 0$
Wrong ✗		Correct ✓		Wrong ✗

$\therefore \dfrac{7-\sqrt{73}}{4} \leq x \leq \dfrac{7+\sqrt{73}}{4}$

Example 3: If $y = \dfrac{x^2+5}{x+2}$ find the range of values of y for which x is real.

SOLUTION

$$y = \frac{x^2+5}{x+2} \Rightarrow xy + 2y = x^2 + 5 \Rightarrow x^2 - xy + (5-2y) = 0 \ \text{(Q in } x)$$

$\therefore$ Real roots $\Rightarrow b^2 \geq 4ac$

$\Rightarrow y^2 \geq 4(5-2y) \Rightarrow y^2 + 8y - 20 \geq 0$

$\Rightarrow \boxed{(y-2)(y+10) \geq 0}$ ....Test Box

Roots of equality: -10, 2

←	-10	↔	2	→
-11		0		3
(-13)(-1) ≥ 0	|	(-2)(10) ≥ 0	|	(1)(13) ≥ 0
Correct ✓		Wrong ✗		Correct ✓

$\therefore y \leq -10,\ y \geq 2$

[C] **Rationals**: $\dfrac{P(x)}{Q(x)} > 0$

STEPS

1. Simplify the functions on either side of the inequality sign if possible.
2. Multiply both sides by the denominator squared unless you are certain that it is positive.
3. Get all terms on one side.
4. Take out HCF.
5. Solve the corresponding equation.
6. Do region test on the roots in ascending order on Test Box.

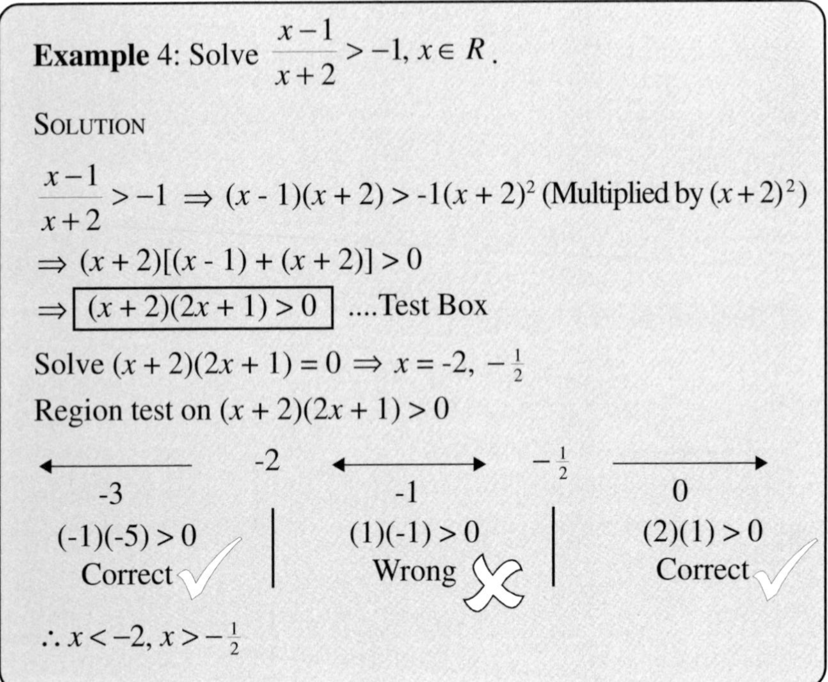

Example 4: Solve $\dfrac{x-1}{x+2} > -1, x \in R$.

SOLUTION

$\dfrac{x-1}{x+2} > -1 \Rightarrow (x - 1)(x + 2) > -1(x + 2)^2$ (Multiplied by $(x+2)^2$)

$\Rightarrow (x + 2)[(x - 1) + (x + 2)] > 0$

$\Rightarrow \boxed{(x + 2)(2x + 1) > 0}$ ....Test Box

Solve $(x + 2)(2x + 1) = 0 \Rightarrow x = -2, -\frac{1}{2}$

Region test on $(x + 2)(2x + 1) > 0$

←	-2	↔	$-\frac{1}{2}$	→
-3		-1		0
$(-1)(-5) > 0$		$(1)(-1) > 0$		$(2)(1) > 0$
Correct ✓		Wrong ✗		Correct ✓

$\therefore x < -2, x > -\frac{1}{2}$

[D] **Modulus** $|ax + b| > c$

STEPS

1. Solve the corresponding modulus equality.
2. Do region test on roots in ascending order on Test Box.

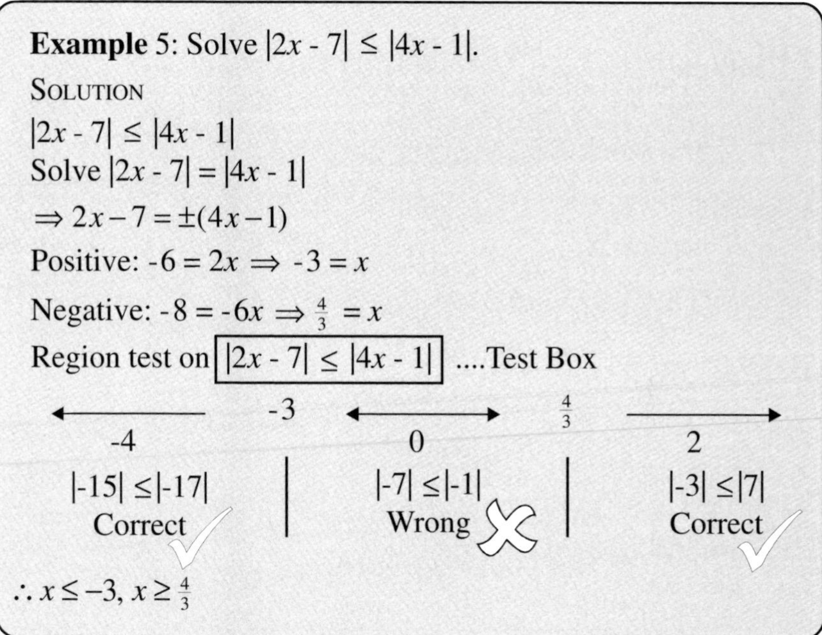

Example 5: Solve $|2x - 7| \leq |4x - 1|$.

Solution

$|2x - 7| \leq |4x - 1|$

Solve $|2x - 7| = |4x - 1|$

$\Rightarrow 2x - 7 = \pm(4x - 1)$

Positive: $-6 = 2x \Rightarrow -3 = x$

Negative: $-8 = -6x \Rightarrow \frac{4}{3} = x$

Region test on $\boxed{|2x - 7| \leq |4x - 1|}$ ....Test Box

$\therefore x \leq -3,\ x \geq \frac{4}{3}$

3.3 Proving inequalities

Inequalities are difficult to prove. The best method is known as *reductio ad absurdum* which means "deduce garbage".

Steps

1. Assume the opposite to the given statement to be proved.
2. Tidy up the algebra.
3. Deduce rubbish - our assumption is false.
4. The statement is correct.

Example 6: Prove $a + \frac{1}{a} \geq 2$ for all positive a.

Solution

To prove $a + \frac{1}{a} \geq 2$ for all $a > 0$

Assume $a + \frac{1}{a} < 2$ for all $a > 0$

$\Rightarrow a^2 + 1 < 2a \Rightarrow a^2 - 2a + 1 < 0$

$\Rightarrow (a - 1)^2 < 0$ (This is Rubbish)

$\therefore\ a + \frac{1}{a} \geq 2$

Example 7: Prove $\frac{a}{b^2} + \frac{b}{a^2} \geq \frac{1}{a} + \frac{1}{b}$ for all $a, b > 0$.

SOLUTION

Assume $\frac{a}{b^2} + \frac{b}{a^2} < \frac{1}{a} + \frac{1}{b}$ for all $a, b > 0$

$\Rightarrow a^3 + b^3 < ab^2 + a^2b$

$\Rightarrow a^3 + b^3 - ab^2 - a^2b < 0$

$\Rightarrow a^2(a - b) - b^2(a - b) < 0$

$\Rightarrow (a - b)(a^2 - b^2) < 0$

$\Rightarrow (a - b)(a - b)(a + b) < 0$

$\Rightarrow (a - b)^2(a + b) < 0$ (Rubbish - not true because LHS is positive)

$\therefore \frac{a}{b^2} + \frac{b}{a^2} \geq \frac{1}{a} + \frac{1}{b}$ for all $a, b > 0$

3.4 GRAPHS OF INEQUALITIES

There are 2 types:

[A] **Linear**

[B] **Modulus**

[A] **Linear** (half planes)

STEPS

1. Draw equality (**E**) as a straight line.
2. Choose a point above or below line (region test).
3. Plonk this point into the inequality (**I**).
4. If it works shade the region. If it does not, shade the other.

Example 8: Plot $x + y \leq 2$.

SOLUTION

E: $x + y = 2$

I: Plonk (2, 2) into $x + y \leq 2$

$\Rightarrow$ $4 \leq 2$ (Wrong)

$\therefore$ other region.

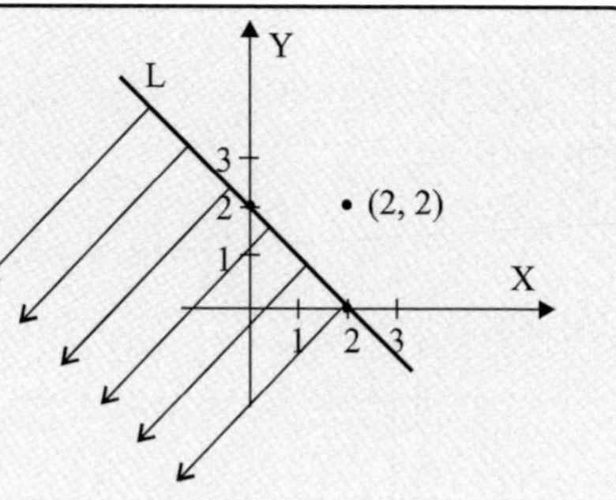

[B] **Modulus**

(i) *x* or *y* inside the mod sign (Graph is V shaped)

STEPS

1. Draw up a table by using values of x determined by putting yoke inside mod = 0 and solving in your head.
2. Choose 2 values to the right and 2 to the left.
3. Plot V, i.e. the equality.
4. Choose a point inside or outside the V (region test).
5. Plonk it into the inequality.
6. If it works, shade the region. If it does not work, shade the other.

Example 9: Plot $y \geq |x + 2|$.

SOLUTION

E: $y = |x + 2|$

Table: x = (-2)

x	-4	-3	(-2)	-1	0
$x + 2$	-2	-1	0	1	2
$y = \|x + 2\|$	2	1	0	1	2

I: Plonk (-2, 2) into $y \geq |x + 2|$

$2 \geq |-2 + 2|$ (Correct)

Therefore shade this region (inside V)

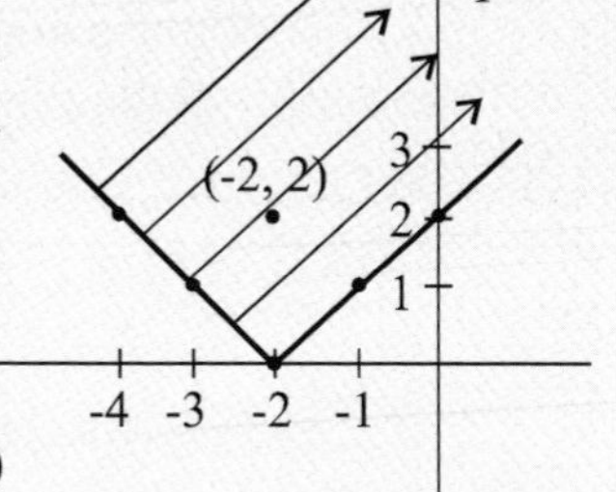

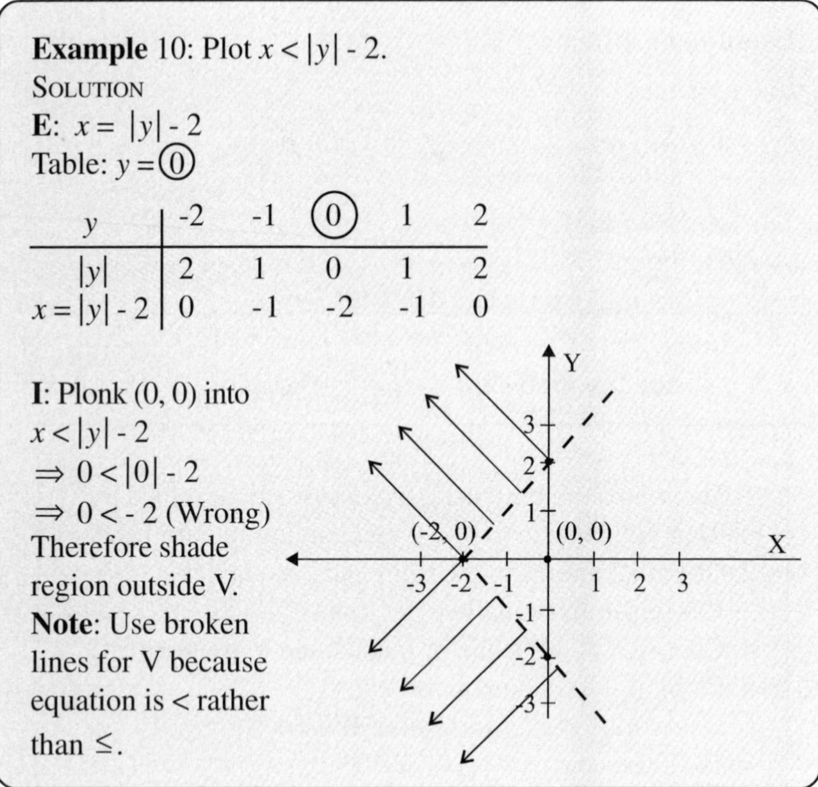

Example 10: Plot $x < |y| - 2$.

SOLUTION

E: $x = |y| - 2$

Table: $y = \textcircled{0}$

y	-2	-1	(0)	1	2
$\lvert y \rvert$	2	1	0	1	2
$x = \lvert y \rvert - 2$	0	-1	-2	-1	0

I: Plonk (0, 0) into
$x < |y| - 2$
$\Rightarrow 0 < |0| - 2$
$\Rightarrow 0 < -2$ (Wrong)
Therefore shade region outside V.

Note: Use broken lines for V because equation is < rather than ≤.

(ii) ***x* and *y* both inside the mod sign** (Graph is in the shape of parallel lines)

STEPS

1. Solve the equality to get 2 parallel lines.
2. Plot the lines.
3. Choose a point inside or outside the parallel lines.
4. If it works, shade the region. If it does not work, shade the other region.

Example 11: Plot $|x+y| \leq 2$.

SOLUTION

E: $|x+y| = 2$

$\Rightarrow x+y = \pm 2$

$\Rightarrow$ *K*: $x+y=2$ and
L: $x+y=-2$

I: Plonk (0, 0) into

$|x+y| \leq 2$

$\Rightarrow |0+0| \leq 2$ (True)

Therefore, shade the region between the parallel lines.

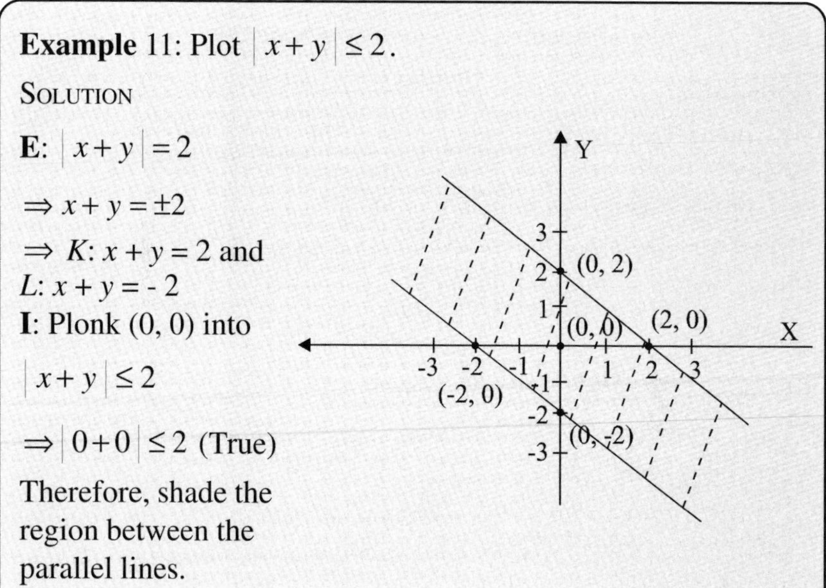

Exercise 20 (Answers: page **90**)
Inequalities

1. **Linear/Quadratic**
Solve
(a) $3x + 5 > 4$
(b) $x - 1 > -7x + 3$
(c) $6 - 2x^2 \geq x$
(d) $3x^2 > 5x + 2$

2. **Modulus**
Solve
(a) $|x - 1| > 2$
(b) $|2x - 3| \leq 5$
(c) $\left|\frac{x}{x+1}\right| > 3$
(d) $|5 - 3x| \leq |x + 1|$

3. **Rational**
Solve
(a) $\frac{x-2}{x+1} < 2$
(b) $\frac{x+1}{x-3} < 5$
(c) $x+1 > \frac{3}{x-1}$
(d) $\frac{x+5}{x+1} < 4$

4. Plot
(a) $y = |x - 1|$
(b) $y \leq |x - 3|$
(c) $y = |x| - 3$
(d) $y = |3x| + 1$
(e) $y < |x + 1|$
(f) $|x+2y| \geq 4$

5. Prove
(a) $a^2 + b^2 \geq 2ab$ for all a, b.
(b) $\frac{2ab}{b+a} \leq \sqrt{ab}$ for all positive a, b.
(c) $\sqrt{\frac{a^2+b^2}{2}} \geq \frac{a+b}{2}$ for all positive a, b.
(d) $\frac{x^2}{1+x^4} \leq \frac{1}{2}$ for all x.
(e) $(a+b)\left(\frac{1}{a}+\frac{1}{b}\right) \geq 4$ for all positive a, b.

ALGEBRA REVISION QUESTIONS

These 3 part questions are similar to the questions on the LC paper. The answers to these questions and hints to help you solve them are available on our website:
www.studentxpress.ie

1. (a) Solve $\log_9 (x + 2) - \log_3 x = 0$.
(b) Show that $x^2 + ax + b = 0$ and $x^2 + bx + a = 0$ have a common root of 1 if $a + b = -1$.
(c) Solve (i) $\sqrt{x-5} + 2 = \sqrt{x+7}$, (ii) $2^{2x+1} - 16.2^x + 32 = 0$.

2. (a) If $\dfrac{ax}{b-c} = \dfrac{by}{c-a} = \dfrac{cz}{a-b}$ show $ax + by + cz = 0$.
(b) Solve (i) $x + \sqrt{5x+19} = -1$, (ii) $\log_2 x + \dfrac{12}{\log_2 x} = 7$.
(c) If $\alpha, n\alpha$ are the roots of $ax^2 + bx + c = 0$ show $nb^2 = (1 + n)^2 ac$.

3. (a) Solve $(1 - \frac{1}{x})^2 = 2$. Give your answer in the form $a + \sqrt{b}$.
(b) Solve $x^3 + 3x^2 + x - 2 = 0$ given one integer root.
(c) If $F(\frac{a}{b}) = F(a) - F(b)$ for all positive values of a and b, show
(i) $F(1) = 0$, (ii) $F(\frac{1}{x}) = -F(x)$, (iii) $F(y^2) = 2F(y)$.

4. (a) Solve $\log_4 (6x + 1) - 2 = 2 \log_4 x$.
(b) One root of $x^3 + kx + 4 = 0$ is 2.
(i) Find k, (ii) find the other roots.
(c) Find k if the curves C_1: $y = (1 - k) - x - x^2$ and
C_2: $y = x^2 + 2kx + \frac{3}{2}$ intersect at one point only.

5. (a) If $f(x) = \frac{1}{x^n}$ and $f(x) = f(\frac{1}{x})$ show $n = 0$.

(b) If α, β are roots of a quadratic $(k+2)x^2+(2k+1)x+k=0$ find k if $\alpha=\beta$.

(c) Prove $(ax+by)^2 \le (a^2+b^2)(x^2+y^2)$ for all $a, b, x, y \in R$.

6. (a) (i) If $27^x = 9$ and $2^{x-y} = 64$ find x, y.

(ii) If $f(x) = \dfrac{2^x}{2^{2x}+1}$, find $f(-1)$.

(b) If α, β are the roots of $f(x) = x^2 + 2kx + k + 2 = 0$ show that $(\alpha - \beta)^2 = 4(k^2 - k - 2)$. If the roots differ by 4, find the values of k.

(c) If α, β are roots of $x^2 + 2bx + c = 0$ show that $\alpha^3 + \beta^3 = 2b(3c - 4b^2)$.

7. (a) If $(x+1)$ and $(x-3)$ are factors of $f(x) = kx^3 - 6x^2 + bx - 6$, find k and b and the other root.

(b) (i) Solve $\dfrac{x}{x+1} > 2$, (ii) Solve $\left|\dfrac{2+x}{x-3}\right| > 4$.

(c) If the roots of the equation $px^2 + qx + r$ are in the ratio 5:3, show that $15q^2 = 64pr$.

8. (a) Solve $\left|\dfrac{7x-3}{2x+1}\right| = 4$.

(b) Find the co-ordinates of the points of intersection of the curves:

$$y = 2x^2 - 7x - 17 = 0$$
$$y = 2x^2 + 9x - 13 = 0$$

(c) If $x, y \in R$ and $x + y = 1$ show that $4xy \le 1$. Deduce that $x^2 + y^2 \ge \frac{1}{2}$.

9. (a) Solve $4x^{-1} - 9x^{-\frac{1}{2}} + 2 = 0$.

(b) Solve (i) $\sqrt{2x+6}-\sqrt{x+4}=1$.

(ii) $\sqrt{2}x+\sqrt{5}y=\sqrt{2}$;

$3\sqrt{5}x-\sqrt{2}y=3\sqrt{5}$.

(c) Prove that if the sum of the reciprocals of the roots of $ax^2 + bx + c = 0$ is 1 then $b + c = 0$.

10. (a) Solve $\frac{4^{3+x}}{8^{10x}}=\frac{2^{10-2x}}{64^{3x}}$.

(b) (i) Solve $e^{\ln x} + \ln e^x = 8$, (ii) Solve $25^x = 5^{x+1} - 6$.

(c) If one root of $ax^2 + bx + c = 0$ is the square of the other show that $c(a - b)^3 = a(c - b)^3$.

11. (a) Solve $\frac{x-1}{x-2}>3, x \in R$.

(b) If $x - 1$ is a factor of $P(x) = 3x^2 - kx^2 + 2x + 3$, find k and the roots of $P(x) = 0$.

(c) (i) Solve $|x + 1| < 2|x - 1|$.

(ii) Sketch the region on the same diagram described by the inequalities: $y \le 4 + |x|$ and $|x| \le y$.

12. (a) Solve $x + y + 2 = 0$;

$x^2 + y^2 = 2$.

(b) If $u = \log_3 x$, write $a \log_3 x = \log_x 3 - a$ as a quadratic in u. Find the sum of the roots of this quadratic.

(c) (i) Show that $ax^2 + 2x - (a - 2) = 0$ has real roots for all $a \in R$.

(ii) Prove $(a + b)^2 - 2b(a - b) \ge 2b^2 + 2ab$ for all $a, b \in R$.

13. (a) Show $\frac{1+\sqrt{3}}{\sqrt{2}-1}=(\sqrt{2}+1)(\sqrt{3}+1)$.

(b) If α, β are the roots of $x^2 - 3x - 2 = 0$ find $\alpha + \beta, \alpha\beta$. If the roots of $x^2 + ax - b = 0$ are α^2, β^2 find a and b.

(c) Find the value of a for which the roots of $x^2 + 2x - a = 0$ differ by 3.

14. (a) Express $\dfrac{\sqrt{3}+1}{\sqrt{3}-1}$ in the form $a + b\sqrt{c}$, $a, b, c \in N$.

(b) (i) Solve $\dfrac{x}{2x-1} < 2$, (ii) $|x - 3| > 2|x - 1|$.

(c) $f(x) = ax^3 + bx^2 + cx + d$, $a, b, c, d \in R$. If $k \in R$ such that $f(k) = 0$ prove $x - k$ is a factor of $f(x)$.

15. (a) Solve

$$\begin{aligned} 2x - y + 3z &= 20 \\ 7x + y + z &= 23 \\ 3x + y - z &= 3 \end{aligned}$$

(b) If α, β are the roots of $px^2 + qx + r = 0$ show $\dfrac{\alpha}{\beta} + \dfrac{\beta}{\alpha} = \dfrac{q^2}{pr} - 2$.

(c) Find the range of values of k for which $(2 - 3k)x^2 + (4 - k)x + 2$ has no real roots.

16. (a) Solve

$$\begin{aligned} x^2 - 2 &= 2y^2 \\ 3x &= y + 7 \end{aligned}$$

(b) $(x + 4)$ is a factor of $P(x) = x^3 - kx^2 - 22x + 56 = 0$. Find k. Find all the roots of $P(x) = 0$.

(c) If the product of the roots of the quadratic $\dfrac{1}{x+a} + \dfrac{1}{x+b} = \dfrac{1}{c}$ is 1, find c in terms of a and b.

Answers and hints to Algebra Revision Questions available on:
www.studentxpress.ie

ANSWERS

Exercise 1 [*Polynomial Operations* (page **7**)]

1. (a) $x^2 - 6x + 9$ (b) $4x^2 + 28x + 49$ (c) $x^3 + 2x^2 - x - 2$
   (d) $12x^2 - 23x + 5$ (e) $25x^2 - 4$
2. (a) $2x^2 + 2x - 3$ (b) $x - 3$ (c) $x + 3$
   (d) $4x^2 - 3x - 9$ (e) $4x^2 + 2x + 1$
   (f) $2x^2 - 15x + 75 - \dfrac{375}{x+5}$
3. (a) $x^2(3 + xy)(9 - 3xy + x^2y^2)$
   (b) $(4x - 1)(2x - 3)$
   (c) $(x^2 + y^2)(x - y)(x + y)$
   (d) $(x - y)(x + y)(x^2 - xy + y^2)(x^2 + xy + y^2)$
   (e) $(x - 2)(x^2 + 1)$
   (f) $(3x - y)(3x - y)$
   (g) $a(x - 1)(x^2 + x + 1)$
   (h) $4(10x + 3)(x + 1)$
   (i) $(x^2 + 1)^2$
   (j) $(a - b)(a - b - 1)$

Exercise 2 [*Fractional Expressions* (page **10**)]

1. (a) -2 (b) b (c) -2
   (d) $\dfrac{(\alpha-\beta)(\alpha+\beta)}{\alpha\beta}$ (e) $\dfrac{x^2-2}{2x}$ (f) $\dfrac{yz+xz+xy}{xyz}$
   (g) $\dfrac{7x^2-2x-3}{6(x+1)^2}$ (h) $\dfrac{-x}{(x-1)(x-2)}$ (i) 1
   (j) $\dfrac{1}{x-4}$ (k) $\dfrac{x+3}{x^2-3x+9}$ (l) $x^2 + 4$
2. (a) $-\dfrac{1}{a(a+h)}$ (b) $-t^3$ (c) $-ab$

(d) $\frac{a^2+ab+4a+2b}{(a+b+2)(a+2)}$ (e) $\frac{3x+5}{x+3}$ (f) $\frac{5y-2}{2(y+2)}$

Exercise 3 [*Exponents* (page **14**)]

(a) $\frac{2n^3}{m^5}$ (b) uv (c) $\frac{1}{a^2+b^2}$

(d) $\frac{x-1}{x^2(x^2+1)}$ (e) $\frac{1}{u^6v^{15}w^3}$ (f) $\frac{(x-y)(x^2+xy+y^2)}{x^5y^2}$

(g) $\frac{(a+b)^2}{b^2}$ (h) $-5(a-2b)$ (i) $\frac{y^3-x^2}{y^3+x^2}$

2. (a) $\frac{1}{x^9}$ (b) $x^{\frac{13}{6}}$ (c) $x^{\frac{17}{6}}$

(d) $\frac{x^{\frac{15}{2}}z^{\frac{3}{4}}}{y^{12}}$ (e) $\frac{xy^2}{4}$ (f) $\frac{3^{2x}}{y^8}$

(g) $\frac{2^{\frac{x}{2}}}{3^{\frac{x^2}{2}}}$ (h) $\frac{1}{e^{\frac{2x^2}{3}}}$ (i) e^{2x}

(j) $\frac{y}{x}$

Exercise 4 [*Surd Expressions* (page **16**)]

1. (a) $2\sqrt{2}$ (b) $2^3=8$ (c) $\sqrt{24}=2\sqrt{6}$

(d) $\frac{\sqrt{3}}{3}$ (e) $8\sqrt{5}$ (f) 4

(g) $5-2\sqrt{6}$ (h) -1 (i) $\sqrt{2}$

(j) $6\sqrt{3}$

2. (a) $\frac{3\sqrt{7}}{7}$ (b) $\frac{2\sqrt{85}}{17}$ (c) $\frac{3\sqrt{190}}{19}$

(d) $\frac{4\sqrt{cd}}{d}$ (e) $-2(1+\sqrt{2})$ (f) $\frac{-(9\sqrt{3}+17)}{46}$

(g) $\frac{3}{46}(4\sqrt{3}+\sqrt{2})$ (h) $\frac{8+6\sqrt{2}+4\sqrt{5}+3\sqrt{10}}{-2}$

(i) $\frac{c^2-2c\sqrt{d}+d}{c^2-d}$ (j) $\sqrt{y^2+9}+3$ (k) $\frac{5(3\sqrt{x}+2x)}{9-4x}$

3. (a) $\frac{1}{\sqrt{a}+\sqrt{b}}$ (b) $\frac{x-y}{x+y+2\sqrt{xy}}$

(c) $\frac{1}{\sqrt{3+x}-\sqrt{3}}$

Exercise 5 [*Logs* (page **19**)]

1. (a) $\log_3(\frac{1}{9})=-2$ (b) $\log_4 1=0$ (c) $\log_{25} 625=2$
(d) $\log_{10} 0.01=-2$ (e) $\log_x y=3$ (f) $\log_2 y=2x$
(g) $\log_2 32=5$ (h) $\log_{36}(\frac{1}{6})=-\frac{1}{2}$
(i) $\log_r t=s$ (j) $\log_{-2} 16=4$
2. (a) $256=2^8$ (b) $243=3^5$ (c) $10{,}000=10^4$
(d) $1=5^0$ (e) $9=27^{\frac{2}{3}}$ (f) $27=3^3$
(g) $4=(\frac{1}{2})^{-2}$ (h) $16=2^4$ (i) $16=(\sqrt{2})^8$
(j) $9=(-3)^2$ (k) $25=625^{\frac{1}{2}}$
3. (a) 2 (b) 3 (c) -2
(d) $\frac{3}{4}$ (e) $\frac{1}{4}$ (f) $-\frac{1}{2}$
(g) $\frac{1}{2}$ (h) -2 (i) 4
(j) 2

4. (a) $\log_a 9$ (b) $\log_7 128$ (c) $\log_4(\frac{1}{2})$
   (d) $\log_a 10$ (e) $\log_2(xy^2)$ (f) $\log_3 28$
   (g) $\log_a(\sqrt{x}y^2)$ (h) $\log_7\left(\frac{x^2z^4}{y^3}\right)$ (i) $\log_a\left(\frac{xy^{\frac{5}{2}}}{\sqrt{z}}\right)$
   (j) $\log_b\left(\frac{x^{\frac{4}{3}}}{y^{\frac{2}{3}}}\right)$ (k) $\log_{10} 1000 = 3$
   (l) $\log_2 1 = 0$
5. (a) $\log_a x + \log_a y$ (b) $2\log_3 x + \log_3 y$
   (c) $\frac{1}{2}(\log_5 x - 3\log_5 y)$ (d) $\frac{1}{4}(\log_3 x - \log_3 y)$
   (e) $\frac{1}{2}(3\log_4 x + \log_4 y)$ (f) $\frac{1}{2}(5\log_7 x - 2\log_7 y)$
   (g) $-2\log_2 x$ (h) $2\log_b x - \frac{1}{2}\log_b(x^2-1)$
   (i) $\frac{1}{5}(\log_3 x + 2\log_3 y)$
6. (a) $\frac{1}{\log_4 2}$ (b) $\frac{1}{\log_8 2}$ (c) $\frac{1}{\log_{16} 2}$
   (d) $\frac{1}{\log_8 16}$ (e) $\log_8 2$ (f) $\log_a b$
7. (a) $\log_2 4$ (b) $\log_2 4$ (c) $\log_2 8$
   (d) $\log_3 2$ (e) $\log_a b$ (f) $\log_4 3$
   (g) $\log_3 9$ (h) $\log_{10} 1000$ (i) $\log_a b$
   (j) $\log_2 e$ (k) $\log_2 4$, $\log_4 2$ (l) $\log_4 8$, $\log_8 4$
   (m) $\log_a x$, $\log_x a$
8. (a) 0 (b) 0 (c) 0
   (d) 0

Exercise 6 [*Simplifying Algebraic Expressions* (page **22**)]

1. $\dfrac{1+3x^{\frac{5}{2}}}{x^{\frac{3}{2}}}$ 2. $\dfrac{2x-1}{(x-1)^{\frac{3}{2}}}$ 3. $\dfrac{2x+5}{6(2x+1)^{\frac{4}{3}}}$

4. $\dfrac{x+6}{3(x+2)^2}$ 5. $\dfrac{x^2-x-3}{3}$ 6. $\dfrac{5-4x^2}{(x-1)^2}$

7. $\dfrac{x+1}{x^3}$ 8. $\dfrac{1+2x^4}{6x^5}$ 9. $\dfrac{3x-2}{2(x-1)^3}$

10. $\dfrac{2+x^4}{6x^4}$

Exercise 7 [*Identities* (page **24**)]

1. $A = 1, B = 1, C = 1$ 2. $A = -3, B = 5$
3. $A = 3, B = -13$ 4. $A = \frac{5}{2}, \ B = -\frac{5}{2}$
5. $a = 5, b = 25$ 6. $A = 3, B = -2$
7. $A = 2, B = -4$ 8. $a = 2, b = 8$
9. $l = 2, m = -1, p = 6$

Exercise 8 [*Factorials* (page **27**)]

1. (a) 24 (b) 5,040 (c) 2 (d) 1
(e) 11,880 (f) 9,900 (g) 364 (h) 252
(i) $\frac{1}{13}$ (j) 100

3. (a) $(n - 1)!(n + 1)$ (b) $\dfrac{n+2}{(n+1)!}$

(c) 1 (d) $\dfrac{1}{(n+2)(n+1)n(n-1)}$

(e) $(n - r)$ (f) $\dfrac{n}{(n+1)!}$

4. (a) 7 (b) 2 (c) 5 (d) 3

Exercise 9 [*Binomial Coefficients* (page **30**)]

1. (a) 330 (b) 1,140 (c) 101 (d) 4,950
   (e) 45 (f) 1,365 (g) 1 (h) 17
   (i) 1 (j) 45
4. (a) 1 (b) $n = 100$, $r = 57$ or 43 (c) 6
   (d) 4

Exercise 10 [*Factor Theorem* (page **33**)]

1. (i) Yes (ii) No (iii) No
2. (i) $\frac{7}{3}$ (ii) $-\frac{1}{4}$ (iii) $-\frac{2}{9}$ (iv) $-\frac{13}{3}$
   (v) $a = 3$, $b = 3$
3. (i) $x^2 + x - 2$ (ii) $x^3 - 7x - 6$
   (iii) $x^2 - 3x$ (iv) $x^3 - \frac{1}{2}x^2 - \frac{5}{2}x - 1$
4. (i) -10 (ii) $\frac{3}{4}$ (iii) 13 (iv) 2
5. (i) $a = -1$, $b = 9$ (ii) -5, 8

Exercise 11 [*Linear Equations* (page **34**)]

1. $\frac{11}{5}$ 2. $-\frac{3}{4}$ 3. $\frac{5}{4}$ 4. $\frac{4}{3}$ 5. 54 6. $\frac{31}{18}$

Exercise 12 [*Quadratics* (page **43**)]

1. (i) $\frac{1}{2}$, -4 (ii) $1 \pm \sqrt{10}$ (iii) $\frac{1}{4}$, $\frac{1}{2}$ (iv) $2 \pm \sqrt{3}$
2. (i) 7 (ii) -3 (iii) $-\frac{7}{3}$ (iv) 55
   (v) 49 (vi) $\frac{55}{9}$ (vii) 406 (viii) 61
   (ix) $\pm\sqrt{61}$ (x) $\pm 7\sqrt{61}$ (xi) 3007 (xii) -13,365
3. (i) $-\frac{3}{2}$ (ii) $-\frac{7}{2}$ (iii) $\frac{37}{4}$ (iv) $-\frac{153}{8}$
   (v) $\frac{3}{7}$ (vi) $\frac{37}{49}$ (vii) $\frac{977}{16}$ (viii) $\frac{9}{4}$
   (ix) $\frac{65}{4}$ (x) $\frac{\pm\sqrt{65}}{2}$ (xi) $\frac{\pm 3\sqrt{65}}{4}$ (xii) $\frac{50421}{64}$
4. (i) $2b^2 = 9ac$ (ii) $3b^2 = 16ac$ (iii) $10b^2 = 49ac$
   (iv) $12b^2 = 49ac$
5. 2, 7

6. (i) $x^2 - 4x + 3 = 0$ (ii) $2x^2 - 3x - 2 = 0$
(iii) $6x^2 + x - 1 = 0$ (iv) $x^2 + 4x + 4 = 0$
(v) $x^2 - (1+\sqrt{2})x + \sqrt{2} = 0$ (vi) $x^2 - 4x - 3 = 0$
(vii) $x^2 - (\sqrt{2}+\sqrt{3})x + \sqrt{6} = 0$ (viii) $pqx^2 - (p^2 + q^2)x + pq = 0$
(ix) $x^2 - p^2 = 0$ (x) $x^2 - (\alpha+\beta)x + \alpha\beta = 0$
(xi) $3x^2 + 20x - 7 = 0$ (xii) $x^2 + x + (-p^2 - 2 + 3p) = 0$

7. (i) $5x^2 - 4x + 1 = 0$ (ii) $x^2 - 6x + 25 = 0$
(iii) $x^2 - 8x + 17 = 0$ (iv) $5x^2 - 6x + 5 = 0$
(v) $5x^2 - 6x + 2 = 0$

8. (i) $4x^2 - 21x + 1 = 0$ (ii) $x^2 - 21x + 4 = 0$
(iii) $16x^2 - 42x + 1 = 0$ (iv) $2x^2 + 15x + 26 = 0$
(v) $2x^2 + 25x + 25 = 0$ (vi) $8x^2 + 95x + 1 = 0$
(vii) $4x^2 + 95x + 2 = 0$

9. $a = -2$, $x = -1, 3$; $x = 0, 4$

10. (i) $\frac{25}{3}$ (ii) 30 (iii) ± 4 (iv) 2 (v) 0

11. (i) $b^2 - 4ac = 17 > 0$: Real and irrational because 17 is not a perfect square,
(ii) $b^2 - 4ac = 53 > 0$: Real and irrational because 53 is not a perfect square,
(iii) $b^2 - 4ac = -8 < 0$: Unreal,
(iv) $b^2 - 4ac = 49 > 0$: Real and rational,
(v) $b^2 - 4ac = 9 > 0$: Real and rational because 9 is a perfect square,
(vi) $b^2 - 4ac = 0$: Equal.

13. 7

Exercise 13 [*Cubic Equations* (page **49**)]

2. $(2x^2 + 7x + 19) + \dfrac{51}{x-3}$

3. (a) $x^3 - 7x + 6 = 0$ (b) $x^3 - 8x^2 + 16x = 0$
(c) $6x^3 - 13x^2 + x + 2 = 0$ (d) $3x^3 - 2x^2 - 9x + 6 = 0$

4 (i) 2, -1, 1 (ii) -2, $-\frac{1}{3}$, $\frac{1}{2}$ (iii) -3

5. (a) $-2\pm\sqrt{3}$, 4 (b) -1, $-\frac{1}{2}$, $\frac{3}{2}$

(c) $\frac{2}{3}$, $-3\pm\sqrt{5}$ (d) -2, $\dfrac{-3\pm\sqrt{5}}{2}$

6. k = -6; 2, $\pm\sqrt{3}$

7. (a) 3, $\dfrac{-3\pm\sqrt{17}}{2}$ (b) 1, -1, $\frac{1}{2}$

(c) -2 (d) 2, $\dfrac{-1\pm\sqrt{5}}{2}$

(e) -1, $-\frac{1}{2}$, $\frac{2}{3}$

8. $a = 2$, $b = -3$

10. $k = -8$, $(x - 2)(x + 6)$

11. $(3 - x)(2 - x)(1 + x)$

13. $g(x) = 4x^3 - 3x^2 - 4x + 3$

Exercise 14 [*Literal Equations* (page **52**)]

1. $R_1 = \dfrac{RR_2}{2R_2 - R}$ 2. $h = \dfrac{\sqrt{gT^2 - 4\pi k^2}}{2\pi}$ 3. $f_1 = -f - 2f_2$

4. $h = \dfrac{s - 2\pi r^2}{2\pi r}$ 5. $r = R\sqrt{\dfrac{f-P}{f+P}}$ 6. $W = \dfrac{Ldp}{h - Ld}$

7. $L = \dfrac{-mcR - 1}{cm^2}$ 8. $r = \dfrac{E - IR}{I}$ 9. $u = \left(\dfrac{rR}{sb}\right)\left(\dfrac{b-s}{r+R}\right) + 1$

10. $r = \dfrac{s-a}{s-l}$ 11. $z = \left(\dfrac{n}{p-r}\right)^2$ 12. $v = \dfrac{k^{\frac{2}{3}}x}{k^{\frac{2}{3}} - p^{\frac{2}{3}}}$

Exercise 15 [*Modulus Equations* (page **54**)]

1. ± 3 2. 18, -4 3. $\frac{1}{2}$, $-\frac{9}{2}$ 4. -5, $\frac{9}{5}$

5. $\frac{8}{5}$, $\frac{4}{5}$ 6. $-\frac{2}{3}$, $-\frac{1}{2}$ 7. -7, $-\frac{1}{15}$ 8. $\frac{4}{3}$, $-\frac{2}{7}$

9. $\frac{1}{3}$ 10. 4

Exercise 16 [*Exponential Equations* (page **56**)]

1. (a) -2   (b) $\frac{1}{6}$ (c) 0   (d) $-\frac{5}{4}$

   (e) $\frac{3}{5}$ (f) 4   (g) $\frac{1}{2}$ (h) $\frac{6}{5}$

   (i) $\frac{4}{3}$ (j) $-\frac{1}{2}$, 1

2. (a) $\dfrac{\log_{10} 5}{\log_{10} 3}$ (b) $\dfrac{\log_{10} 5}{\log_{10} 16}$ (c) $-\log_{10} 9$ (d) $\dfrac{\log_{10} 16}{\log_{10} 3}$

   (e) $\dfrac{1}{3}\left(\dfrac{1}{\log_{10} 3} - 1\right)$ (f) $\dfrac{1}{2}\left(\dfrac{1}{\log_{10} 5} + 1\right)$

   (g) $\dfrac{\log_{10} 7}{\log_{10} 25}$ (h) $\dfrac{3}{4}$ (i) $-\frac{3}{2}\log_{10} 4$ (j) $\dfrac{\log_{10} 11}{5\log_{10} 5}$

3. (a) 1, 3   (b) $\dfrac{\log_{10} 2}{\log_{10} 3}$ (c) 1, 3   (d) 2, 1

   (e) 1, $\frac{3}{2}$ (f) 1, $\dfrac{\log_{10}(\frac{3}{2})}{\log_{10} 2}$ (g) 1, $\dfrac{\log_{10} 5}{\log_{10} 4}$ (h) ln 2, -ln 3

   (i) 2, 0   (j) ln 2   (k) -1

Exercise 17 [*Log Equations* (page **59**)]

1. (a) 8   (b) ± 3 (c) 10^8 (d) -1, 6

   (e) 50   (f) 302   (g) $-\frac{4}{3}$, $\frac{1}{2}$

2. (a) 16   (b) 8   (c) $-\frac{1}{4}$ (d) 8

   (e) $\frac{5}{4}$ (f) 3, 6

3. (a) $\frac{5}{2}$ (b) $4^{\frac{2}{3}}$, 8   (c) 9   (d) 18

   (e) 64, 2   (f) 4, 8

Exercise 18 [*Surd Equations* (page **60**)]

1. 0, 4 2. 2 3. 12 4. 8 5. 9 6. 12
7. $\frac{56}{5}$ 8. $\frac{25}{16}$ 9. $\frac{4}{3}$ 10. $\frac{1}{3}$ 11. 4 12. $\frac{1}{64}$
13. 11 14. 8 15. $\frac{1}{3}$

Exercise 19 [*Simultaneous Equations* (page **65**)]

1. (a) (4, -3) (b) (-3, -2) (c) (7, 9)
2. (a) (2, 3, -1) (b) (-2, 4, 5) (c) ($\frac{3}{2}$, 1, $-\frac{3}{2}$)
   (d) ($\frac{4}{5}$, $\frac{12}{13}$, $\frac{6}{7}$) (e) ($\frac{1}{2}$, -1, 2) (f) (-1, -2, -3)
   (g) ($a + b$, $3a + 2b$, $4a - b$) (h) (12, 18, 20)
3. (a) (-1, 2), ($-\frac{1}{2}$, $\frac{5}{2}$) (b) (3, -5), (-1, 3) (c) (3, 2), (6, 1)
   (d) (2, 4), ($-\frac{1}{2}$, $-\frac{7}{2}$)(e) ($1-3\sqrt{2}$, $1+2\sqrt{2}$), ($1+3\sqrt{2}$, $1-2\sqrt{2}$)
   (f) (5, -2), (3, $-\frac{2}{3}$) (g) (1, 1), ($-\frac{19}{13}$, $-\frac{35}{13}$)
   (h) (a, $\frac{a^2}{b}$), ($-\frac{a}{2}$, $-\frac{2a^2}{b}$) (i) (5, 0), (-4, 3)
4. (a) $x = 1, y = 4$ (b) $x = 27, y = \frac{1}{3}$ (c) $x = 27, y = \frac{1}{3}$
   (d) $x = 27, y = 16$

Exercise 20 [*Inequalities* (page **74**)]

1. (a) $x > -\frac{1}{3}$ (b) $x > \frac{1}{2}$ (c) $-2 \leq x \leq \frac{3}{2}$
   (d) $x \leq -\frac{1}{3}$, $x \geq 2$
2. (a) $x < -1, x > 3$ (b) $-1 \leq x \leq 4$ (c) $-\frac{3}{2} < x < -\frac{3}{4}$, $x \neq -1$
   (d) $1 \leq x \leq 3$
3. (a) $x < -4, x > -1$ (b) $x < 3, x > 4$ (c) $-2 < x < 1, x > 2$
   (d) $x < -1, x > \frac{1}{3}$

Complex Numbers

1. COMPLEX NUMBER ALGEBRA

1.1 FORM OF A COMPLEX NUMBER

Always write a complex number as Re + iIm where $i = \sqrt{-1}$.

Example 1: $-3i + 2 = +2 - 3i$

Example 2: $\frac{1}{2} = \frac{1}{2} + 0i$

Example 3: $-\frac{\sqrt{3}}{2}i = 0 - \frac{\sqrt{3}}{2}i$

1.2 POWER OF i: $i^p = i^{\text{remainder when } p \text{ is divided by } 4}$

Remember: $i^2 = -1$

Example 4: Evaluate i^{37}

SOLUTION:

$i^{37} = i^1 = i$

Example 5: Evaluate i^{47}

SOLUTION

$i^{47} = i^3 = i^2.i = -i$

A power of i is always one of 4 answers: i, -1, $-i$, 1

1.3 OPERATIONS

[A] +, -, × **by scalar**: Multiply out brackets and gather up into form Re + iIm

TRICK

Never do a complex number operation unless it is in the form Re + iIm

Example 6: Simplify $3i - 2(5 + 7i) - 6(2 + i)$

SOLUTION

$3i - 2(5 + 7i) - 6(2 + i) = 3i - 10 - 14i - 12 - 6i = -22 - 17i$

Example 7: Simplify $5xi - 2y + 7(4 - xi) - y(2 - 3i)$

SOLUTION

$5xi - 2y + 7(4 - xi) - y(2 - 3i) = 5xi - 2y + 28 - 7xi - 2y + 3yi$

$= (28 - 4y) + i(-2x + 3y)$

[B] **Multiplication**: Multiply out brackets and put $i^2 = -1$.

Example 8: Simplify $(4 - 3i)(2 + 7i)$.

SOLUTION

$(4 - 3i)(2 + 7i) = 8 - 6i + 28i - 21i^2 = 8 + 22i + 21 = 29 + 22i$

Exercise 1 (Answers: page **134**)

Addition, Subtraction, Multiplication by a Scalar, Multiplication

1. **Simplify**

(a) $-7i + 10i$

(b) $4i + (-10i)$

(c) $(3 + 2i) + (5 - i)$

(d) $(-2 + 3i) + (7 + 8i)$

(e) $(4 - 3i) + (5 - 2i)$

(f) $2i - (4 - 3i)$

(g) $3i - (5 - 2i)$

(h) $(3 - i) - (5 + 2i)$

(i) $(-2 + 8i) - (7 + 3i)$

(j) $(4 - 2i) - (5 - 3i)$

(k) $(2 + 3i) + (5 - 3i) - (4 + 7i)$

2. **Simplify**

(a) $3(2 - i) - (4 - i)$

(b) $(2 + 3i) - 4(1 - i)$

(c) $(3 - 2i) -2(1 - i)$

(d) $2(3 + i) - 4(1 - i)$

(e) $3(3 - i) - 4(1 + 3i) - 5(7 - i)$

3. **Simplify**

(a) $(1 + 3i)(5 + 2i)$

(b) $(3 - 6i)(2 + 9i)$

(c) $2i(8 - 5i)$

(d) $(3 + 3i)(4 - 4i)$

(e) $(3 - 2i)(3 + 2i)$

(f) $(1 - i\sqrt{2})(1 + i\sqrt{2})$

(g) $(-2 - 5i)(-2 - 5i)$

(h) $(6 + i)(5 - 7i)(-3i + 2)$

(i) $(\sqrt{3} - i)(\sqrt{3} + i)$

(j) $(6 - 2i)(2 - 6i)$

(k) $(1 - i)(2 - i)(1 + i)$

[C] **Conjugate (bar)**: $\overline{\text{Re} + i\,\text{Im}} = \text{Re} - i\,\text{Im}$

Example 9: $\overline{-7i+3} = \overline{3-7i} = 3+7i$

Example 10: $\overline{2i-3+a-7i} = \overline{(a-3)-5i} = (a-3)+5i\ ,\ a \in R$

Example 11: $\overline{\tfrac{1}{2}i} = \overline{0+\tfrac{1}{2}i} = -\tfrac{1}{2}i$

Example 12: $\overline{3} = \overline{3+0i} = 3-0i = 3$

Conjugate trick: If you multiply a complex number $a + ib$ by its conjugate $a - ib$ you get a result that's easy to remember.

$$(a + ib)(a - ib) = a^2 + iab - iab - i^2b^2 = a^2 + b^2$$

Example 13: Simplify $(3 + 2i)(3 - 2i)$.

SOLUTION

$(3 + 2i)(3 - 2i) = 9 + 4 = 13$

Example 14: Simplify $(-5 - 6i)(-5 + 6i)$.

SOLUTION

$(-5 - 6i)(-5 + 6i) = 61$

Example 15: Simplify $(1 - i)(2 + 3i)(1 + i)$.

SOLUTION

$(1 - i)(2 + 3i)(1 + i) = (1 - i)(1 + i)(2 + 3i) = 2(2 + 3i)$

$= 4 + 6i$

TRICK

If you multiply a complex number $a + ib$ by its conjugate $a - ib$ you get $a^2 + b^2$. This trick is very important in dividing complex numbers and forming equations.

[D] **Division**: Multiply above and below by the conjugate of the number on the bottom. Use **the conjugate** trick and do bottom multiplication first.

Example 16: Evaluate $\frac{2-3i}{4+i}$.

SOLUTION

$$\frac{2-3i}{4+i}=\frac{2-3i}{(4+i)}.\frac{4-i}{(4-i)}=\frac{8-12i-2i+3i^2}{17}$$

$$=\frac{8-14i-3}{17}=\frac{5-14i}{17}=\frac{5}{17}-\frac{14}{17}i$$

You can do divisions really quickly if the number of the top is purely real.

Example 17: Evaluate $\frac{-6}{2-i}$.

SOLUTION

$$\frac{-6}{2-i}=\frac{-6}{2-i}.\frac{2+i}{2+i}=\frac{-12-6i}{5}=-\frac{12}{5}-\frac{6i}{5}$$

TWO NIFTY LITTLE TRICKS

Idea: Move and change sign

1. $\frac{1}{i}=\frac{1}{i}.\frac{-i}{-i}=\frac{-i}{1}=-i$

2. $\frac{1}{\cos A+i\sin A}$

$$=\frac{1}{\cos A+i\sin A}.\frac{\cos A-i\sin A}{\cos A-i\sin A}$$

$$=\frac{\cos A-i\sin A}{\cos^2 A+\sin^2 A}=\cos A-i\sin A$$

TRICK

Move and change sign

$$\frac{1}{i}=-i$$

$$\frac{1}{\cos A\oplus i\sin A}=\cos A-i\sin A$$

Example 18 **Example** 19

$$\frac{1}{3i}=-\frac{i}{3} \qquad \frac{2}{i}=-2i$$

Example 20: $\frac{5+i}{i} = (5+i).-i = -5i - i^2 = 1-5i$

Example 21: $\frac{5}{\cos A + i\sin A} = 5(\cos A - i\sin A)$

Exercise 2 (Answers: page **134**)

Real and Imaginary parts, Conjugate, Division

1. Find the real and imaginary parts of the following:

(a) $2 + 3i$
(b) $2 - 3i$
(c) $-i$
(d) 3
(e) $-3i$
(f) -4
(g) $x - yi$
(h) $-2i + 3$
(i) $\sqrt{3} - \sqrt{3}i$
(j) $-3 - 4i$
(k) $-2 - \sqrt{2}i$

2. Write in the form $a + bi$:

(a) $\overline{2}$
(b) $\overline{3-i}$
(c) $\overline{2+i}$
(d) $\overline{-5-5i}$
(e) $\overline{-2i}$
(f) $\overline{2-\sqrt{2}i}$
(g) $\overline{3-2i}$
(h) $\overline{-i-3}$
(i) $\overline{-4i-7}$
(j) $\overline{-i-1}$
(k) $\overline{2-i+3-2i}$
(l) $\overline{2-i-3+2i}$
(m) $\overline{x-iy}$

3. If $z = 2 + 3i$ and $w = 4 - 5i$ evaluate in the form $a + bi$:

(a) $z + w$
(b) $z - w$
(c) zw
(d) $\frac{z}{w}$
(e) $\overline{z+w}$
(f) $\overline{z-w}$

(g) $\overline{zw}$

(h) $\overline{\left(\frac{z}{w}\right)}$

(i) $\bar{z} + \bar{w}$

(j) $\bar{z} - \bar{w}$

(k) $\bar{z}\,\bar{w}$

(l) $\frac{\bar{z}}{\bar{w}}$

4. Express in the form $a + bi$:

(a) $\dfrac{1+5i}{1-i}$

(b) $\dfrac{5-i}{6+2i}$

(c) $\dfrac{4-7i}{3-i}$

(d) $\dfrac{47+33i}{5-3i}$

(e) $\dfrac{2-3i}{3i}$

(f) $\dfrac{5+6i}{2-7i}$

(g) $\dfrac{3i}{2+i}$

(h) $\dfrac{2}{1+i}$

(i) $\dfrac{1-i}{1-i\sqrt{2}}$

(j) $\dfrac{1-\sqrt{3}i}{1+\sqrt{3}i}$

5. Simplify and write your answer in the form $a + bi$:

(a) $\dfrac{\overline{(3+4i)}}{3-4i}$

(b) $\dfrac{2-i}{\overline{(3-i)}}$

(c) $\overline{\left(\dfrac{1-2i}{1+i}\right)}$

(d) $\overline{\left(\dfrac{2+2i}{3+2i}\right)}$

(e) $\overline{(3+2i)(1-i)(2-i)}$

(f) $(3-i)\dfrac{2-i}{\overline{1-i}}$

(g) $\overline{(2+i)}\ \dfrac{1}{1-i}$

(h) $(1-i)(1+i)\overline{(2-3i)}$

(i) $\dfrac{2-i}{\overline{-i}}.i^2$

(j) $i^3.\dfrac{\overline{1-i}}{3+i}$

(k) $\dfrac{(3-i)i}{3+i}$

(l) $\dfrac{\frac{1}{i}+i}{\frac{1}{i}-i}$

(m) $\dfrac{\frac{1}{1-i}+\frac{1}{1+i}}{\frac{1}{i}}$

(n) $\dfrac{3+4i}{3-4i}-\dfrac{3-4i}{3+4i}$

(o) $\dfrac{i(1-2i)^2-4(i-3)}{i(2i+i^2)}$

[E] **Equality**

Trick: Put Re on left = Re on right and Im on left = Im on right. This is true for all complex number equations.

Example 22: If $3x + 2i - 3iy - 7 = 0$ find $x, y \in R$.

SOLUTION

$3x + 2i - 3iy - 7 = 0 + 0i$

$\Rightarrow (3x - 7) + i(2 - 3y) = 0 + 0i$

$\therefore$ Re = Re $\Rightarrow 3x - 7 = 0 \Rightarrow x = \frac{7}{3}$

and Im = Im $\Rightarrow 2 - 3y = 0 \Rightarrow y = \frac{2}{3}$

Exercise 3 (Answers: page **135**)

Equality

Solve for x and y:

1. $(2x + y + 2) + i(3x + 2y + 5) = 0$
2. $2z + \bar{z} = 3 - 2i$ where $z = x + iy$
3. $\dfrac{x+iy}{2-i} = 5+3i$
4. $\dfrac{5x+7iy}{5-2i} = 2+5i$
5. $x + 3y + (2x + y)i = 9 - 2i$
6. $6(x - iy) + 18i(x + 2) = 5(6 - y)$

7. $2x(1 + 2i) - y = 7 + y(1 - i) - x$

8. $2x - 1 + 6xi = -y(1 - 5i) - 9i$

9. $x + 3xi - 2yi = 4y - 6 - 13i$

10. $\frac{2}{y+3} + (x-4)i = 4 + \frac{(x+1)}{2}i$

[F] **Brackets**: Expand out as normal. You can use the Binomial Theorem.

Example 23: Evaluate $(2 - i)^3$.

SOLUTION

$(2 - i)^3 = (2 - i)(2 - i)(2 - i) = (2 - i)(4 - 4i - 1)$
$= (2 - i)(3 - 4i) = 6 - 3i - 8i + 4i^2$
$= 6 - 11i - 4 = 2 - 11i$

Example 24: Evaluate $(1 + i)^4$.

SOLUTION

$(1 + i)^4 = 1 + 4i + 6i^2 + 4i^3 + i^4 = 1 + 4i - 6 - 4i + 1 = -4$

Exercise 4 (Answers: page **135**)

Brackets

Evaluate in the form $a + bi$:

1. $(5 + 6i)^2$
2. $(1 - i)^3$
3. $(1 + i)^4$
4. $(2 + i)^4 - (2 - i)^4$
5. $(3 + i)^2 + (3 - i)^2$
6. $\frac{1}{(4+i)^2}$
7. $\frac{1}{(2-i)^3}$
8. $\frac{3}{(1+i)^4}$
9. $(3 - i)^3$
10. $(2 - i)^2(3 + i)^2$

[G] **Square Roots**

There are 3 ways to ask this:

1. Evaluate $\sqrt{a+ib}$,
2. Solve $z^2 = a + ib$,
3. If $\sqrt{a+ib} = c + id$ find $a, b \in R$.

No matter how it's asked begin as in No. 3.

STEPS

1. Put $\sqrt{a+ib} = c + id$.
2. Square both sides: $a+ib=(c^2-d^2)+i2cd$.
3. Put Re = Re $\Rightarrow c^2-d^2=a$,
   Put Im = Im $\Rightarrow 2cd=b \Rightarrow cd=\frac{b}{2}$.
4. Solve simultaneously by guessing at 2 numbers multiplied together to give $\frac{b}{2}$ whose difference of squares is a.
5. There are 2 answers $(\pm)$.

Example 25: Evaluate $\sqrt{-63+16i}$.

SOLUTION

Step 1: $\sqrt{-63+16i} = c + id$

Step 2: $\Rightarrow -63 + 16i = (c^2 - d^2) + 2cdi$

Step 3: $\therefore\ cd = 8$ and $c^2 - d^2 = -63$

Step 4: $\therefore\ c = 1, d = 8$ or $c = -1, d = -8$ (Clever guess)

Step 5: $\therefore\ 1 + 8i, -1 - 8i$ are the roots.

Exercise 5 (Answers: page **136**)

Square Roots

Find the following in the form $a + bi$:

1. $\sqrt{3+4i}$
2. $\sqrt{-5+12i}$
3. $\sqrt{-21-20i}$
4. $\sqrt{-2-2i\sqrt{3}}$
5. $\sqrt{15+8i}$
6. $\sqrt{7-24i}$
7. $\sqrt{-9-40i}$
8. $\sqrt{-1+4i\sqrt{5}}$
9. $\sqrt{-13+84i}$
10. $\sqrt{-45-28i}$
11. $\sqrt{-8+15i}$
12. $\sqrt{5-12i}$
13. $\sqrt{55-48i}$
14. $\sqrt{-39-80i}$
15. $\sqrt{-33-56i}$
16. $\sqrt{77+36i}$
17. $\sqrt{4+3i}$
18. $\sqrt{35+12i}$
19. $\sqrt{11-60i}$
20. $\sqrt{-65+72i}$

[H] **Argand Diagram** (Modulus, Argument)

1. **Argand diagram**: This is drawn by plotting a complex number on a 2-d diagram with Re = x and Im = y.

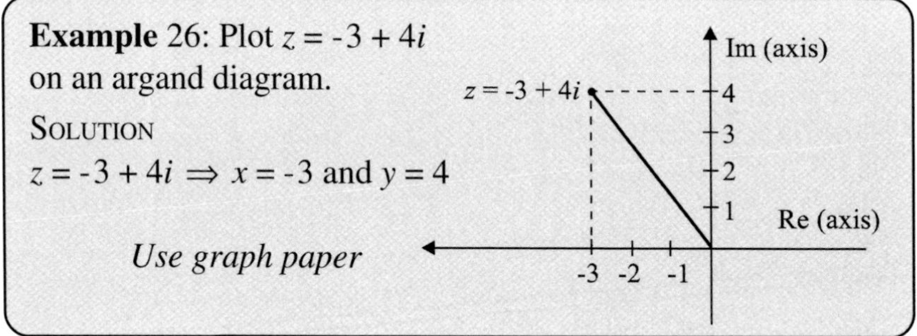

Example 26: Plot $z = -3 + 4i$ on an argand diagram.

SOLUTION

$z = -3 + 4i \Rightarrow x = -3$ and $y = 4$

Use graph paper

2. **Modulus** ($|z|$): This is the distance of the complex number from the origin.

Notation: $|z|$ = Distance $oz = r$

$$|z| = r = \sqrt{x^2 + y^2} = \sqrt{\text{Re}^2 + \text{Im}^2}$$

This is Pythagoras.

Trick: You can use the distance formula.

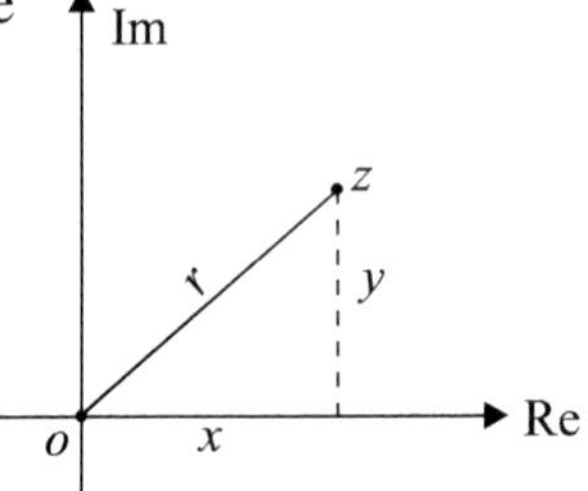

Example 27: Evaluate $|3 - 2i|$.

SOLUTION

$$|3-2i| = \sqrt{(3)^2 + (-2)^2} = \sqrt{13} \text{ (Don't include } i\text{)}$$

Example 28: Evaluate $|z|$ if $z = 3 + xi - y + 13i$.

SOLUTION

$z = 3 + xi - y + 13i = (3 - y) + i(x + 13)$

$$\therefore |z| = \sqrt{(3-y)^2 + (x+13)^2}$$

Example 29: Evaluate $|zw|$ if $z = 3 - 4i$ and $w = 5 + 12i$.

SOLUTION

$|zw| = |z||w| = |3 - 4i||5 + 12i| = (5)(13) = 65$

Example 30: Evaluate $\left|\frac{z}{w}\right|$ if $z = 2 + 4i$ and $w = 1 - i$.

SOLUTION

$$\left|\frac{z}{w}\right| = \frac{|z|}{|w|} = \frac{|2+4i|}{|1-i|} = \frac{\sqrt{20}}{\sqrt{2}} = \sqrt{10}$$

TRICKS

$$|zw| = |z|.|w|$$

$$\left|\frac{z}{w}\right| = \frac{|z|}{|w|}$$

Example 31: If $z = x + iy$ plot $|z - 2 - 3i| = 2$ on an Argand diagram.

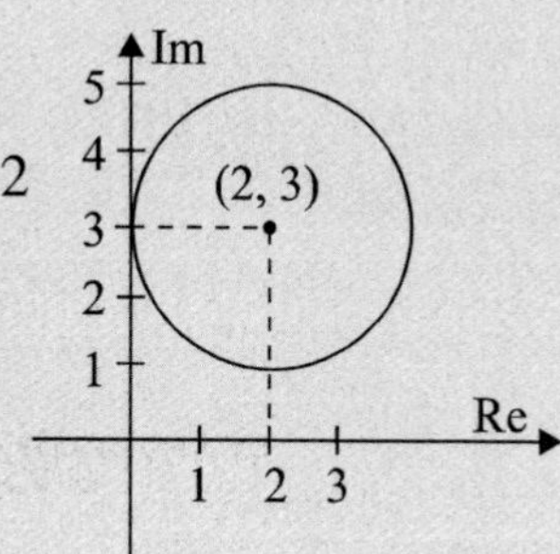

Solution

$|z - 2 - 3i| = 2 \Rightarrow |x + iy - 2 - 3i| = 2$

$\Rightarrow |(x - 2) + i(y - 3)| = 2$

$\Rightarrow \sqrt{(x-2)^2 + (y-3)^2} = 2$

$\Rightarrow (x - 2)^2 + (y - 3)^2 = 4$

Circle centre (2, 3) and radius 2

3. **Argument** ($\arg z = \theta$): This is the angle that the line joining the complex number to the origin makes with the +Re axis.

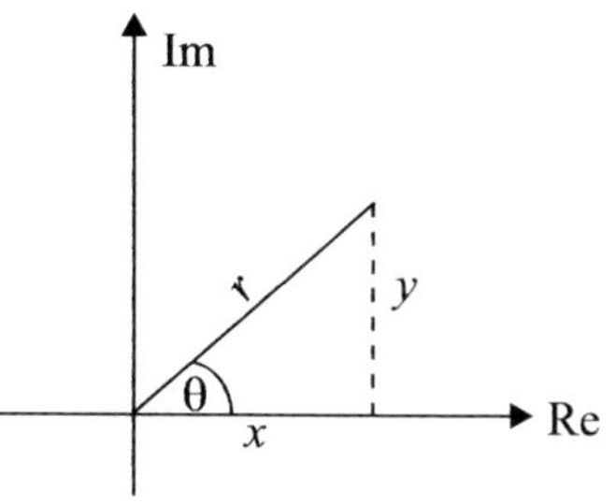

$$\arg z = \theta = \tan^{-1}\left(\frac{y}{x}\right) = \tan^{-1}\left(\frac{\text{Im}}{\text{Re}}\right)$$

$$\therefore \tan\theta = \frac{\text{Im}}{\text{Re}}$$

Steps for finding θ:

Steps

Step 1: Draw a picture first - find the quadrant it is in.

Step 2: Find $|\tan\theta| = \left|\frac{\text{Im}}{\text{Re}}\right|$.

Step 3: Find θ using the quadrant diagram to the right.

2nd. Quadrant	1st. Quadrant
180° - Angle	✓
180° + Angle	360° - Angle
3rd. Quadrant	4th. Quadrant

Example 32: Find arg z if $z = -3 - 3i$.

SOLUTION

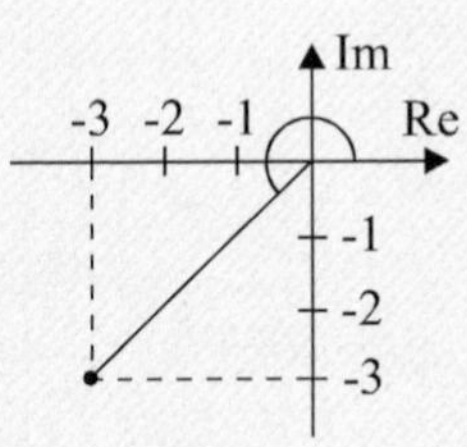

Step 1. Draw a picture.

Step 2. $|\tan\theta| = 1$

Step 3. $\therefore\ \theta = 45^\circ$ in 3rd quadrant

$\therefore\ \theta = 180^\circ + 45^\circ = 225^\circ = \frac{5\pi}{4} = \arg z$

Example 33: Find arg z if $z = -3 + 4i$.

SOLUTION

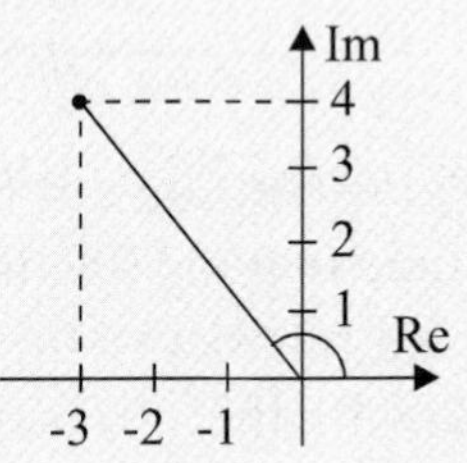

Step 1. Draw a picture.

Step 2. $|\tan\theta| = \frac{4}{3}$

Step 3. θ is in second quadrant.

$\therefore \theta = 180^\circ - \tan^{-1}(\frac{4}{3}) = \pi - \tan^{-1}(\frac{4}{3})$

Example 34: Plot $\arg z = \frac{\pi}{4}$ on the Argand diagram if $z = x + iy$.

SOLUTION

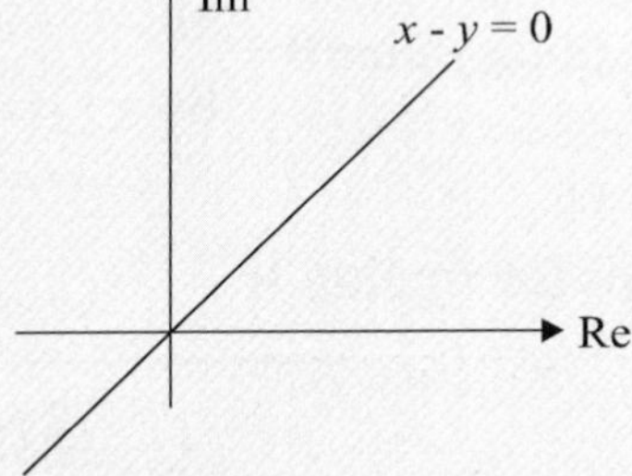

$$\arg z = \frac{\pi}{4} \Rightarrow \tan^{-1}\left(\frac{y}{x}\right) = \frac{\pi}{4}$$

$$\Rightarrow \frac{y}{x} = \tan\left(\frac{\pi}{4}\right) = 1 \Rightarrow y = x$$

$\Rightarrow x - y = 0$ (straight line through the origin)

Example 35: Plot $z = \frac{1}{\sqrt{2}} + \frac{1}{\sqrt{2}}i$ and $w = 1 + 0i$ on the Argand diagram. Plot $z + w$ on the same diagram and hence find $\tan\frac{\pi}{8}$.

SOLUTION

$|z| = 1,\ \arg z = \frac{\pi}{4}$

$|w| = 1,\ \arg w = 0$

> **TRICK**
> Complex numbers add like vectors in Argand diagram, i.e. triangle/ parallelogram law.

Cont....

$z+w=(1+\frac{1}{\sqrt{2}})+\frac{1}{\sqrt{2}}i$

$\arg(z+w)=\frac{\pi}{8}$

$\therefore \tan(\frac{\pi}{8})=\dfrac{\frac{1}{\sqrt{2}}}{1+\frac{1}{\sqrt{2}}}=\dfrac{1}{\sqrt{2}+1}=\sqrt{2}-1$

Exercise 6 (Answers: page **136**)

Argand Diagram, Modulus, Argument

1. For each of the following find $|z|$ and arg z and plot on the Argand diagram:
(a) $z = 4 - 2i$
(b) $z = 3 + 4i$
(c) $z = 1 + i\sqrt{2}$
(d) $z = \sqrt{3} - i$
(e) $z = \frac{1}{2} - i\frac{\sqrt{3}}{2}$
(f) $z = -\frac{1}{\sqrt{2}} - \frac{1}{\sqrt{2}}i$
(g) $z = -5 - 12i$
(h) $z = 4 - 4i$
(i) $z = 1 + i\sqrt{3}$
(j) $z = i$
(k) $z = -8 + 15i$
(l) $z = -i\sqrt{5}$
(m) $z = 4i - 1$
(n) $z = i^2 + 2i^3$
(o) $z = 1 + \frac{2}{i}$
(p) $z = i(3 + i)$
(q) $z = (1 - i)(1 + i)$

2. Given $|z|$ and arg z find z in the form $a + bi$:
(a) $|z| = 3$, $\arg z = \frac{\pi}{3}$
(b) $|z| = 1$, $\arg z = \frac{3\pi}{4}$
(c) $|z| = \frac{1}{2}$, $\arg z = \frac{11\pi}{6}$
(d) $|z| = 2$, $\arg z = -\frac{\pi}{4}$
(e) $|z| = 3$, $\arg z = 210^{\circ}$
(f) $|z| = 2$, $\arg z = -150^{\circ}$

3. Find $|z|$ and arg z for:
(a) $z = x + iy$
(b) $z = (3 + 2i)(1 - i)$
(c) $z = \dfrac{2-i}{1+i}$
(d) $z = x + 3 - iy + 2i$
(e) $z = 3 - i + x - iy$
(f) $z = x - iy + c$
(g) $z = x - 3 + 2x - 3iy$
(h) $z = 2 - i - x - iy$
(i) $z = x + iy - a - ib$

2. PROPERTIES

If you are asked to prove properties of complex numbers simply show $LHS = RHS$.

STEPS

1. Don't cross over.
2. For one complex number, z: Put $z = a + ib$.
For 2 complex numbers, z and w: Put $z = a + ib$ and $w = c + id$.
Remember: Always put a complex number in the form Re + iIm before doing an operation.

Example 1: Show $z+\bar{z}=2\text{Re}(z)$ where $\text{Re}(z)$ means the real part of z.

SOLUTION

Let $z = a + ib$

LHS	*RHS*
$z+\bar{z}$	$2\,\text{Re}(z)$
$= a + ib + a - ib$	$= 2\text{Re}(a + ib)$
$= 2a$	$= 2a$

Example 2: Show $\overline{zw}=\bar{z}\bar{w}$.

SOLUTION

Let $z = a + ib$ and $w = c + id$

LHS	*RHS*
$\overline{zw}$	$\bar{z}.\bar{w}$
$=\overline{(a+ib)(c+id)}$	$=\overline{(a+ib)}\,\overline{(c+id)}$
$=\overline{ac+ibc+iad-bd}$	$=(a-ib)(c-id)$
$=\overline{(ac-bd)+i(bc+ad)}$	$=ac-ibc-iad-bd$
$=(ac-bd)-i(bc+ad)$	$=(ac-bd)-i(bc+ad)$

Example 3: Show $|zw| = |z||w|$.

SOLUTION

Let $z = a + ib$ and $w = c + id$

LHS

$|zw|$

$= |(a+ib)(c+id)|$

$= |(ac-bd)+i(bc+ad)|$

$= \sqrt{(ac-bd)^2+(bc+ad)^2}$

$= \sqrt{a^2c^2+b^2c^2+b^2d^2+a^2d^2}$

RHS

$|z||w|$

$= |(a+ib)||(c+id)|$

$= \sqrt{a^2+b^2}.\sqrt{c^2+d^2}$

$= \sqrt{(a^2+b^2)(c^2+d^2)}$

$= \sqrt{a^2c^2+b^2c^2+b^2d^2+a^2d^2}$

Exercise 7

Properties of Conjugates

1. If $z = a + ib$ and $w = c + id$ show that $\overline{z+w} = \overline{z}+\overline{w}$.
2. If $z = a + ib$ and $w = c + id$ show that $\overline{z-w} = \overline{z}-\overline{w}$.
3. If $z = a + ib$ show that $\overline{\overline{z}} = z$.
4. If $z = a + ib$ show that $z-\overline{z} = 2i\,\text{Im}(z)$.
5. If $z = a + ib$ show that $z\overline{z} = |z|^2$.
6. If $z = a + ib$ and $w = c + id$ show that $\overline{\left(\frac{z}{w}\right)} = \frac{\overline{z}}{\overline{w}}$.

3. EQUATIONS

For all equations you can put: Re = Re and Im = Im

Example 1: Solve for a and b
$a + ib = 2 - 3i$.

SOLUTION
$a = 2$ and $b = -3$

Example 2: Solve for x and y
$(x - 2) + i(y + 7) = 0$.

SOLUTION
$(x - 2) + i(y + 7) = 0 + 0i$
$x - 2 = 0 \Rightarrow x = 2$
$y + 7 = 0 \Rightarrow y = -7$

TYPES OF EQUATION

3.1 EQUATIONS INVOLVING z (TYPE 1)

STEPS

1. Isolate z.
2. Put $z = x + iy$.
3. Read off x and y.

Example 3: If $\frac{1}{z-i} + 3 - 2i = 1$ where $z = x + iy$ find $x, y \in R$.

SOLUTION

Step 1. $\frac{1}{z-i} + 3 - 2i = 1 \Rightarrow \frac{1}{z-i} = -3 + 2i + 1 = -2 + 2i$

$\Rightarrow z - i = \frac{1}{-2+2i} = \frac{-2-2i}{8} = -\frac{1}{4} - \frac{1}{4}i$ (Division)

$\Rightarrow z = -\frac{1}{4} - \frac{1}{4}i + i$

Step 2. $\Rightarrow x + iy = -\frac{1}{4} + \frac{3}{4}i$

Step 3. $\therefore x = -\frac{1}{4}$ and $y = \frac{3}{4}$

3.2 EQUATIONS INVOLVING z AND $\bar{z}$ (TYPE 2)

STEPS

1. Put $z = x + iy$ and $\bar{z} = x - iy$.
2. Set Re = Re and Im = Im.
3. Solve.

Example 4: Solve $2z\bar{z} + 2\bar{z} - 5 = 27 + 4i$ for $x, y \in R$ if $z = x + iy$.

SOLUTION

Step 1. $2z\bar{z} + 2\bar{z} - 5 = 27 + 4i$

$\Rightarrow 2(x + iy)(x - iy) + 2(x - iy) - 5 = 27 + 4i$

$\Rightarrow 2(x^2 + y^2) + 2x - 2iy - 5 = 27 + 4i$

$\Rightarrow (2x^2 + 2y^2 + 2x - 5) + i(-2y) = 27 + 4i$

Step 2. $\Rightarrow$ (i) $2x^2 + 2y^2 + 2x - 5 = 27$ and (ii) $-2y = 4$

Step 3. $\therefore\ y = -2$

Putting this value into (i) gives:

$2x^2 + 8 + 2x - 5 = 27$

$\therefore\ 2x^2 + 2x - 24 = 0$

$\Rightarrow x^2 + x - 12 = 0$

$\Rightarrow (x - 3)(x + 4) = 0$

$\therefore\ x = 3, x = -4$

$\therefore\ z = 3 - 2i$ and $z = -4 - 2i$

3.3 POLYNOMIAL EQUATIONS: Q AND C (TYPE 3)

[A] **Quadratics**

The methods are the same as for algebra.

1. Magic to solve: $z = \dfrac{-b \pm \sqrt{b^2 - 4ac}}{2a} = \alpha, \beta$

2. Sum S: $\alpha+\beta=\dfrac{-\,\text{2nd}}{\text{1st}}$; Prod P: $\alpha\beta=\dfrac{\text{3rd}}{\text{1st}}$

3. Form a quadratic: $z^2 - Sz + P = 0$

Example 5: Solve $9z^2 + 12z + 29 = 0$.

SOLUTION

$9z^2 + 12z + 29 = 0$

$$\Rightarrow z=\frac{-12\pm\sqrt{144-1044}}{18}=\frac{-12\pm\sqrt{-900}}{18}$$

$$\therefore z=\frac{-12\pm 30i}{18}=\frac{-12+30i}{18},\ \frac{-12-30i}{18}$$

$$=-\frac{2}{3}+\frac{5}{3}i,\ -\frac{2}{3}-\frac{5}{3}i=\alpha,\beta$$

Example 6: Form quadratic equations from the following roots using $z^2 - Sz + P = 0$:

(i) 2, - 3, (ii) $2 - 3i$, $2 + 3i$, (iii) 2, $2 + 3i$, (iv) $1 - i$, $2 + 3i$.

SOLUTION

These roots represent all 4 possibilities:

(i) 2 real roots: 2, - 3

$2, -3 \Leftrightarrow z^2 - (-1)z + (-6) = 0 \Leftrightarrow 1z^2 + 1z - 6 = 0$

(ii) 2 complex conjugate roots: $2 - 3i$, $2 + 3i$

Using the CON trick: S = 4 and P = 13

$2 - 3i, 2 + 3i \Leftrightarrow 1z^2 - 4z + 13 = 0$

(iii) 1 real and 1 complex root: 2, $2 + 3i$

$2, 2 + 3i \Leftrightarrow z^2 - (4 + 3i)z + (4 + 6i) = 0$

(iv) 2 complex roots: $1 - i$, $2 + 3i$

$1 - i, 2 + 3i \Leftrightarrow z^2 - (3 + 2i)z + 5 + i = 0$

Example 7: Find $\sqrt{8-6i}$.
Hence solve $z^2 - (3 + 3i)z + (-2 + 6i) = 0$.

SOLUTION

Step 1. $\sqrt{8-6i} = c + id$

Step 2. $\Rightarrow 8 - 6i = (c^2 - d^2) + 2cdi$

Step 3. $\therefore cd = -3$ and $c^2 - d^2 = 8$

Step 4. $\therefore c = 3$, $b = -1$ or $a = -3$, $b = 1$ (Clever guess)

Step 5. $\therefore \pm(3 - i)$ are the roots.

$z^2 - (3 + 3i)z + (-2 + 6i) = 0$

$$\Rightarrow z = \frac{(3+3i) \pm \sqrt{(3+3i)^2 - 4(-2+6i)}}{2}$$

$$= \frac{3+3i \pm \sqrt{8-6i}}{2} = \frac{3+3i \pm (3-i)}{2}$$

$= 3 + i, 2i$

So a quadratic with all real coefficients has real roots or complex conjugate roots. This is also true for cubics. This leads to the **Conjugate Root Trick (CRT).**

CRT

If a complex number is a root of a polynomial equation with **all real coefficients** so is its conjugate.

NOTES

1. It is important to know when it can be used, i.e. for all real coefficients.
2. Remember for roots, plonk in always works.

Example 8: If $1 + i$ is a root of $z^2 - az + b = 0$ find $a, b \in R$.

SOLUTION

CRT does apply since $a, b \in R$.

$\alpha = 1 + i,\ \beta = 1 - i$

$S = \alpha + \beta = a = (1 + i) + (1 - i) = 2$

$P = \alpha\beta = b = (1 + i)(1 - i) = 2$

Example 9: If $2 - i$ is a root of $z^2 + kiz - ai = 0$ find $a, k \in R$ and the other roots.

SOLUTION

CRT does not apply since ki and $-ai$ are not real. Plonk $2 - i$ into the equation.

$(2 - i)^2 + ki(2 - i) - ai = 0$

$\Rightarrow 3 - 4i + 2ki + k - ai = 0$

$\Rightarrow (3 + k) + i(2k - 4 - a) = 0 + 0i$

$\Rightarrow k = -3$ and $2k - 4 - a = 0$ (Re = Re, Im = Im)

$\therefore\ a = -10$

So the quadratic is $z^2 - 3iz + 10i = 0$

$\alpha = 2 - i,\ \beta = ?$

Sum: $\alpha + \beta = 2 - i + \beta = 3i$

$\therefore\ \beta = -2 + 4i$

Exercise 8 (Answers: page **137**)

Quadratic Equations

1. If $z = x + iy$, $x, y \in R$ find z and hence x and y:

(a) $\frac{1}{z} - 1 = 2 - i$

(b) $\frac{1}{z-1} + 1 - i = 3 + i$

(c) $\frac{3-2i}{z+i} = 3 - i$

(d) $\frac{1}{z-1-2i} = 2 - 3i$

(e) $\frac{1}{z-1} = \frac{1+i}{1-i}$

(f) $\frac{1}{z} = \frac{1}{2+i} - \frac{1}{1-2i}$

2. Solve

(a) $z\bar{z} + 2z - 9 - 6i = 0$ if $z = x + iy$

(b) $z\bar{z} - 3\bar{z} + 2 = 1 - 3i$ if $z = x + iy$

(c) $z\bar{z} + z - 12 = 1 + i$ if $z = x + iy$

3. Given the 2 roots of a quatratic, form the quadratic equation:

(a) 1, -3

(b) $1 + i$, 2

(c) $2 - i$, $2 + i$

(d) $3 - i$, $2 + i$

(e) 2, 2

(f) $3 - i$, $3 + i$

4. Solve the quadratics:

(a) $z^2 - 4z + 13 = 0$

(b) $5z^2 + 6z + 7 = 0$

(c) $z^2 + 2iz - 5 = 0$

(d) $z^2 - 8z + 25 = 0$

(e) $z^2 - 2z - 11 = 0$

---

5. (a) If $(p + iq)^2 = 15 - 8i$ find $p, q \in R$. Hence solve $(1 + i)z^2 + (-2 + 3i)z - 3 + 2i = 0$.

(b) Solve $z^2 + (-4 + i)z + (6 - 2i) = 0$.

(c) If $(x + iy)^2 = -5 + 12i$, $x, y \in R$ find x and y. Hence, solve $z^2 + 4z + 9 - 12i = 0$.

(d) Find $\sqrt{3+4i}$. Hence solve $z^2 + 2iz - 4 - 4i = 0$.

6. (a) If i is a root of $z^2 - 3z + k = 0$, find k.
(b) If i is a root of $z^2 - az + b = 0$, $a, b \in R$, find a, b.
(c) If $2 - i$ is a root of $z^2 + bz + c = 0$, find b and $c \in R$.
(d) If $1 - i$ is a root of $z^2 + (a + 3i)z + ki = 0$, find $a, k \in R$ and the other root.
(e) If $1 - 2i$ is a root of a quadratic equation with real coefficients find the equation.
(f) If $\dfrac{1+2i}{1-i}$ is a root of $az^2 + bz + 5 = 0$, find $a, b \in R$.

---

7. Form the quadratics with all real coefficients given one root:
(a) $1 + 4i$
(b) $-2 + 3i$
(c) $\dfrac{1-i}{2}$
(d) $-2-i\sqrt{3}$
(e) $-i$
(f) $i\sqrt{7}$
(g) $-5 - i$
(h) $-i\sqrt{5}$
(i) $\dfrac{1-i\sqrt{2}}{3}$
(j) $\dfrac{1}{1+i}$

8. For each of the following quadratics say whether the roots are (i) real and unequal, (ii) real and equal, (iii) complex:
(a) $z^2 - 4z - 5 = 0$
(b) $2z^2 - 4z + 1 = 0$
(c) $z^2 + 6z - 9 = 0$
(d) $z^2 - 2z + 4 = 0$
(e) $z^2 + 14z + 49 = 0$
(f) $z^2 + 1 = 0$
(g) $4z^2 - 5 = 0$
(h) $3z^2 - 2z + 2 = 0$
(i) $4z^2 + 2z + 1 = 0$
(j) $5z^2 + z - 2 = 0$
(k) $\dfrac{17}{8-z} = z$

[B] **Cubics**

The methods for solving cubics in this section are the same as in algebra.

1. Solve by guessing a root (unless given) and then factorising.

2. S: $\alpha+\beta+\gamma = \frac{-\text{2nd}}{\text{1st}}$; SPP: $\alpha\beta+\beta\gamma+\alpha\gamma = \frac{\text{3rd}}{\text{1st}}$

P: $\alpha\beta\gamma = \frac{-\text{4th}}{\text{1st}}$

3. Form a cubic: $z^3 - Sz^2 + SPPz - P = 0$.

Example 10: Form the cubic equation with roots $1 + i$, $1 - i$, 3.

SOLUTION

Use $z^3 - Sz^2 + SPPz - P = 0$

$S = 1 + i + 1 - i + 3 = 5$

$SPP = (1 - i)(1 + i) + (1 - i)3 + (1 + i)3$

$= 2 + 3 - 3i + 3 + 3i = 8$

$P = (1 - i)(1 + i)3 = 6$

$\therefore\ z^3 - 5z^2 + 8z - 6 = 0$

Example 11: Solve $z^3 - 5z^2 + 11z - 15 = 0$ if $1 + 2i$ is a root.

SOLUTION

$z^3 - 5z^2 + 11z - 15 = 0$

All coefficients are real (CRT is on)

$\alpha = 1 + 2i,\ \beta = 1 - 2i,\ \gamma = ?$

$S = 2 + \gamma = 5\ \therefore\ \gamma = 3$

OR

$1 + 2i,\ 1 - 2i$ roots $\Rightarrow z^2 - Sz + P = z^2 - 2z + 5$ is a factor

$\therefore\ z^3 - 5z^2 + 11z - 15 = (z^2 - 2z + 5)(z - 3)$

$\therefore$ Roots are $1 + 2i$, $1 - 2i$, 3

Example 12: Find $k \in R$ if $2 - 3i$ is a root of
$z^3 - kz^2 + z + 39 = 0$.

SOLUTION

$z^3 - kz^2 + z + 39 = 0$

All coefficients are real (CRT is on)

$\alpha = 2 - 3i,\ \beta = 2 + 3i,\ \gamma = ?$

$S = 4 + \gamma = k$

$P = 13\gamma = -39 \Rightarrow \gamma = -3$

$\therefore\ 4 - 3 = k \Rightarrow k = 1$

OR

$2 - 3i, 2 + 3i$ are roots $\Rightarrow z^2 - 4z + 13$ is a factor

$\therefore\ z^3 - kz^2 + z + 39 = (z^2 - 4z + 13)(z + 3)$

$\Rightarrow z^3 - kz^2 + z + 39 = z^3 - z^2 + z + 39$

$\therefore\ k = 1$

Exercise 9 (Answers: page **138**)

Cubic Equations

1. Form the cubic equations with roots:

(a) $1, -2, 7$

(b) $i, 3, 5$

(c) $1 + i, -3, 2$

(d) $1 - i, 2, 3 - i$

(e) $1 + i, 1 - i, 3$

(f) $i, -3i, 7i$

(g) $1 - i, 2 + i, 3 - 2i$

2. Solve the cubics:

(a) $z^3 - z^2 + 2 = 0$

(b) $z^3 - 6z^2 + 13z - 10 = 0$

(c) $z^3 - z^2 + z - 1 = 0$

3. Solve
(a) $z^3 - 10z^2 + 31z - 30 = 0$ if 5 is a root.
(b) $z^3 - 5z^2 + 11z - 15 = 0$ if $1 + 2i$ is a root.
(c) $z^3 - 2z^2 + 5z + 26 = 0$ if $2 - 3i$ is a root.
(d) $z^3 - (-5 - i)z^2 + (6 + 5i)z + 6i = 0$ if $-i$ is a root.
(e) $z^3 - 2z^2 + z + 100 = 0$ if $3 + 4i$ is a root.
(f) $z^3 - 3z^2 + 4z - 12 = 0$ if $2i$ is a root.

4. (a) Find $k \in R$ if $3 - 2i$ is a root of $z^3 - 23z + k = 0$
(b) Find $k \in R$ if $2 - 3i$ is a root of $z^3 - kz^2 + z + 39 = 0$
(c) Find $k \in R$ if $2 - i$ is a root of $x^3 - kx^2 + 17x - 15 = 0$
(d) Find $k \in R$ if $1 + 3i$ is a root of $z^3 - 6z^2 + kz - 40 = 0$
(e) Find $k \in R$ if $3 + 4i$ is a root of $z^3 - 4z^2 + 13z + k = 0$
(f) Find $k \in R$ if $\frac{1}{2} - \frac{1}{3}i$ is a root of $kz^3 - 252z^2 + 229z - 78 = 0$

4. POLAR FORM AND DE MOIVRE'S THEOREM

4.1 POLAR FORM

Complex numbers can be written in 2 different ways: **Cartesian** form (normal) and **Polar** form.

You must be able to move from one form to another with ease.

$z = x + iy$... **Cartesian**

$\cos\theta = \frac{x}{r}$, $\sin\theta = \frac{y}{r}$

$\Rightarrow \; x = r\cos\theta$, $y = r\sin\theta$

$\Rightarrow \; z = r\cos\theta + i\,r\sin\theta$

$\therefore \; z = r(\cos\theta + i\sin\theta)$ ....**Polar**

$|z|$ $\arg z$

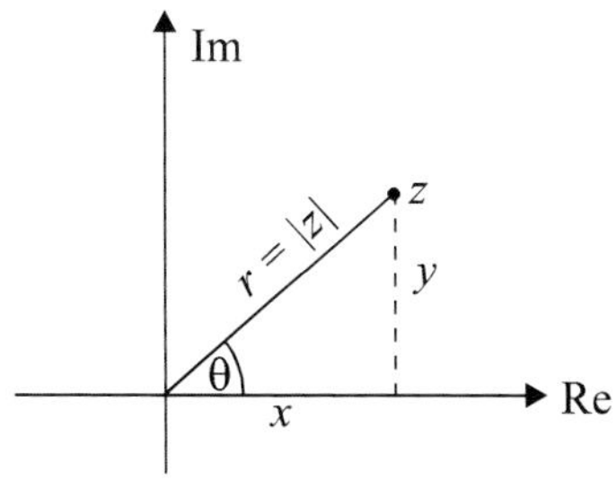

Steps for changing from Cartesian to Polar:

STEPS

1. Find $r = |z| = \sqrt{\mathrm{Re}^2 + \mathrm{Im}^2}$ first.

2. Draw a free-hand picture to see what quadrant θ is in.

3. Find θ from $|\tan\theta| = \left|\frac{\mathrm{Im}}{\mathrm{Re}}\right|$ and by looking at the picture.

4. Write $z = r(\cos\theta + i\sin\theta)$. For general polar form add $2n\pi$ to θ.

Example 1: Write $z = \frac{\sqrt{3}}{2} - \frac{1}{2}i$ in polar form.

SOLUTION

Step 1. $r = |z| = \sqrt{\frac{3}{4} + \frac{1}{2}} = 1$

Step 2. z is in the fourth quadrant.

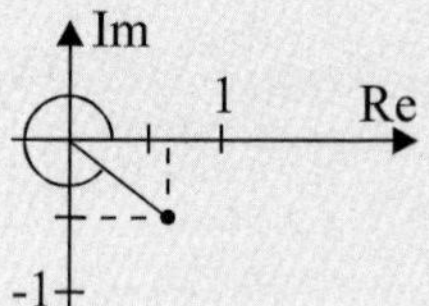

Step 3. $|\tan\theta| = \left|\frac{\mathrm{Im}}{\mathrm{Re}}\right| = \frac{1}{\sqrt{3}}$

$\therefore\ \theta = 30^{\circ}$ in the fourth quadrant $= 2\pi - \frac{\pi}{6} = \frac{11\pi}{6}$

Step 4. $z = 1(\cos(\frac{11\pi}{6}) + i\sin(\frac{11\pi}{6}))$

Example 2: Write $z = -1 - i\sqrt{3}$ in **general** polar form.

SOLUTION

Step 1. $r = |z| = \sqrt{1+3} = 2$

Step 2. z is in the third quadrant.

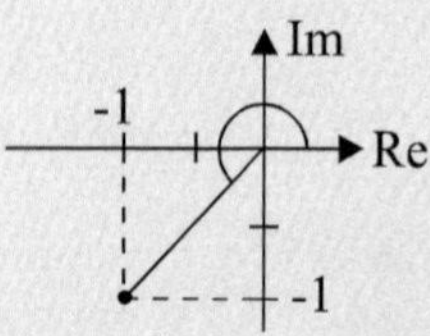

Step 3. $|\tan\theta| = \left|\frac{\mathrm{Im}}{\mathrm{Re}}\right| = \left|\frac{-\sqrt{3}}{-1}\right| = \sqrt{3}$

$\therefore\ \theta = 60^{\circ}$ in the third quadrant $= \pi + \frac{\pi}{3} = \frac{4\pi}{3}$

Cont....

Step 4. $z = 2\left\{\cos\left(\frac{4\pi}{3} + 2n\pi\right) + i\sin\left(\frac{4\pi}{3} + 2n\pi\right)\right\}$

Steps for changing from Polar to Cartesian:

STEPS

1. Look up cos and sin of the angle.
2. Multiply in by the modulus.

Example 3: Write $z = \sqrt{2}\left\{\cos\frac{3\pi}{4} + i\sin\frac{3\pi}{4}\right\}$ in Cartesian form.

SOLUTION

$$z = \sqrt{2}\left\{\cos\frac{3\pi}{4} + i\sin\frac{3\pi}{4}\right\} = \sqrt{2}(\cos 135^\circ + i\sin 135^\circ)$$

$$= \sqrt{2}\left\{-\frac{1}{\sqrt{2}} + i\frac{1}{\sqrt{2}}\right\} = -1 + i$$

4.2 DE MOIVRE OBJECTS

The object is in the form $(\cos\theta + i\sin\theta)$. We shall call it a De Moivre Object (**DMO**). There are 4 nifty tricks that we can do with it.

[A] **De Moivre Tricks**

1. **Trick**: If you multiply DMO's you just add the angles.

$(\cos A \oplus i\sin A)(\cos B \oplus i\sin B)$

$= (\cos A\cos B - \sin A\sin B) + i(\cos A\sin B + \cos B\sin A)$

$= \cos(A+B) + i\sin(A+B)$

---

2. **Trick**: If you move a DMO from top to bottom or vice versa you change the sign between cos and sin.

This works for $\cos\theta \pm i\sin\theta$

$$\frac{1}{\cos A \pm i\sin A} = \frac{1}{\cos A \pm i\sin A}\,\frac{\cos A \mp i\sin A}{\cos A \mp i\sin A}$$

$$= \frac{\cos A \mp i\sin A}{\cos^2 A + \sin^2 A} = \cos A \mp i\sin A$$

---

3. **Trick**: If you divide 2 DMO's you subtract their angles.

$$\frac{\cos A \oplus i\sin A}{\cos B \oplus i\sin B} = (\cos A + i\sin A)(\cos B - i\sin B)$$

$= (\cos A\cos B + \sin A\sin B) + i(\sin A\cos B - \cos A\sin B)$

$= \cos(A-B) + i\sin(A-B)$

---

4. **Trick**: $(\cos A + i\sin A)^n$

$$= \underbrace{(\cos A + i\sin A)(\cos A + i\sin A)\,.........\,(\cos A + i\sin A)}_{n\text{ times}}$$

$(\cos nA + i\sin nA)$ by **Trick** 1. This is an example of De Moivre's Theorem (DMT).

A SUMMARY OF DE MOIVRE'S TRICKS

DMO 1

If you multiply DMO's you just add the angles.

$$(\cos A \oplus i\sin A)(\cos B \oplus i\sin B) \;= \cos(A+B) + i\sin(A+B)$$

DMO 2

If you move a DMO from top to bottom or vice versa you change the sign between cos and sin.

$$\frac{1}{\cos A \pm i\sin A} = \cos A \mp i\sin A$$

DMO 3

If you divide 2 DMO's you subtract their angles.

$$\frac{\cos A \oplus i\sin A}{\cos B \oplus i\sin B} = \cos(A-B) + i\sin(A-B)$$

DMO 4

De Moivre's Theorem (DMT)

$$(\cos A + i\sin A)^n = (\cos nA + i\sin nA),\ n \in N_0$$

Trick: Don't be too hasty in changing complex numbers out of polar form. If you know the 4 DMO tricks it is usually easier to work in polars.

Example 4: Draw $3\left\{\cos\frac{\pi}{3} + i\sin\frac{\pi}{3}\right\}$ on an argand diagram.

SOLUTION

$z = 3\left\{\cos\frac{\pi}{3} + i\sin\frac{\pi}{3}\right\}$

$r = |z| = 3,\ \theta = \frac{\pi}{3} = 60°$

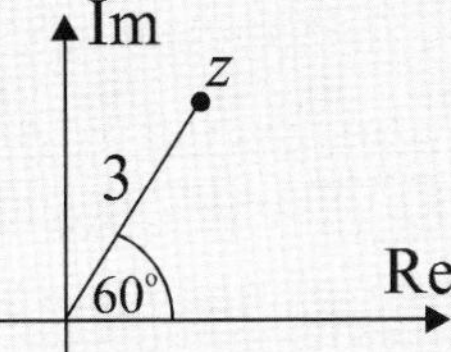

Example 5: Simplify $3\left(\cos\frac{\pi}{6}+i\sin\frac{\pi}{6}\right)2\left(\cos\frac{\pi}{3}+i\sin\frac{\pi}{3}\right)$.

SOLUTION

$$3\left(\cos\frac{\pi}{6}+i\sin\frac{\pi}{6}\right)2\left(\cos\frac{\pi}{3}+i\sin\frac{\pi}{3}\right)=6\left(\cos\frac{\pi}{2}+i\sin\frac{\pi}{2}\right)$$

$= 6(0 + i) = 6i$ (Used **DMO** 1)

Example 6: Solve $z\left(\cos\frac{\pi}{4}+i\sin\frac{\pi}{4}\right)=1$.

SOLUTION

$$z\left(\cos\frac{\pi}{4}+i\sin\frac{\pi}{4}\right)=1\Rightarrow z=\frac{1}{\cos\frac{\pi}{4}+i\sin\frac{\pi}{4}}=\cos\frac{\pi}{4}-i\sin\frac{\pi}{4}$$

$=\frac{1}{\sqrt{2}}-i\frac{1}{\sqrt{2}}$ (Used **DMO** 2)

Example 7: Simplify $\left(\frac{\cos 3\theta+i\sin 3\theta}{\cos\theta-i\sin\theta}\right)\left(\frac{\cos 2\theta-i\sin 2\theta}{\cos\theta+i\sin\theta}\right)$ in the form $\cos A+i\sin A$.

SOLUTION

$$\left(\frac{\cos 3\theta+i\sin 3\theta}{\cos\theta-i\sin\theta}\right)\left(\frac{\cos 2\theta-i\sin 2\theta}{\cos\theta+i\sin\theta}\right)$$

$$=\frac{\cos 3\theta+i\sin 3\theta}{\cos 2\theta+i\sin 2\theta}\frac{\cos\theta+i\sin\theta}{\cos\theta+i\sin\theta}=\frac{\cos 3\theta+i\sin 3\theta}{\cos 2\theta+i\sin 2\theta}$$

$=\cos\theta+i\sin\theta$ (Used **DMO** 1, 2 & 3)

Example 8: Simplify $(\cos\frac{\pi}{3}+i\sin\frac{\pi}{3})^5$.

SOLUTION

$(\cos\frac{\pi}{3}+i\sin\frac{\pi}{3})^5=\cos\frac{5\pi}{3}+i\sin\frac{5\pi}{3}$

$=\cos 300^\circ+i\sin 300^\circ=\frac{1}{2}-i\frac{\sqrt{3}}{2}$ (Using **DMO** 4)

Example 9: Write down the modulus and argument of

$z_1=\cos\frac{\pi}{6}+i\sin\frac{\pi}{6}$, $z_2=2\left\{\cos\frac{\pi}{3}+i\sin\frac{\pi}{3}\right\}$, z_1z_2 and plot them on the Argand diagram.

SOLUTION

$$z_1=\cos\frac{\pi}{6}+i\sin\frac{\pi}{6}\Rightarrow|z_1|=1,\ \arg z_1=\frac{\pi}{6}$$

$$z_2=2\left\{\cos\frac{\pi}{3}+i\sin\frac{\pi}{3}\right\}\Rightarrow|z_2|=2,\ \arg z_2=\frac{\pi}{3}$$

$$z_1z_2=2\left\{\cos\frac{\pi}{2}+i\sin\frac{\pi}{2}\right\}\Rightarrow|z_1z_2|=2,\ \arg z_1z_2=\frac{\pi}{2}$$

Draw complex numbers in Polar form on the Argand diagram with a protractor and a ruler.

Trick: Make sure that a DMO is always in the right form before manipulating it.

$\cos A-i\sin A=\cos(-A)+i\sin(-A)$

$\sin A+i\cos A=\cos(90-A)+i\sin(90-A)$

[B] **De Moivre's Theorem (DMT)**

This theorem is a theorem concerning DMO's.

Statement of DMT:

$$(\cos\theta\pm i\sin\theta)^p=\cos p\theta\pm i\sin p\theta \text{ for all } p\in R.$$

NOTES

1. The proof of De Moivre's for $p \in N_0$ (whole positive number powers) is by induction (page 424) and is required.
2. There are 3 uses to be treated.
3. All it says is that if you put a DMO to any power you simply multiply the angle by that power.

USES

USE 1. **Powers of complex numbers**

The DMT can be used to evaluate high whole number powers of complex numbers, e.g. $(1 - i)^{100}$, $(-3 - 3i)^{-20}$

STEPS

1. Write complex number in polar form.
2. Apply DMT.
3. Change to Cartesian.

Remember: $2n\pi = 0$ for $n \in N$, i.e. an even number of $\pi = 0$.

Example 10: Evaluate $(-1 - i)^{-30}$ using DMT.

SOLUTION

Step 1. $z = -1 - i,\ r = |z| = \sqrt{2},\ |\tan\theta| = 1$

$\therefore\ \theta = 45^\circ$ in third quadrant $\Rightarrow\ \theta = \pi + \frac{\pi}{4} = \frac{5\pi}{4}$

Im
Re
-1
-1

$$\therefore z = \sqrt{2}\left\{\cos\frac{5\pi}{4} + i\sin\frac{5\pi}{4}\right\}$$

Step 2/3. $\therefore z^{-30} = (\sqrt{2})^{-30}\left\{\cos\left(\frac{-75\pi}{2}\right) + i\sin\left(\frac{-75\pi}{2}\right)\right\}$

$$= \frac{1}{2^{15}}\left\{\cos\frac{3\pi}{2} - i\sin\frac{3\pi}{2}\right\} = \frac{i}{2^{15}}$$

USE 2. **Roots of Complex Numbers**

The DMT can be used to evaluate fractional powers of complex numbers, e.g. $(1-i)^{\frac{1}{3}}$

> **STEPS**
> 1. Write the complex number in general polar form.
> 2. Apply DMT.
> 3. List all roots (start at $n = 0$).
> 4. Change to Cartesian for nice angles.

Example 11: Use DMT to find the 3 cube roots of 1 - i.

SOLUTION

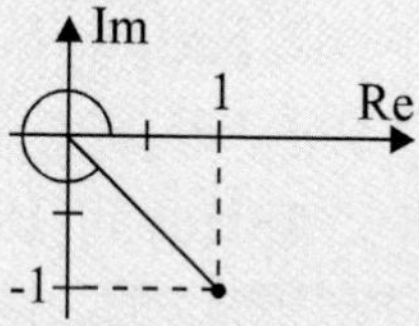

Step 1. $z = 1 - i,\ r = |z| = \sqrt{2}$

$|\tan\theta| = 1 \Rightarrow \theta = 45^{o}$ in 4th quadrant.

$\Rightarrow \theta = 2\pi - \frac{\pi}{4} = \frac{7\pi}{4}$

$$\therefore z = \sqrt{2}\left\{\cos\left(\frac{7\pi}{4}+2n\pi\right)+i\sin\left(\frac{7\pi}{4}+2n\pi\right)\right\}$$

$$\Rightarrow z = \sqrt{2}\left\{\cos\left(\frac{7\pi+8n\pi}{4}\right)+i\sin\left(\frac{7\pi+8n\pi}{4}\right)\right\}$$

Step 2. $\therefore z^{\frac{1}{3}} = 2^{\frac{1}{6}}\left\{\cos\left(\frac{7\pi+8n\pi}{12}\right)+i\sin\left(\frac{7\pi+8n\pi}{12}\right)\right\}$ by DMT

Step 3/4. $n = 0 \Rightarrow z_1 = 2^{\frac{1}{6}}\left\{\cos\frac{7\pi}{12}+i\sin\frac{7\pi}{12}\right\}$

$$n = 1 \Rightarrow z_2 = 2^{\frac{1}{6}}\left\{\cos\frac{15\pi}{12}+i\sin\frac{15\pi}{12}\right\} = 2^{\frac{1}{6}}\left\{-\frac{1}{\sqrt{2}}-\frac{1}{\sqrt{2}}i\right\}$$

$$n = 2 \Rightarrow z_3 = 2^{\frac{1}{6}}\left\{\cos\frac{23\pi}{12}+i\sin\frac{23\pi}{12}\right\}$$

NOTES

1. **General** Polar form means that you add $2n\pi$ to the angle.
2. There will be 2 square roots, 3 cube roots, etc..

USE 3. **Proofs of certain trig identities**

The DMT can be used to express cosines and sines of multiple angles in terms of single angles, e.g. to prove

$\cos 4\theta = 8\cos^4\theta - 8\cos^2\theta + 1$

STEPS

1. Write down DMT for number in multiple angle.
2. Expand out LHS.
3. Put Re = Re and Im = Im.
4. Tidy up LHS using $\cos^2\theta + \sin^2\theta$.

Example 12: Prove $\cos 3\theta = 4\cos^3\theta - 3\cos\theta$.

SOLUTION

Step 1. $(\cos\theta + i\sin\theta)^3 = \cos 3\theta + i\sin 3\theta$

Step 2. $\Rightarrow \cos^3\theta + 3\cos^2\theta(i\sin\theta) + 3\cos\theta(i\sin\theta)^2 + (i\sin\theta)^3$

$= \cos 3\theta + i\sin 3\theta$

$\Rightarrow \cos^3\theta + i3\cos^2\theta\sin\theta - 3\cos\theta\sin^2\theta - i\sin^3\theta$

$= \cos 3\theta + i\sin 3\theta$

Step 3. Put Re = Re.

$\Rightarrow \cos^3\theta - 3\cos\theta\sin^2\theta = \cos 3\theta$

Step 4. $\Rightarrow \cos^3\theta - 3\cos\theta(1 - \cos^2\theta) = \cos 3\theta$

$\Rightarrow 4\cos^3\theta - 3\cos\theta = \cos 3\theta$

Exercise 10 (Answers: page **138**)
Polar Form and De Moivre's Theorem

1. Write the following complex numbers in polar form:
(a) 1
(b) -4
(c) $-\frac{1}{\sqrt{2}}-\frac{1}{\sqrt{2}}i$
(d) -64i
(e) 8
(f) -16
(g) $-\frac{1}{2}+\frac{\sqrt{3}}{2}i$
(h) $\frac{\sqrt{3}}{2}i+\frac{1}{2}$
(i) $\frac{\sqrt{3}}{2}+\frac{1}{2}i$
(j) -i
(k) $8(-1+i\sqrt{3})$
(l) $4i + 4$
(m) $-3 - 3i$
(n) $1 - i$
(o) $-1 - i$
(p) $2 - 2i$
(q) $-1-i\sqrt{3}$
(r) $1 + i$
(s) $5\sqrt{3}-5i$
(t) $1+i\sqrt{3}$

2. Write the following in Cartesian Form:
(a) $z=2(\cos\frac{\pi}{6}+i\sin\frac{\pi}{6})$
(b) $z=3(\cos\pi+i\sin\pi)$
(c) $z=1(\cos\frac{5\pi}{3}+i\sin\frac{5\pi}{3})$
(d) $z=5(\cos\frac{\pi}{2}+i\sin\frac{\pi}{2})$
(e) $z=8(\cos\frac{11\pi}{6}+i\sin\frac{11\pi}{6})$
(f) $z=\cos(-\frac{\pi}{3})+i\sin(-\frac{\pi}{3})$
(g) $z=4(\cos 2n\pi+i\sin 2n\pi)$ for $n \in N$.
(h) $z=6(\cos\frac{7\pi}{4}+i\sin\frac{7\pi}{4})$

3. Use De Moivre's to evaluate in the form $a + ib$:
(a) $(1 + i)^3$
(b) $(1 - i)^4$
(c) $(\frac{\sqrt{3}}{2}+\frac{1}{2}i)^{100}$
(d) $(-1 + i)^6$
(e) $(1+i\sqrt{3})^7$
(f) $(\frac{\sqrt{3}}{2}-\frac{1}{2}i)^{10}$
(g) $(-\frac{1}{\sqrt{2}}-\frac{1}{\sqrt{2}}i)^{20}$
(h) $(\frac{1}{2}+\frac{\sqrt{3}}{2}i)^{102}$
(i) $(4 + 4i)^8$
(j) $(\cos\frac{\pi}{3}+i\sin\frac{\pi}{3})^{15}$
(k) $(\cos\frac{3\pi}{2}+i\sin\frac{3\pi}{2})^{100}$
(l) $(\frac{1}{2}-i\frac{\sqrt{3}}{2})^{12}$

(m) $(\cos\frac{\pi}{5}+i\sin\frac{\pi}{5})^{10}$

(n) $(1-i\sqrt{3})^{10}$

(o) $(\cos\frac{3\pi}{5}+i\sin\frac{3\pi}{5})^{15}$

(p) $(\cos\frac{8\pi}{3}+i\sin\frac{8\pi}{3})^{6}$

(q) $(-3 - 3i)^{20}$

4. Use De Moivre to evaluate:

(a) $(1)^{\frac{1}{3}}$

(b) $(-16)^{\frac{1}{4}}$

(c) $(-i)^{\frac{1}{5}}$

(d) $(-3i+3)^{\frac{1}{3}}$

(e) $(1-i)^{\frac{1}{4}}$

(f) $(1+i)^{\frac{1}{3}}$

5. Use De Moivre's to evaluate the roots of the equations:

(a) $z^3 = +1$

(b) $z^2 = -4$

(c) $z^6 + 64i = 0$

(d) $z^3 + 8 = 0$

(e) $z^4 = -16$

(f) $2z^2 + 1 - i\sqrt{3} = 0$

(g) $z^5 = -i$

(h) $z^4 = 8(-1+i\sqrt{3})$

(i) $z^3 = 3i - 3$

(j) $z^2 = 1 - i$

(k) $z^4 = 1$

(l) $z^2 = 2 + 2i\sqrt{3}$

(m) $z^6 + 64 = 0$

(n) $z^2 + 9i = 0$

---

6. Use De Moivre to write in the form $\cos\theta + i\sin\theta$:

(a) $(\cos A + i\sin A)^2(\cos 2A + i\sin 2A)^3$

(b) $\dfrac{\cos A - i\sin A}{(\cos 2A - i\sin 2A)^3}$

(c) $\dfrac{(\cos A - i\sin A)^3(\cos 2A - i\sin 2A)^2}{(\cos 3A + i\sin 3A)^2}$

(d) $\dfrac{(\cos 2A + i\sin 2A)^2(\cos 3A - i\sin 3A)^4}{(\cos A - i\sin A)^5(\cos 4A + i\sin 4A)^3}$

(e) $\dfrac{(1+i\tan A)^2}{(1-i\tan A)^2}$

7. Use De Moivre to show that:

(a) $\cos 2\theta = \cos^2\theta - \sin^2\theta$ and
$\sin 2\theta = 2\sin\theta\cos\theta$

Deduce from these 2 results that $\tan 2\theta = \dfrac{2\tan\theta}{1-\tan^2\theta}$ and
$\cos 2\theta = 2\cos^2\theta - 1$.

(b) $\cos 3\theta = \cos^3\theta - 3\cos\theta\sin^2\theta$ and
$\sin 3\theta = 3\sin\theta\cos^2\theta - \sin^3\theta$

Deduce from these 2 results that $\tan 3\theta = \dfrac{3\tan\theta - \tan^3\theta}{1-3\tan^2\theta}$ and
$\cos 3\theta = 4\cos^3\theta - 3\cos\theta$ and $\sin 3\theta = 3\sin\theta - 4\sin^3\theta$.

(c) $\cos 4\theta = \cos^4\theta - 6\cos^2\theta\sin^2\theta + \sin^4\theta$ and
$\sin 4\theta = 4\cos^3\theta\sin\theta - 4\cos\theta\sin^3\theta$

Deduce from these 2 results that $\tan 4\theta = \dfrac{4\tan\theta - 4\tan^3\theta}{1-6\tan^2\theta+\tan^4\theta}$
and $\cos 4\theta = 8\cos^4\theta - 8\cos^2\theta + 1$.

COMPLEX NUMBER REVISION QUESTIONS

> These 3 part questions are similar to the questions on the LC paper. The answers to these questions and hints to help you solve them are available on our website:
> **www.studentxpress.ie**

1. (a) Express $(\cos 5\pi + i\sin 5\pi)^{\frac{1}{3}}$ in the form $\dfrac{a+ib}{c}$.

(b) (i) If $z = \cos\frac{\pi}{3} + i\sin\frac{\pi}{3}$ evaluate $|1 + z|$.

(ii) Express $\sqrt{2 - 2i\sqrt{3}}$ in the form $a + ib$.

(c) Express $\dfrac{1 + i\tan\theta}{1 - i\tan\theta}$ in the form $\cos A + i\sin A$ and hence

$\left(\dfrac{1 + i\tan\theta}{1 - i\tan\theta}\right)^7$ in the same form.

2. (a) If $z_1 = a + ib$, $z_2 = c + id$ show $z_1\bar{z}_2 + \bar{z}_1 z_2 = 2\,\text{Re}(z_1\bar{z}_2)$.

(b) (i) If $z(\cos\frac{5\pi}{4} + i\sin\frac{5\pi}{4}) = 1$ find z in the form $x + iy$.

(ii) Evaluate $\left(\dfrac{-1 + i\sqrt{3}}{\sqrt{3} + i}\right)^{99}$.

(c) Solve $z^3 = 1$. If 1 and ω are two of the roots show that ω^2 is the third root. Form the quadratic equation with roots ω and $\frac{1}{\omega}$.

3. (a) Evaluate $\sqrt{3 - 4i}$.

(b) If $z = \dfrac{2 + i}{1 - i}$ find $z + \frac{1}{z}$ in the form $a + ib$.

(c) Use De Moivre's to prove $\sin 3\theta = 3\sin\theta - 4\sin^3\theta$.

4. (a) Evaluate $\dfrac{1}{\cos\frac{3\pi}{4} - i\sin\frac{3\pi}{4}}$ in the form $x + iy$.

(b) (i) Express $\dfrac{(\cos\theta + i\sin\theta)^4}{(\cos\theta - i\sin\theta)^3}$ in the form $\cos A + i\sin A$.

(ii) Express in the form $a + ib$ the complex number z with $|z| = 2$ and $\arg z = -\frac{\pi}{3}$.

(c) Solve $z^2 = \frac{1}{2} + i\frac{\sqrt{3}}{2}$.

5. (a) Show $z = i$ is a solution of $z^2 - z(1 + 2i) - (1 - i) = 0$. Find the other solution.
(b) If $z = x + iy$ and $w = u + iv$ and $z + iw = 1$ and $iz + w = 1 + i$ find $x, y, u, v \in R$.
(c) If $z = \cos\theta + i\sin\theta$ and $z - (\cos\frac{\pi}{3} + i\sin\frac{\pi}{3})\bar{z} = 0$ find θ.

6. (a) If $\dfrac{1+2i}{1-i}$ is a root of the quadratic $ax^2 + bx + 5 = 0$, $a, b \in R$, find a, b.
(b) Prove (i) $\overline{z_1 + z_2} = \bar{z}_1 + \bar{z}_2$, (ii) $\overline{z_1 z_2} = \bar{z}_1\,\bar{z}_2$.
(c) If $z = \cos\theta + i\sin\theta$ show $z^n + z^{-n} = 2\cos n\theta$ and $z^n - z^{-n} = 2i\sin n\theta$.

7. (a) Express $\dfrac{1 + i\tan\frac{\pi}{6}}{1 - i\tan\frac{\pi}{6}}$ in the form $\cos\theta + i\sin\theta$.

(b) Solve the equation $(1 + iz)(\sqrt{3} - i) = (1 - iz)(\sqrt{3} + i)$.
(c) Solve $z^3 = 1$. If the roots are $1, z_1, z_2$, show that
(i) $1 + z_1 + z_2 = 0$,
(ii) $z_1 = z_2^2$,
(iii) $z_2 = z_1^2$.

8. (a) If $(p + iq)^2 = 15 - 8i$, find $p, q \in R$.

(b) Use De Moivre's Theorem to evaluate $\left(\frac{1-i\sqrt{3}}{4}\right)^{12}$.

(c) Solve $z^5 = 1$. If α is one root show that $1, \alpha^2, \alpha^3, \alpha^4$ are the others.

9. (a) Express $\frac{\left[\sqrt{3}(\cos\alpha + i\sin\alpha)\right]^4}{\cos 2\alpha - i\sin 2\alpha}$ in the form $r(\cos\theta + i\sin\theta)$.

(b) If $1 + 2i$ is a root of $z^3 + az^2 + cz + 5 = 0$, $a, c \in R$, find a and c.

(c) Solve $z^3 = -1$. If λ is one root show that the others are -1 and $-\lambda^2$. Show that $\lambda^2 - \lambda + 1 = 0$.

10. (a) If $\sqrt{-21-20i} = a + ib$, find $a, b \in R$.

(b) If $z_1 = \frac{a}{1-i}$ and $z_2 = \frac{b}{2+i}$ and $2z_1 + z_2 = 3$, find a and b.

(c) If $2 + i$ is a root of $z^3 + az^2 + bz + 10 = 0$, $a, b \in R$, find a, b.

11. (a) If $z = -1 + i\sqrt{3}$, find z^2 and find $k \in R$ if $zk + z^2$ is real.

(b) If $z = 1 + 7i$, $z_1 = 3 + 4i$, $z_2 = 7 - 2i$ find a and b if $z = az_1 + bz_2$, $a, b \in R$.

(c) If ki is a root of $3z^3 - z^2 + 12z - 4 = 0$, find $k \in R$ and the other roots.

12. (a) If $\frac{1+i}{1-i} = k\left(\frac{1-i}{1+i}\right)$, find $k \in R$.

(b) Use De Moivre to evaluate $(1 + i)^{100}$.

(c) If $3 + 4i$ is a root of $x^3 - 4x^2 + kx - a = 0$, $k, a \in R$, find the other roots and the values of k and a.

13. (a) If $z = 2p + (p - 1)i$ is a real number, find $p, z \in R$.
(b) The roots of $(1 + i)z^2 - 2iz + 3 + i = 0$ are α and β. Find $\alpha + \beta$, $\alpha\beta$. Form the quadratic equation with roots $\alpha + 3\beta$, $3\alpha + \beta$.
(c) If $1 + i$ is a root of $z^3 + pz^2 + qz - p = 0$ where $p, q \in R$, find p, q and the other roots.

14. (a) If $\sqrt{-5+12i} = a + ib$, find $a, b \in R$.
(b) In the quadratic equation $x^2 + (p + iq)x + 3i = 0$, p and q are real numbers. If the sum of the squares of the roots is 8, find p and q.

(c) If $z = \cos\theta + i\sin\theta$ prove $\dfrac{2}{1+z} = 1 - i\tan(\frac{\theta}{2})$.

15. (a) Solve $z^2 - 2z + 5 = 0$ giving your answer in the form $x + iy$.
(b) Evaluate $(\frac{\sqrt{3}}{2} + \frac{1}{2}i)^{12}$ in the form $p + iq$, $p, q \in R$ using De Moivre's theorem.

(c) Express $z = \dfrac{1+i}{\sqrt{3}-i}$ in polar form.

Find z^n, $n \in N_0$ using De Moivre's Theorem. Find the least value of n for which z^n is real.

16. $p(z) = z^2 + bz + c$. $2 + i$ is a root of $p(z) = 0$. Find $b, c \in R$.

(b) If $A = \begin{pmatrix} 1 & i \\ -i & 1 \end{pmatrix}$ where $i = \sqrt{-1}$ evaluate A^2. Hence, evaluate A^8.

(c) Express 1 in polar form. Use De Moivre to solve $z^3 = 1$. If 1, ω, ω^2 are the cube roots of 1 show that $1 + \omega + \omega^2 = 0$ and hence show that $(3 + 4\omega + 3\omega^2)^3 = 1$.

Answers and hints to Complex Number Revision Questions available on: **www.studentxpress.ie**

ANSWERS

Exercise 1 [*Addition, Subtraction, Multiplication by a scalar, Multiplication* (page **93**)]

1. (a) $3i$ (b) $-6i$ (c) $8+i$ (d) $5+11i$
   (e) $9-5i$ (f) $-4+5i$ (g) $-5+5i$ (h) $-2-3i$
   (i) $-9+5i$ (j) $-1+i$ (k) $3-7i$
2. (a) $2-2i$ (b) $-2+7i$ (c) 1 (d) $2+3i$
   (e) $-30-10i$
3. (a) $-1+17i$ (b) $60+15i$ (c) $10+16i$ (d) 24
   (e) 13 (f) 3 (g) $-21+20i$ (h) $-37-185i$
   (i) 4 (j) $-40i$ (k) $4-2i$

Exercise 2 [*Real & Imaginary parts, Conjugates, Division* (page **96**)]

1. (a) Re = 2, Im = 3 (b) Re = 2, Im = - 3 (c) Re = 0, Im = - 1
   (d) Re = 3, Im = 0 (e) Re = 0, Im = - 3 (f) Re = - 4, Im = 0
   (g) Re = x, Im = $-y$ (h) Re = 3, Im = - 2 (i) Re = $\sqrt{3}$, Im = $-\sqrt{3}$
   (j) Re = -3, Im = - 4 (k) Re = - 2, Im = $-\sqrt{2}$
2. (a) $2+0i$ (b) $3+i$ (c) $2-i$
   (d) $-5+5i$ (e) $2i$ (f) $2+\sqrt{2}\,i$
   (g) $3+2i$ (h) $-3+i$ (i) $-7+4i$
   (j) $-1+i$ (k) $5+3i$ (l) $-1-i$
   (m) $x+iy$
3. (a) $6-2i$ (b) $-2+8i$ (c) $23+2i$
   (d) $-\frac{7}{41}+\frac{22}{41}i$ (e) $6+2i$ (f) $-2-8i$
   (g) $23-2i$ (h) $-\frac{7}{41}-\frac{22}{41}i$ (i) $6+2i$
   (j) $-2-8i$ (k) $23-2i$ (l) $-\frac{7}{41}-\frac{22}{41}i$
4. (a) $-2+3i$ (b) $\frac{7}{10}+\frac{2}{5}i$ (c) $\frac{19}{10}-\frac{17}{10}i$

(d) $4 + 9i$ (e) $-1-\frac{2}{3}i$ (f) $-\frac{32}{53}+\frac{47}{53}i$

(g) $\frac{3}{5}+\frac{6}{5}i$ (h) $1 - i$ (i) $\frac{(1+\sqrt{2})}{3}-\frac{(1-\sqrt{2})}{3}i$

(j) $-\frac{1}{2}-\frac{\sqrt{3}}{2}i$

5. (a) 1 (b) $\frac{1}{2}-\frac{1}{2}i$ (c) $-\frac{1}{2}+\frac{3}{2}i$

(d) $\frac{10}{13}-\frac{2}{13}i$ (e) $9 + 7i$ (f) $- 5i$

(g) $\frac{3}{2}+\frac{1}{2}i$ (h) $4 + 6i$ (i) $1 + 2i$

(j) $\frac{1}{5}-\frac{2}{5}i$ (k) $\frac{3}{5}+\frac{4}{5}i$ (l) 0

(m) i (n) $\frac{48}{25}i$ (o) $- 5 + 6i$

Exercise 3 [*Equality* (page **98**)]

1. (1, - 4) 2. (1, - 2) 3. (13, 1)
4. (4, 3) 5. (- 3, 4) 6. (0, 6)
7. $(\frac{7}{11}, -\frac{28}{11})$ 8. $(-\frac{1}{4}, \frac{3}{2})$ 9. $(-4, \frac{1}{2})$
10. $(9, -\frac{5}{2})$

Exercise 4 [*Brackets* (page **99**)]

1. $- 11 + 60i$ 2. $- 2 - 2i$ 3. $- 4$
4. $48i$ 5. 16 6. $\frac{15}{289}-\frac{8}{289}i$
7. $\frac{2}{125}+\frac{11}{125}i$ 8. $-\frac{3}{4}$ 9. $18 - 26i$
10. $48 - 14i$

Exercise 5 [*Square Roots* (page **101**)]

1. $\pm(2+i)$ 2. $\pm(2+3i)$ 3. $\pm(2-5i)$

4. $\pm(1-i\sqrt{3})$ 5. $\pm(4+i)$ 6. $\pm(4-3i)$

7. $\pm(4-5i)$ 8. $\pm(2+i\sqrt{5})$ 9. $\pm(6+7i)$

10. $\pm(2-7i)$ 11. $\pm\frac{1}{\sqrt{2}}(3+5i)$ 12. $\pm(3-2i)$

13. $\pm(8-3i)$ 14. $\pm(5-8i)$ 15. $\pm(4-7i)$

16. $\pm(9+2i)$ 17. $\pm\frac{1}{\sqrt{2}}(3+i)$ 18. $\pm(6+i)$

19. $\pm(6-5i)$ 20. $\pm(4+9i)$

Exercise 6 [*Argand Diagram, Modulus, Argument* (page **105**)]

1. (a) $2\sqrt{5}$, $2\pi-\tan^{-1}(\frac{1}{2})$ (b) 5, $\tan^{-1}(\frac{4}{3})$
   (c) $\sqrt{3}$, $\tan^{-1}(\sqrt{2})$ (d) 2, $\frac{11\pi}{6}$
   (e) 1, $\frac{5\pi}{3}$ (f) 1, $\frac{5\pi}{4}$
   (g) 13, $\pi+\tan^{-1}(\frac{12}{5})$ (h) $4\sqrt{2}$, $\frac{7\pi}{4}$
   (i) 2, $\frac{\pi}{3}$ (j) 1, $\frac{\pi}{2}$
   (k) 17, $\pi-\tan^{-1}(\frac{15}{8})$ (l) $\sqrt{5}$, $\frac{3\pi}{2}$
   (m) $\sqrt{17}$, $\pi-\tan^{-1}4$ (n) $\sqrt{5}$, $\pi+\tan^{-1}2$
   (o) $\sqrt{5}$, $2\pi-\tan^{-1}2$ (p) $\sqrt{10}$, $\pi-\tan^{-1}3$
   (q) 2, 0
2. (a) $\frac{3}{2}+\frac{3\sqrt{3}}{2}i$ (b) $-\frac{1}{\sqrt{2}}+\frac{i}{\sqrt{2}}$
   (c) $\frac{\sqrt{3}}{4}-\frac{1}{4}i$ (d) $\sqrt{2}-\sqrt{2}i$
   (e) $\frac{-3\sqrt{3}}{2}-\frac{3}{2}i$ (f) $-\sqrt{3}-i$
3. (a) $\sqrt{x^2+y^2}$, $\tan^{-1}(\frac{y}{x})$ (b) $\sqrt{26}$, $2\pi-\tan^{-1}(\frac{1}{5})$
   (c) $\sqrt{\frac{5}{2}}$, $2\pi-\tan^{-1}3$

(d) $\sqrt{(x+3)^2+(2-y)^2}$, $\tan^{-1}(\frac{2-y}{x+3})$

(e) $\sqrt{(x+3)^2+(y+1)^2}$, $\tan^{-1}(\frac{-(y+1)}{x+3})$

(f) $\sqrt{(x+c)^2+y^2}$, $\tan^{-1}(\frac{-y}{x+c})$

(g) $\sqrt{(3x-3)^2+9y^2}$, $\tan^{-1}(\frac{y}{1-x})$

(h) $\sqrt{(2-x)^2+(y+1)^2}$, $\tan^{-1}(\frac{y+1}{x-2})$

(i) $\sqrt{(x-a)^2+(y-b)^2}$, $\tan^{-1}(\frac{y-b}{x-a})$

Exercise 8 [*Quadratic Equations* (page **113**)]

1. (a) $\frac{3}{10}+\frac{1}{10}i$ (b) $\frac{5}{4}-\frac{1}{4}i$ (c) $\frac{11}{10}-\frac{13}{10}i$

   (d) $\frac{15}{13}+\frac{29}{13}i$ (e) $1 - i$ (f) $\frac{1}{2}+\frac{3}{2}i$
2. (a) $3i$, $-2 + 3i$ (b) $2 - i$, $1 - i$ (c) $3 + i$, $-4 + i$
3. (a) $z^2 + 2z - 3 = 0$ (b) $z^2 - (3 + i)z + (2 + 2i) = 0$

   (c) $z^2 - 4z + 5 = 0$ (d) $z^2 - 5z + (7 + i) = 0$

   (e) $z^2 - 4z + 4 = 0$ (f) $z^2 - 6z + 10 = 0$
4. (a) $2\pm 3i$ (b) $-\frac{3}{5}\pm\frac{\sqrt{26}}{5}i$ (c) $\pm 2-i$

   (d) $4\pm 3i$ (e) $1\pm 2\sqrt{3}$
5. (a) $p=\pm 4$, $q=\pm 1$, $z = -1$ or $\frac{1}{2}-\frac{5}{2}i$ (b) $2 + i$, $2 - 2i$

   (c) $x=\pm 2$, $y=\pm 3$, $z = 3i$ or $z = -4 - 3i$

   (d) $2\pm i$, $2 - 2i$, 2
6. (a) $1 + 3i$ (b) $a = 0$, $b = 1$ (c) $b = -4$, $c = 5$

   (d) $a = -3$, $k = -4$ (e) $z^2 - 2z + 5 = 0$ (f) $a = 2$, $b = 2$
7. (a) $z^2 - 2z + 17 = 0$ (b) $z^2 + 4z + 13 = 0$ (c) $2z^2 - 2z + 1 = 0$

   (d) $z^2 + 4z + 7 = 0$ (e) $z^2 + 1 = 0$ (f) $z^2 + 7 = 0$

(g) $z^2 + 10z + 26 = 0$ (h) $z^2 + 5 = 0$ (i) $3z^2 - 2z + 1 = 0$
(j) $2z^2 - 2z + 1 = 0$

8. (a) Real and unequal (b) Real and unequal
(c) Real and unequal (d) Complex
(e) Real and equal (f) Complex
(g) Real and unequal (h) Complex
(i) Complex (j) Real and unequal
(k) Complex

Exercise 9 [*Cubic Equations* (page **116**)]

1. (a) $z^3 - 6z^2 - 9z + 14 = 0$
(b) $z^3 - (8 + i)z^2 + (15 + 8i)z - 15i = 0$
(c) $z^3 - iz^2 + (-7 - i)z + 6 + 6i = 0$
(d) $z^3 - (6 - 2i)z^2 + (10 - 8i)z - (4 - 8i) = 0$
(e) $z^3 - 5z^2 + 8z - 6 = 0$
(f) $z^3 - 5iz^2 + 17z - 21i = 0$
(g) $z^3 - (6 - 2i)z^2 + (12 - 7i)z - (7 - 9i) = 0$
2. (a) $-1, 1 + i, 1 - i$ (b) $2 - i, 2 + i, 2$ (c) $1, i, -i$
3. (a) 2, 3, 5 (b) $1 + 2i, 1 - 2i, 3$ (c) $2 + 3i, 2 - 3i, -2$
(d) $-3, -2, -i$ (e) $3 + 4i, 3 - 4i, -4$ (f) $-2i, 2i, 3$
4. (a) 78 (b) 1 (c) 7
(d) 18 (e) 50 (f) 36

Exercise 10 [*Polar Form and De Moivre's Theorem* (page **127**)]

1. (a) $\cos 0 + i\sin 0$ (b) $4(\cos\pi + i\sin\pi)$
(c) $\cos\frac{5\pi}{4} + i\sin\frac{5\pi}{4}$ (d) $64(\cos\frac{3\pi}{2} + i\sin\frac{3\pi}{2})$
(e) $8(\cos 0 + i\sin 0)$ (f) $16(\cos\pi + i\sin\pi)$
(g) $\cos\frac{2\pi}{3} + i\sin\frac{2\pi}{3}$ (h) $\cos\frac{\pi}{3} + i\sin\frac{\pi}{3}$
(i) $\cos\frac{\pi}{6} + i\sin\frac{\pi}{6}$ (j) $\cos\frac{3\pi}{2} + i\sin\frac{3\pi}{2}$
(k) $16(\cos\frac{2\pi}{3} + i\sin\frac{2\pi}{3})$ (l) $4\sqrt{2}(\cos\frac{\pi}{4} + i\sin\frac{\pi}{4})$
(m) $3\sqrt{2}(\cos\frac{5\pi}{4} + i\sin\frac{5\pi}{4})$ (n) $\sqrt{2}(\cos\frac{7\pi}{4} + i\sin\frac{7\pi}{4})$
(o) $\sqrt{2}(\cos\frac{5\pi}{4} + i\sin\frac{5\pi}{4})$ (p) $2\sqrt{2}(\cos\frac{7\pi}{4} + i\sin\frac{7\pi}{4})$

(q) $2(\cos\frac{4\pi}{3}+i\sin\frac{4\pi}{3})$ (r) $\sqrt{2}(\cos\frac{\pi}{4}+i\sin\frac{\pi}{4})$

(s) $10(\cos\frac{11\pi}{6}+i\sin\frac{11\pi}{6})$ (t) $2(\cos\frac{\pi}{3}+i\sin\frac{\pi}{3})$

2. (a) $\sqrt{3}+i$ (b) -3 (c) $\frac{1}{2}-i\frac{\sqrt{3}}{2}$ (d) $5i$

(e) $4\sqrt{3}-4i$ (f) $\frac{1}{2}-i\frac{\sqrt{3}}{2}$ (g) 4 (h) $3\sqrt{2}-3\sqrt{2}i$

3. (a) -2 + 2i (b) -4 (c) $-\frac{1}{2}+\frac{\sqrt{3}}{2}i$ (d) $8i$

(e) $64+64\sqrt{3}i$ (f) $\frac{1}{2}+\frac{\sqrt{3}}{2}i$ (g) -1 (h) 1

(i) 2^{20} (j) -1 (k) 1 (l) 1

(m) 1 (n) $512(-1+i\sqrt{2})$ (o) -1

(p) 1 (q) $-(3\sqrt{2})^{20}$

4. (a) 1, $\frac{1}{2}(-1+\sqrt{3}i)$, $\frac{1}{2}(-1-\sqrt{3}i)$

(b) $\sqrt{2}+i\sqrt{2}$, $-\sqrt{2}+i\sqrt{2}$, $-\sqrt{2}-i\sqrt{2}$, $\sqrt{2}-i\sqrt{2}$

(c) $\cos\frac{3\pi}{10}+i\sin\frac{3\pi}{10}$, $\cos\frac{7\pi}{10}+i\sin\frac{7\pi}{10}$, $\cos\frac{11\pi}{10}+i\sin\frac{11\pi}{10}$, $-i$,
$\cos\frac{19\pi}{10}+i\sin\frac{19\pi}{10}$

(d) $18^{\frac{1}{6}}(\cos\frac{7\pi}{12}+i\sin\frac{7\pi}{12})$, $18^{\frac{1}{6}}(-\frac{1}{\sqrt{2}}-\frac{1}{\sqrt{2}}i)$, $18^{\frac{1}{6}}(\cos\frac{23\pi}{12}+i\sin\frac{23\pi}{12})$

(e) $2^{\frac{1}{8}}(\cos\frac{7\pi}{16}+i\sin\frac{7\pi}{16})$, $2^{\frac{1}{8}}(\cos\frac{15\pi}{16}+i\sin\frac{15\pi}{16})$,
$2^{\frac{1}{8}}(\cos\frac{23\pi}{16}+i\sin\frac{23\pi}{16})$, $2^{\frac{1}{8}}(\cos\frac{31\pi}{16}+i\sin\frac{31\pi}{16})$

(f) $2^{\frac{1}{6}}(\cos\frac{\pi}{12}+i\sin\frac{\pi}{12})$, $2^{\frac{1}{6}}(-\frac{1}{\sqrt{2}}+\frac{1}{\sqrt{2}}i)$, $2^{\frac{1}{6}}(\cos\frac{17\pi}{12}+i\sin\frac{17\pi}{12})$

5. (a) 1, $\frac{1}{2}(-1+i\sqrt{3})$, $\frac{1}{2}(-1-i\sqrt{3})$

(b) $2i$, $-2i$

(c) $2(\frac{1}{\sqrt{2}}+\frac{1}{\sqrt{2}}i)$, $2(\cos\frac{19\pi}{12}+i\sin\frac{19\pi}{12})$, $2(\cos\frac{23\pi}{12}+i\sin\frac{23\pi}{12})$,
$2(\cos\frac{7\pi}{12}+i\sin\frac{7\pi}{12})$, $2(\cos\frac{11\pi}{12}+i\sin\frac{11\pi}{12})$, $2(-\frac{1}{\sqrt{2}}-\frac{1}{\sqrt{2}}i)$

(d) -2, $1 \pm i\sqrt{3}$

(e) $\sqrt{2}+i\sqrt{2}$, $-\sqrt{2}+i\sqrt{2}$, $-\sqrt{2}-i\sqrt{2}$, $\sqrt{2}-i\sqrt{2}$

(f) $\frac{1}{2}+i\frac{\sqrt{3}}{2}$, $-\frac{1}{2}-i\frac{\sqrt{3}}{2}$

(g) $\cos\frac{3\pi}{10}+i\sin\frac{3\pi}{10}$, $\cos\frac{7\pi}{10}+i\sin\frac{7\pi}{10}$, $\cos\frac{11\pi}{10}+i\sin\frac{11\pi}{10}$, $-i$

$\cos\frac{19\pi}{10}+i\sin\frac{19\pi}{10}$

(h) $\sqrt{3}+i$, $-1+i\sqrt{3}$, $-\sqrt{3}-i$, $1-i\sqrt{3}$

(i) $3^{\frac{1}{3}}2^{\frac{1}{6}}(\frac{1}{\sqrt{2}}+\frac{1}{\sqrt{2}}i)$, $3^{\frac{1}{3}}2^{\frac{1}{6}}(\cos\frac{11\pi}{12}+i\sin\frac{11\pi}{12})$,

$3^{\frac{1}{3}}2^{\frac{1}{6}}(\cos\frac{19\pi}{12}+i\sin\frac{19\pi}{12})$

(j) $2^{\frac{1}{4}}(\cos\frac{7\pi}{8}+i\sin\frac{7\pi}{8})$, $2^{\frac{1}{4}}(\cos\frac{15\pi}{8}+i\sin\frac{15\pi}{8})$

(k) ± 1, $\pm i$

(l) $\sqrt{3}+i$, $-\sqrt{3}-i$

(m) $\pm 2i$, $\pm(1+i\sqrt{3})$, $\pm(1-i\sqrt{3})$

(n) $3(\frac{1}{\sqrt{2}}-\frac{1}{\sqrt{2}}i)$, $3(-\frac{1}{\sqrt{2}}+\frac{1}{\sqrt{2}}i)$

6. (a) $\cos 8A+i\sin 8A$ (b) $\cos 5A+i\sin 5A$
   (c) $\cos 13A-i\sin 13A$ (d) $\cos 15A-i\sin 15A$
   (e) $\cos 4A+i\sin 4A$

Matrices

1. DEFINITION OF A MATRIX

A matrix is an ordered array of objects (usually numbers) in rows (going across) and columns (going down).

Example: $\begin{pmatrix} 1 & 3 \\ -1 & 7 \end{pmatrix}$ 2 rows, 2 columns

$\begin{pmatrix} -\frac{2}{3} \\ -7 \end{pmatrix}$ 2 rows, 1 column

$\begin{pmatrix} -32 & \frac{1}{2} \end{pmatrix}$ 1 row, 2 columns

NOTES

1. Matrices are labelled with capital letters

$$A = \begin{pmatrix} 2 & -5 \\ 7 & 2 \end{pmatrix}$$

2. The entries are labelled by small letters and there are no commas between them.

$$A = \begin{pmatrix} a & b \\ c & d \end{pmatrix} = \begin{pmatrix} -1 & 3 \\ 4 & 0 \end{pmatrix} \Rightarrow a = -1,\ b = 3,\ c = 4 \text{ and } d = 0$$

3. The order of a matrix = No. of rows × No. of columns.
On the LC you need to only deal with:

2 × 2 Matrices: $\begin{pmatrix} -5 & 6 \\ \frac{1}{2} & 0 \end{pmatrix}$

2 × 1 Matrices: $\begin{pmatrix} -\sqrt{2} \\ 7 \end{pmatrix}$

1 × 2 Matrices: $\begin{pmatrix} -\frac{3}{2} & \frac{1}{\sqrt{3}} \end{pmatrix}$

1 × 1 Matrices: (-15)

2. OPERATIONS

2.1 ADDITION AND SUBTRACTION

You can only add/subtract matrices of the same order.
Trick: Add/subtract the corresponding entries.

Example 1: Evaluate $A + B$ if $A = \begin{pmatrix} 2 & -1 \\ 4 & 6 \end{pmatrix}$ and $B = \begin{pmatrix} 3 & 7 \\ -2 & 1 \end{pmatrix}$.

SOLUTION

$$A + B = \underset{2\times2}{\begin{pmatrix} 2 & -1 \\ 4 & 6 \end{pmatrix}} + \underset{2\times2}{\begin{pmatrix} 3 & 7 \\ -2 & 1 \end{pmatrix}} = \underset{2\times2}{\begin{pmatrix} 5 & 6 \\ 2 & 7 \end{pmatrix}}$$

Example 2: Evaluate $A - B$ if $A = \begin{pmatrix} 4 \\ -1 \end{pmatrix}$ and $B = \begin{pmatrix} 3 \\ 7 \end{pmatrix}$.

SOLUTION

$$A - B = \underset{2\times1}{\begin{pmatrix} 4 \\ -1 \end{pmatrix}} - \underset{2\times1}{\begin{pmatrix} 3 \\ 7 \end{pmatrix}} = \underset{2\times1}{\begin{pmatrix} 1 \\ -8 \end{pmatrix}}$$

2.2 MULTIPLICATION BY A SCALAR

Trick: Multiply each number by the scalar. It doesn't matter if the scalar is in front of or behind the matrix.

Example 3: $2\begin{pmatrix} -3 & 1 \\ \frac{1}{2} & 7 \end{pmatrix} = \begin{pmatrix} -6 & 2 \\ 1 & 14 \end{pmatrix}$

Example 4: $\begin{pmatrix} -3 \\ 5 \end{pmatrix}\frac{1}{2} = \begin{pmatrix} -\frac{3}{2} \\ \frac{5}{2} \end{pmatrix}$

Example 5: Evaluate $2A - B + \frac{1}{2}C$ if $A = \begin{pmatrix} 2 & 3 \\ -1 & 4 \end{pmatrix}$,

$B = \begin{pmatrix} -3 & 0 \\ -1 & 2 \end{pmatrix}$, $C = \begin{pmatrix} 4 & 5 \\ -1 & 7 \end{pmatrix}$.

SOLUTION

$$2A - B + \tfrac{1}{2}C = 2\begin{pmatrix} 2 & 3 \\ -1 & 4 \end{pmatrix} - \begin{pmatrix} -3 & 0 \\ -1 & 2 \end{pmatrix} + \tfrac{1}{2}\begin{pmatrix} 4 & 5 \\ -1 & 7 \end{pmatrix}$$

$$= \begin{pmatrix} 4 & 6 \\ -2 & 8 \end{pmatrix} - \begin{pmatrix} -3 & 0 \\ -1 & 2 \end{pmatrix} + \begin{pmatrix} 2 & \frac{5}{2} \\ -\frac{1}{2} & \frac{7}{2} \end{pmatrix} = \begin{pmatrix} 9 & \frac{17}{2} \\ -\frac{3}{2} & \frac{19}{2} \end{pmatrix}$$

2.3 MULTIPLICATION

This is the hardest and most important operation.

Trick: Never change the order of multiplication. AB means A on the left and B on the right.

Trick: Before you do multiplication check that the number of columns of the left matrix equals the number of rows of the right matrix.

$$AB = \begin{pmatrix} 3 & -1 \\ 2 & 4 \end{pmatrix} \begin{pmatrix} 2 \\ 7 \end{pmatrix} = \begin{pmatrix} \\ \end{pmatrix}$$

$$2 \times \cancel{2} — \cancel{2} \times 1 \qquad 2 \times 1$$

Cross out the common numbers leaving the outer numbers as the order of the resultant matrix.

The Multiplication Process

Example: $AB = \begin{pmatrix} 4 & -1 \\ 2 & 3 \end{pmatrix} \begin{pmatrix} 2 & 4 \\ 3 & 7 \end{pmatrix} = \begin{pmatrix} & \\ & \end{pmatrix}$

$2 \times 2 - 2 \times 2 \qquad 2\times2$

STEPS

1. Multiply first row entries in left matrix by corresponding entries in first column of right matrix, writing your answer in first row, first column of receiver matrix.

$$4 \times 2 + (-1) \times 3 = 5$$

$$\begin{pmatrix} 4 & -1 \\ 2 & 3 \end{pmatrix} \begin{pmatrix} 2 & 4 \\ 3 & 7 \end{pmatrix} = \begin{pmatrix} 5 & \\ & \end{pmatrix}$$

2. Multiply first row entries in left matrix by corresponding entries in second column of right matrix writing your answer in the first row, second column of receiver.

$$4 \times 4 + (-1) \times 7 = 9$$

$$\begin{pmatrix} 4 & -1 \\ 2 & 3 \end{pmatrix} \begin{pmatrix} 2 & 4 \\ 3 & 7 \end{pmatrix} = \begin{pmatrix} 5 & 9 \\ & \end{pmatrix}$$

3. Then start on the second row of the left matrix and do the same with the 2 columns of the right matrix.

$$2 \times 2 + 3 \times 3 = 13$$

$$\begin{pmatrix} 4 & -1 \\ 2 & 3 \end{pmatrix} \begin{pmatrix} 2 & 4 \\ 3 & 7 \end{pmatrix} = \begin{pmatrix} 5 & 9 \\ 13 & \end{pmatrix}$$

$$2 \times 4 + 3 \times 7 = 29$$

$$\begin{pmatrix} 4 & -1 \\ 2 & 3 \end{pmatrix} \begin{pmatrix} 2 & 4 \\ 3 & 7 \end{pmatrix} = \begin{pmatrix} 5 & 9 \\ 13 & 29 \end{pmatrix}$$

Example 6: If $A = (3 \ \ -1)$, $B = \begin{pmatrix} 4 \\ 7 \end{pmatrix}$ find AB.

SOLUTION

$$(3 \ \ -1) \quad \begin{pmatrix} 4 \\ 7 \end{pmatrix} = (5)$$

$$\underbrace{1 \times \not{2} - \not{2} \times 1} \qquad 1 \times 1$$

Example 7: If $A = \begin{pmatrix} 7 & -1 \\ 3 & 0 \end{pmatrix}$, $B = \begin{pmatrix} 1 & -\frac{1}{2} \\ 6 & 2 \end{pmatrix}$ find BA.

SOLUTION

$$BA = \begin{pmatrix} 1 & -\frac{1}{2} \\ 6 & 2 \end{pmatrix}\begin{pmatrix} 7 & -1 \\ 3 & 0 \end{pmatrix} = \begin{pmatrix} \frac{11}{2} & -1 \\ 48 & -6 \end{pmatrix}$$

$$\underbrace{2 \times \not{2} - \not{2} \times 2} \qquad 2 \times 2$$

Example 8: If $A = \begin{pmatrix} 3 \\ 5 \end{pmatrix}$, $B = (-7 \ \ 11)$, find AB.

SOLUTION

$$AB = \begin{pmatrix} 3 \\ 5 \end{pmatrix} \quad (-7 \ \ 11) = \begin{pmatrix} -21 & 33 \\ -35 & 55 \end{pmatrix}$$

$$\underbrace{2 \times \not{1} - \not{1} \times 2} \qquad 2 \times 2$$

Example 9: Simplify $(x\ \ y)\begin{pmatrix}2 & -3\\ 4 & 7\end{pmatrix}\begin{pmatrix}x\\ y\end{pmatrix}$.

SOLUTION

$$(x\ \ y)\begin{pmatrix}2 & -3\\ 4 & 7\end{pmatrix}\begin{pmatrix}x\\ y\end{pmatrix} = (x\ \ y)\begin{pmatrix}2x-3y\\ 4x+7y\end{pmatrix}$$

$2 \times \not{2} - \not{2} \times 1$ $\quad$ 2×1

$$= (x\ \ y)\begin{pmatrix}2x-3y\\ 4x+7y\end{pmatrix} = (2x^2 - 3xy + 4xy + 7y^2) = (2x^2 + xy + 7y^2)$$

$1 \times \not{2} - \not{2} \times 1$ $\quad$ 1×1

Tricks

1. $AB \neq BA$. Never change the order.
2. $(AB)C = A(BC)$. You can group 2 side by side matrices.
3. $A^2 = AA$.

Example 10: Evaluate AB, BA if $A = \begin{pmatrix}1 & 4\\ -3 & 7\end{pmatrix}$, $B = \begin{pmatrix}2 & -2\\ 4 & 0\end{pmatrix}$.

SOLUTION

$$AB = \begin{pmatrix}1 & 4\\ -3 & 7\end{pmatrix}\begin{pmatrix}2 & -2\\ 4 & 0\end{pmatrix} = \begin{pmatrix}18 & -2\\ 22 & 6\end{pmatrix}$$

$2 \times \not{2} - \not{2} \times 2$ $\quad$ 2×2

$$BA = \begin{pmatrix}2 & -2\\ 4 & 0\end{pmatrix}\begin{pmatrix}1 & 4\\ -3 & 7\end{pmatrix} = \begin{pmatrix}8 & -6\\ 4 & 16\end{pmatrix}$$

$2 \times \not{2} - \not{2} \times 2$ $\quad$ 2×2

Example 11: Find *ABC* if $A = \begin{pmatrix} 4 & -8 \\ 3 & 0 \end{pmatrix}$, $B = \begin{pmatrix} 1 & -4 \\ 2 & 1 \end{pmatrix}$, $C = \begin{pmatrix} -7 & 4 \\ 6 & 1 \end{pmatrix}$.

SOLUTION

$$ABC = \begin{pmatrix} 4 & -8 \\ 3 & 0 \end{pmatrix}\begin{pmatrix} 1 & -4 \\ 2 & 1 \end{pmatrix}\begin{pmatrix} -7 & 4 \\ 6 & 1 \end{pmatrix} = A(BC)$$

$$= \begin{pmatrix} 4 & -8 \\ 3 & 0 \end{pmatrix}\begin{pmatrix} -31 & 0 \\ -8 & 9 \end{pmatrix} = \begin{pmatrix} -60 & -72 \\ -93 & 0 \end{pmatrix}$$

Example 12: If $A = \begin{pmatrix} -1 & 2 \\ 4 & 6 \end{pmatrix}$ find A^2.

SOLUTION

$$A^2 = AA = \begin{pmatrix} -1 & 2 \\ 4 & 6 \end{pmatrix}\begin{pmatrix} -1 & 2 \\ 4 & 6 \end{pmatrix} = \begin{pmatrix} 9 & 10 \\ 20 & 44 \end{pmatrix}$$

2.4 EQUALITY

2 matrices of the same order are equal if their corresponding entries are equal.

For a 2×2 matrix: $\begin{pmatrix} a & b \\ c & d \end{pmatrix} = \begin{pmatrix} e & f \\ g & h \end{pmatrix}$

$\Rightarrow a = e, b = f, c = g$ and $d = h$.

Example 13: If $B^2 = I$ where $B = \begin{pmatrix} a & 1 \\ -3 & -2 \end{pmatrix}$ and $I = \begin{pmatrix} 1 & 0 \\ 0 & 1 \end{pmatrix}$, find a.

SOLUTION

$$B^2 = \begin{pmatrix} a & 1 \\ -3 & -2 \end{pmatrix}\begin{pmatrix} a & 1 \\ -3 & -2 \end{pmatrix} = \begin{pmatrix} a^2-3 & a-2 \\ -3a+6 & 1 \end{pmatrix}$$

$$\Rightarrow \begin{pmatrix} a^2-3 & \underline{a-2} \\ -3a+6 & 1 \end{pmatrix} = \begin{pmatrix} 1 & \underline{0} \\ 0 & 1 \end{pmatrix}$$

$\Rightarrow a - 2 = 0$

$\therefore\ a = 2$

Example 14: If $A = \begin{pmatrix} 2 & 1 \\ 4 & 2 \end{pmatrix}$, $B = \begin{pmatrix} 3 & 2 \\ -6 & c \end{pmatrix}$, find c if $AB = O$,

where $O = \begin{pmatrix} 0 & 0 \\ 0 & 0 \end{pmatrix}$.

SOLUTION

$AB = O$

$$\Rightarrow \begin{pmatrix} 2 & 1 \\ 4 & 2 \end{pmatrix}\begin{pmatrix} 3 & 2 \\ -6 & c \end{pmatrix} = \begin{pmatrix} 0 & 0 \\ 0 & 0 \end{pmatrix}$$

$$\Rightarrow \begin{pmatrix} 0 & \underline{4+c} \\ 0 & 8+2c \end{pmatrix} = \begin{pmatrix} 0 & \underline{0} \\ 0 & 0 \end{pmatrix}$$

$\Rightarrow 4 + c = 0$

$\therefore\ c = -4$

Exercise 1 (Answers: page **171**)

Matrix Operations

1. Evaluate

(a) $\begin{pmatrix}1 & 4\\7 & 2\end{pmatrix}-3\begin{pmatrix}1 & 5\\6 & -1\end{pmatrix}+\frac{1}{2}\begin{pmatrix}-2 & 4\\6 & 3\end{pmatrix}$

(b) $\begin{pmatrix}0 & 5\\-1 & 0\end{pmatrix}+\begin{pmatrix}2 & 5\\7 & 9\end{pmatrix}-\begin{pmatrix}1 & -6\\3 & 4\end{pmatrix}3$

(c) $5\begin{pmatrix}1\\7\end{pmatrix}-3\begin{pmatrix}2\\4\end{pmatrix}+7\begin{pmatrix}-6\\0\end{pmatrix}$

---

2. Evaluate

(a) $\begin{pmatrix}1 & 2\\3 & 4\end{pmatrix}\begin{pmatrix}3 & 4\\5 & 6\end{pmatrix}$

(b) $(3 \quad -7)\begin{pmatrix}5\\6\end{pmatrix}$

(c) $\begin{pmatrix}2 & 7\\1 & 0\end{pmatrix}\begin{pmatrix}-3\\-2\end{pmatrix}$

(d) $\begin{pmatrix}\frac{1}{2} & 3\\2 & \frac{1}{4}\end{pmatrix}\begin{pmatrix}8\\4\end{pmatrix}$

(e) $(1 \quad 3)\begin{pmatrix}-1\\4\end{pmatrix}$

(f) $(2 \quad 7)\begin{pmatrix}3\\-4\end{pmatrix}$

(g) $(-1 \quad 0)\begin{pmatrix}3\\-1\end{pmatrix}$

(h) $\begin{pmatrix}2 & 1\\3 & -1\end{pmatrix}\begin{pmatrix}2\\4\end{pmatrix}$

(i) $\begin{pmatrix}-1 & 3\\5 & 2\end{pmatrix}\begin{pmatrix}-1\\-2\end{pmatrix}$

(j) $\begin{pmatrix}-1 & 0\\-1 & 2\end{pmatrix}\begin{pmatrix}4\\5\end{pmatrix}$

3. Evaluate

(a) $\begin{pmatrix}2 & -1\\4 & 2\end{pmatrix}\begin{pmatrix}-1 & 0\\2 & -3\end{pmatrix}$

(b) $\begin{pmatrix}0 & -5\\6 & -1\end{pmatrix}\begin{pmatrix}3 & -1\\-4 & 0\end{pmatrix}$

(c) $\begin{pmatrix}\cos\theta & \sin\theta\\-\sin\theta & \cos\theta\end{pmatrix}\begin{pmatrix}\cos\theta\\\sin\theta\end{pmatrix}$

(d) $\begin{pmatrix}x & 3x\\2y & y\end{pmatrix}\begin{pmatrix}3x\\2y\end{pmatrix}$

4. If $A = \begin{pmatrix} 1 & 0 \\ 0 & 2 \end{pmatrix}$, $B = \begin{pmatrix} 2 & 0 \\ 1 & 0 \end{pmatrix}$ evaluate A^2, A^3, B^2, AB, BA.
Is $AB = BA$?

5. For $A = \begin{pmatrix} 1 & -1 \\ 0 & 2 \end{pmatrix}$, $B = \begin{pmatrix} 1 & 0 \\ 1 & 2 \end{pmatrix}$ verify

(a) $(A+B)(A+B) \neq A^2 + 2AB + B^2$. Why?
(b) $(A+B)(A-B) \neq A^2 - B^2$.
(c) $(A+B)(A+B) = A^2 + AB + BA + B^2$.

6. Show that $A = \begin{pmatrix} 3 & 2 \\ -1 & 2 \end{pmatrix}$ is a solution of $A^2 - 5A + 8I = 0$

where $I = \begin{pmatrix} 1 & 0 \\ 0 & 1 \end{pmatrix}$ and $O = \begin{pmatrix} 0 & 0 \\ 0 & 0 \end{pmatrix}$.

7. If $A = \begin{pmatrix} 1 & 2 \\ 3 & 4 \end{pmatrix}$ find A^2, A^3.

8. If $A = \begin{pmatrix} 1 & 0 \\ 2 & -1 \end{pmatrix}$, $B = \begin{pmatrix} -2 & 1 \\ 3 & 0 \end{pmatrix}$ find

(a) $(A+B)^2$, (b) $A^2 + AB + BA + B^2$, (c) $A^2 + 2AB + B^2$.

9. Find x and y if $(x \quad y)\begin{pmatrix} 2 & 3 \\ 0 & 1 \end{pmatrix} = (6 \quad 10)$.

10. Evaluate $(x \quad y)\begin{pmatrix} a & b+t \\ b-t & c \end{pmatrix}\begin{pmatrix} x \\ y \end{pmatrix}$.

3. SPECIAL MATRICES

3.1 TYPES OF MATRICES

[A] **Additive Identity** (2 × 2)

$O = \begin{pmatrix} 0 & 0 \\ 0 & 0 \end{pmatrix}$ = 2 × 2 Additive Identity

$\Rightarrow A + O = O + A = A$ for all 2 × 2 matrices

Example: $\begin{pmatrix} a & b \\ c & d \end{pmatrix} + \begin{pmatrix} 0 & 0 \\ 0 & 0 \end{pmatrix} = \begin{pmatrix} a & b \\ c & d \end{pmatrix}$

[B] **Multiplicative Identity** (2 × 2)

$I = \begin{pmatrix} 1 & 0 \\ 0 & 1 \end{pmatrix}$ = 2 × 2 Multiplicative Identity

$\Rightarrow AI = IA = A$ for all 2 × 2 matrices

Example: $\underset{2 \times 2}{\begin{pmatrix} a & b \\ c & d \end{pmatrix}} \underset{2 \times 2}{\begin{pmatrix} 1 & 0 \\ 0 & 1 \end{pmatrix}} = \underset{2 \times 2}{\begin{pmatrix} a & b \\ c & d \end{pmatrix}}$

[C] **The Diagonal Matrix**

$D = \begin{pmatrix} a & 0 \\ 0 & b \end{pmatrix}$ = 2 × 2 Diagonal Matrix. It must have 2 zeros on the **off** diagonal.

/ = Off Diagonal   \ = Main Diagonal

Examples: $\begin{pmatrix} 1 & 0 \\ 0 & 5 \end{pmatrix}, \begin{pmatrix} 1 & 0 \\ 0 & 1 \end{pmatrix}, \begin{pmatrix} 0 & 0 \\ 0 & 0 \end{pmatrix}$ are diagonals but,

$\begin{pmatrix} 0 & 1 \\ 2 & 0 \end{pmatrix}, \begin{pmatrix} 1 & 0 \\ 2 & 0 \end{pmatrix}, \begin{pmatrix} 0 & 3 \\ 0 & 0 \end{pmatrix}$ are not diagonals.

TRICK

$$D^n = \begin{pmatrix} a^n & 0 \\ 0 & b^n \end{pmatrix}$$

Example 1: If $D = \begin{pmatrix} -1 & 0 \\ 0 & 3 \end{pmatrix}$ find D^2.

SOLUTION

$$D^2 = DD = \begin{pmatrix} -1 & 0 \\ 0 & 3 \end{pmatrix}\begin{pmatrix} -1 & 0 \\ 0 & 3 \end{pmatrix} = \begin{pmatrix} 1 & 0 \\ 0 & 9 \end{pmatrix} \text{ (Slow)}$$

$$D^2 = \begin{pmatrix} (-1)^2 & 0 \\ 0 & 3^2 \end{pmatrix} = \begin{pmatrix} 1 & 0 \\ 0 & 9 \end{pmatrix} \text{ (Fast)}$$

Example 2: If $D = \begin{pmatrix} -1 & 0 \\ 0 & 1 \end{pmatrix}$ find D^{42}.

SOLUTION

$$D^{42} = \begin{pmatrix} (-1)^{42} & 0 \\ 0 & (1)^{42} \end{pmatrix} = \begin{pmatrix} 1 & 0 \\ 0 & 1 \end{pmatrix}$$

Example 3: Evaluate A^8 if $A = \begin{pmatrix} 2 & 0 \\ 0 & 1 \end{pmatrix}$.

SOLUTION

$$A^8 = \begin{pmatrix} 2^8 & 0 \\ 0 & 1^8 \end{pmatrix} = \begin{pmatrix} 256 & 0 \\ 0 & 1 \end{pmatrix}$$

3.2 INVERSE MATRIX

[A] **Definition**: The inverse A^{-1} of a 2×2 matrix A is a matrix such that $AA^{-1} = I = A^{-1}A$ where $I = \begin{pmatrix} 1 & 0 \\ 0 & 1 \end{pmatrix}$.

[B] **Finding the Inverse** of a 2×2 matrix, A:

If $A = \begin{pmatrix} a & b \\ c & d \end{pmatrix}$, $A^{-1} = \frac{1}{\Delta}\begin{pmatrix} d & -b \\ -c & a \end{pmatrix}$ where $\Delta = (ad - bc)$.

Note: $\Delta = (ad - bc)$ is called the **determinant** of a matrix.

If $\Delta = 0$ the inverse A^{-1} does not exist.

TRICK

Calculating the inverse of $A = \begin{pmatrix} a & b \\ c & d \end{pmatrix}$:

Find $\Delta = (ad - bc)$,

then find $A^{-1} = \frac{1}{\Delta}$ [Inter, Sign, Change, Change]

Example 4: Find A^{-1} if $A = \begin{pmatrix} 2 & -1 \\ 3 & 7 \end{pmatrix}$ and show $AA^{-1} = I$.

SOLUTION

$$A = \begin{pmatrix} 2 & -1 \\ 3 & 7 \end{pmatrix}$$

$$\Delta = 14 - (-3) = 17$$

$$A^{-1} = \tfrac{1}{17}\begin{pmatrix} 7 & 1 \\ -3 & 2 \end{pmatrix}$$

$$AA^{-1} = \begin{pmatrix} 2 & -1 \\ 3 & 7 \end{pmatrix}\begin{pmatrix} 7 & 1 \\ -3 & 2 \end{pmatrix}\tfrac{1}{17} = \tfrac{1}{17}\begin{pmatrix} 17 & 0 \\ 0 & 17 \end{pmatrix} = \begin{pmatrix} 1 & 0 \\ 0 & 1 \end{pmatrix} = I$$

Example 5: Find x if $A = \begin{pmatrix} 2 & x \\ 3 & 7 \end{pmatrix}$ has no inverse.

SOLUTION

$$A = \begin{pmatrix} 2 & x \\ 3 & 7 \end{pmatrix}$$

No inverse $\Rightarrow \; \Delta = 2(7) - 3x = 0$

$\Rightarrow 14 = 3x$

$\Rightarrow \; x = \frac{14}{3}$

Example 6: If $M^{-1} = M$ show that $M^2 = I$ for any 2×2 matrix M.

SOLUTION

$M^{-1} = M \Rightarrow M.M^{-1} = M.M \Rightarrow I = M^2$

Example 7: If $M^{-1} = M$ show $a^2 + k^2 = 1$ where

$M = \begin{pmatrix} a & k \\ k & -a \end{pmatrix}$.

SOLUTION

$$M = \begin{pmatrix} a & k \\ k & -a \end{pmatrix}$$

$M^{-1} = M$

$$\Rightarrow \frac{1}{-a^2 - k^2} \begin{pmatrix} -a & -k \\ -k & a \end{pmatrix} = \begin{pmatrix} a & k \\ k & -a \end{pmatrix}$$

$$\Rightarrow \begin{pmatrix} \frac{a}{a^2+k^2} & \frac{k}{a^2+k^2} \\ \frac{k}{a^2+k^2} & \frac{-a}{a^2+k^2} \end{pmatrix} = \begin{pmatrix} a & k \\ k & -a \end{pmatrix} \Rightarrow \frac{a}{a^2 + k^2} = a \Rightarrow a^2 + k^2 = 1$$

Exercise 2 (Answers: page **171**)

Matrix Algebra

1. If $A=\begin{pmatrix} 2 & -5 \\ -3 & 1 \end{pmatrix}$ find a, c such that $aI + A + cA^2 = O$ where $a, c \in R$ and $O=\begin{pmatrix} 0 & 0 \\ 0 & 0 \end{pmatrix}$.

2. Find a if $B^2 = I$ where $B=\begin{pmatrix} a & 1 \\ -3 & -2 \end{pmatrix}$.

3. Show $AB = BA$ where $A=\begin{pmatrix} 1-3b & b \\ 4b & 1 \end{pmatrix}$ and $B=\begin{pmatrix} 2 & 1 \\ 4 & 5 \end{pmatrix}$.

4. If $A=\begin{pmatrix} 1 & 2 \\ 0 & 1 \end{pmatrix}$ and $I=\begin{pmatrix} 1 & 0 \\ 0 & 1 \end{pmatrix}$ find $p, q \in R$ if $A^2 = pA + qI$.

5. If $A=\begin{pmatrix} 2 & 3 \\ 3 & 5 \end{pmatrix}$ show that $A^2 = 7A - I$. Express A^3 in terms of A and I. (**Hint**: $A^3 = A^2A$)

6. If $A=\begin{pmatrix} 2 & 1 \\ 1 & 2 \end{pmatrix}$ and $B=\begin{pmatrix} 3 & 0 \\ 0 & 1 \end{pmatrix}$ and $X=\begin{pmatrix} x & y \\ x & -y \end{pmatrix}$ show that $AX = XB$, $x, y \in R$.

7. Find c if $X^2 = O$ where $X=\begin{pmatrix} 2 & c \\ 3 & -2 \end{pmatrix}$ and $O=\begin{pmatrix} 0 & 0 \\ 0 & 0 \end{pmatrix}$, $c \in R$.

8. If $M = \begin{pmatrix} 2 & 0 \\ 1 & 3 \end{pmatrix}$ verify $M^2 = 5M - 6I$. Hence show that $M^3 = 19M - 30I$.

9. Find the inverse of:

(a) $\begin{pmatrix} 2 & 3 \\ 1 & 2 \end{pmatrix}$ (b) $\begin{pmatrix} 3 & 1 \\ 2 & 1 \end{pmatrix}$

(c) $\begin{pmatrix} -1 & 0 \\ 0 & -1 \end{pmatrix}$ (d) $\begin{pmatrix} 1 & 0 \\ 0 & -1 \end{pmatrix}$

(e) $\begin{pmatrix} -1 & 0 \\ 0 & 1 \end{pmatrix}$ (f) $\begin{pmatrix} 1 & 0 \\ 0 & 1 \end{pmatrix}$

(g) $\begin{pmatrix} 2 & 3 \\ 4 & -1 \end{pmatrix}$ (h) $\begin{pmatrix} 4 & -2 \\ 3 & 1 \end{pmatrix}$

(i) $\begin{pmatrix} 4 & 1 \\ 2 & 1 \end{pmatrix}$ (j) $\begin{pmatrix} 4 & 2 \\ 0 & 2 \end{pmatrix}$

(k) $\begin{pmatrix} \cos A & -\sin A \\ \sin A & \cos A \end{pmatrix}$

(l) $\begin{pmatrix} \cos 2A & \sin 2A \\ \sin 2A & -\cos 2A \end{pmatrix}$

10. If $A = \begin{pmatrix} 5 & 3 \\ 3 & 2 \end{pmatrix}$ and $B = \begin{pmatrix} 0 & 1 \\ 1 & 0 \end{pmatrix}$ find

(a) A^{-1}
(b) B^{-1}
(c) AB
(d) BA
(e) $(AB)^{-1}$
(f) $B^{-1}A^{-1}$
(g) $A^{-1}B^{-1}$
(h) $A^{-1}A$
(i) $(A^{-1})^{-1}$
(j) $(A^{-1})^2$
(k) $(A^{-1}B^{-1})^2$
(l) $AB\,B^{-1}A^{-1}$
(m) $A^{-1}A^2$
(n) B^2B^{-1}

11. (a) If $\begin{pmatrix} x & 1 \\ 1 & x \end{pmatrix}$ has no inverse, find x.

(b) Find x, if $A = \begin{pmatrix} 3x & 1 \\ x & x \end{pmatrix}$ has no inverse.

(c) Find x, if $A = \begin{pmatrix} 3 & 2 \\ 1 & x \end{pmatrix}$ has no inverse.

4. EQUATIONS

4.1 MATRIX EQUATIONS

Example: If $AB = C$ find A.

$\Rightarrow ABB^{-1} = CB^{-1}$

(Multiply on the right by B^{-1})

$\Rightarrow A = CB^{-1}$

TRICK

To solve for an unknown matrix A isolate it by multiplying both sides by inverse matrices in the right order.

Remember: You cannot change the order of matrix multiplication.

Example: If $BAC = D$, find A.

$BAC = D \Rightarrow B^{-1}BACC^{-1} = B^{-1}DC^{-1}$

$\Rightarrow A = B^{-1}DC^{-1}$

Example 1: If $B = \begin{pmatrix} 2 & 1 \\ -3 & 5 \end{pmatrix}$, $C = \begin{pmatrix} 4 & 0 \\ 5 & 1 \end{pmatrix}$ find A if $AB = C$.

SOLUTION

$AB = C$

$\Rightarrow ABB^{-1} = CB^{-1}$

$$\Rightarrow A = CB^{-1} = \begin{pmatrix} 4 & 0 \\ 5 & 1 \end{pmatrix}\begin{pmatrix} 5 & -1 \\ 3 & 2 \end{pmatrix}\tfrac{1}{13} = \tfrac{1}{13}\begin{pmatrix} 20 & -4 \\ 28 & -3 \end{pmatrix} = \begin{pmatrix} \frac{20}{13} & -\frac{4}{13} \\ \frac{28}{13} & -\frac{3}{13} \end{pmatrix}$$

Example 2: If $A = M + AB$ find B if $A = \begin{pmatrix} 2 & -1 \\ 3 & 1 \end{pmatrix}$ and

$M = \begin{pmatrix} -2 & 0 \\ -1 & 1 \end{pmatrix}$.

SOLUTION

$$A = M + AB \Rightarrow A - M = AB \Rightarrow A^{-1}(A - M) = A^{-1}AB$$

$$\Rightarrow A^{-1}(A - M) = B$$

$$\Rightarrow \tfrac{1}{5}\begin{pmatrix} 1 & 1 \\ -3 & 2 \end{pmatrix}\begin{pmatrix} 4 & -1 \\ 4 & 0 \end{pmatrix} = \tfrac{1}{5}\begin{pmatrix} 8 & -1 \\ -4 & 3 \end{pmatrix} = B$$

$$\therefore B = \begin{pmatrix} \tfrac{8}{5} & -\tfrac{1}{5} \\ -\tfrac{4}{5} & \tfrac{3}{5} \end{pmatrix}$$

4.2 SIMULTANEOUS EQUATIONS

TRICK

Simultaneous equations in 2 or more unknowns can be written as a single matrix equation: $AX = B$

Example: Write $3x - 2y = 7$
$4x + y = -2$
as a single matrix equation.

SOLUTION

$$\begin{matrix} 3x - 2y = 7 \\ 4x + y = -2 \end{matrix} \Rightarrow \begin{pmatrix} 3 & -2 \\ 4 & 1 \end{pmatrix}\begin{pmatrix} x \\ y \end{pmatrix} = \begin{pmatrix} 7 \\ -2 \end{pmatrix}$$

$$A \quad X = B$$

Trick: Make sure x's are under x's, y's are under y's and number is under number.

Check: $\begin{pmatrix} 3 & -2 \\ 4 & 1 \end{pmatrix}\begin{pmatrix} x \\ y \end{pmatrix} = \begin{pmatrix} 7 \\ -2 \end{pmatrix} \Rightarrow \begin{pmatrix} 3x - 2y \\ 4x + y \end{pmatrix} = \begin{pmatrix} 7 \\ -2 \end{pmatrix}$

$\Rightarrow$ $3x - 2y = 7$ and $4x + y = -2$

Example 3: Use matrix methods to solve

$$2x - 7y = -11$$
$$3x + 8y = -2$$

SOLUTION

$2x - 7y = -11$

$3x + 8y = -2$

$$\Rightarrow \begin{pmatrix} 2 & -7 \\ 3 & 8 \end{pmatrix}\begin{pmatrix} x \\ y \end{pmatrix} = \begin{pmatrix} -11 \\ -2 \end{pmatrix}$$

$$A \quad X = B$$

Multiplying both sides on the left by A^{-1}

$$\Rightarrow \begin{pmatrix} x \\ y \end{pmatrix} = \begin{pmatrix} 8 & 7 \\ -3 & 2 \end{pmatrix}\begin{pmatrix} -11 \\ -2 \end{pmatrix}\tfrac{1}{37} = \tfrac{1}{37}\begin{pmatrix} -102 \\ 29 \end{pmatrix} = \begin{pmatrix} -\frac{102}{37} \\ \frac{29}{37} \end{pmatrix}$$

$\therefore x = -\frac{102}{37}$, $y = \frac{29}{37}$

A SPECIAL RESULT

$(A^{-1}MA)^n = A^{-1}M^nA$ for all 2×2 matrices M and A, $n \in N_0$.

PROOF

$$(A^{-1}MA)^n = \underbrace{(A^{-1}MA)(A^{-1}MA)(A^{-1}MA).......(A^{-1}MA)(A^{-1}MA)}_{n \text{ of them}}$$

$$= A^{-1}MAA^{-1}MAA^{-1}MA.......A^{-1}MAA^{-1}MA$$

$$= A^{-1}\underbrace{MMM.......MM}_{n \text{ of them}}A = A^{-1}M^nA$$

Example 4: If $M = \begin{pmatrix} -1 & 6 \\ -2 & 6 \end{pmatrix}$, $A = \begin{pmatrix} 3 & 2 \\ 2 & 1 \end{pmatrix}$ show that

$A^{-1}MA = \begin{pmatrix} 3 & 0 \\ 0 & 2 \end{pmatrix}$. Hence evaluate M^7.

SOLUTION

$$A^{-1}MA = \tfrac{1}{-1}\begin{pmatrix} 1 & -2 \\ -2 & 3 \end{pmatrix}\begin{pmatrix} -1 & 6 \\ -2 & 6 \end{pmatrix}\begin{pmatrix} 3 & 2 \\ 2 & 1 \end{pmatrix}$$

$$= -1\begin{pmatrix} 1 & -2 \\ -2 & 3 \end{pmatrix}\begin{pmatrix} 9 & 4 \\ 6 & 2 \end{pmatrix} = -\begin{pmatrix} -3 & 0 \\ 0 & -2 \end{pmatrix} = \begin{pmatrix} 3 & 0 \\ 0 & 2 \end{pmatrix}$$

$$(A^{-1}MA)^7 = A^{-1}M^7A$$

$$\Rightarrow \begin{pmatrix} 3 & 0 \\ 0 & 2 \end{pmatrix}^7 = A^{-1}M^7A \Rightarrow A\begin{pmatrix} 3 & 0 \\ 0 & 2 \end{pmatrix}^7 A^{-1} = M^7$$

$$\Rightarrow \begin{pmatrix} 3 & 2 \\ 2 & 1 \end{pmatrix}\begin{pmatrix} 2187 & 0 \\ 0 & 128 \end{pmatrix}\begin{pmatrix} -1 & 2 \\ 2 & -3 \end{pmatrix} = M^7$$

$$\Rightarrow \begin{pmatrix} 6561 & 256 \\ 4374 & 128 \end{pmatrix}\begin{pmatrix} -1 & 2 \\ 2 & -3 \end{pmatrix} = M^7$$

$$\Rightarrow \begin{pmatrix} -6049 & 12354 \\ -4118 & 8364 \end{pmatrix} = M^7$$

Exercise 3 (Answers: page **172**)

Equations

1. Solve the following simultaneous equations by the matrix method:

(a) $2x + 3y = 7$
$3x - y = 5$

(b) $2x + y = 4$
$x + y = 3$

(c) $3x + y = 9$
$5x + 2y = 16$

(d) $y = 2x$
$y = 5 - 3x$

(e) $2x - y = 6$
$3x + y = 14$

(f) $2x - 3y = 1$
$x + 2y = 4$

(g) $ax + by = e$
$cx + dy = f$

(h) $5x - 3y + 4 = 0$
$2x - y = -1$

---

2. If $A = \begin{pmatrix} 1 & 1 \\ 1 & 1 \end{pmatrix}$ find (i) A^2, (ii) A^3, (iii) A^{10}, (iv) A^n.

3. Evaluate $\cos A \begin{pmatrix} \cos A & -\sin A \\ \sin A & \cos A \end{pmatrix} + \sin A \begin{pmatrix} \sin A & \cos A \\ \cos A & -\sin A \end{pmatrix}$.

4. If $A = \begin{pmatrix} \lambda & 1+\lambda \\ 1-\lambda & -\lambda \end{pmatrix}$ show (i) $A^2 = I$, (ii) $A^{-1} = A$.

5. If $A = \begin{pmatrix} 2 & 1 \\ 4 & 2 \end{pmatrix}$ and $B = \begin{pmatrix} 3 & 2 \\ -6 & c \end{pmatrix}$, find c if $AB = O$ where

$O = \begin{pmatrix} 0 & 0 \\ 0 & 0 \end{pmatrix}$.

6. If $A=\begin{pmatrix} 2 & 3 \\ c & -2 \end{pmatrix}$ find c if $A^2 = I$.

7. Solve $x^2 - 7x + 10 = 0$. If α, β are the roots of this quadratic with $\alpha < \beta$. Find x, y if $M\begin{pmatrix} 1 \\ x \end{pmatrix}=\alpha\begin{pmatrix} 1 \\ x \end{pmatrix}$ and $M\begin{pmatrix} 3 \\ y \end{pmatrix}=\beta\begin{pmatrix} 3 \\ y \end{pmatrix}$ where $M=\begin{pmatrix} 4 & 2 \\ 1 & 3 \end{pmatrix}$. Show if $A=\begin{pmatrix} 1 & 3 \\ x & y \end{pmatrix}$ that $A^{-1}MA=\begin{pmatrix} 2 & 0 \\ 0 & 5 \end{pmatrix}$. Hence, evaluate M^5.

8. If $I=\begin{pmatrix} 1 & 0 \\ 0 & 1 \end{pmatrix}$, $J=\begin{pmatrix} 0 & 1 \\ -1 & 0 \end{pmatrix}$ show that $J^2 = -I$. Show that $aI + bJ$ has an inverse if $a^2 + b^2 \neq 0$.

9. Find $x, z \in R$ if $A^2 + 3A + 2I = 0$ where $A=\begin{pmatrix} x & 0 \\ 3 & z \end{pmatrix}$, $O=\begin{pmatrix} 0 & 0 \\ 0 & 0 \end{pmatrix}$, $I=\begin{pmatrix} 1 & 0 \\ 0 & 1 \end{pmatrix}$.

10. If $B=\begin{pmatrix} 3 & -1 \\ 1 & 3 \end{pmatrix}$ and $S=\begin{pmatrix} 4 & 3 \\ 3 & -4 \end{pmatrix}$ show $B^{-1}SB=\begin{pmatrix} 5 & 0 \\ 0 & -5 \end{pmatrix}$.

11. (i) If α, β are the roots of $x^2 - 2x - 24 = 0$ find α, β, $\alpha > \beta$.

(ii) If $M = \begin{pmatrix} 4 & 1 \\ 16 & -2 \end{pmatrix}$ find z such that $M\begin{pmatrix} 1 \\ z \end{pmatrix} = \alpha\begin{pmatrix} 1 \\ z \end{pmatrix}$ and find y such that $M\begin{pmatrix} 1 \\ y \end{pmatrix} = \beta\begin{pmatrix} 1 \\ y \end{pmatrix}$.

(iii) If $B = \begin{pmatrix} 1 & 1 \\ z & y \end{pmatrix}$ show $B^{-1}MB = \begin{pmatrix} \alpha & 0 \\ 0 & \beta \end{pmatrix}$.

12. If $M = \begin{pmatrix} 1 & -2 \\ -2 & 4 \end{pmatrix}$ evaluate $(z \quad y)\, M \begin{pmatrix} z \\ y \end{pmatrix}$.

13. If $M = \begin{pmatrix} 1 & 0 \\ 2 & 1 \end{pmatrix}$ find (i) M^2, (ii) M^3, (iii) M^{10}, (iv) M^n.

14. Evaluate $\begin{pmatrix} 1 & k \\ 0 & 1 \end{pmatrix}\begin{pmatrix} p & 0 \\ 0 & q \end{pmatrix}\begin{pmatrix} 1 & 0 \\ h & 1 \end{pmatrix}$.

15. If $A = M + AB$ find B if $A = \begin{pmatrix} 2 & -1 \\ 3 & 1 \end{pmatrix}$ and $M = \begin{pmatrix} 2 & 0 \\ -1 & 1 \end{pmatrix}$.

MATRICES REVISION QUESTIONS

These 3 part questions are similar to the questions on the LC paper. The answers to these questions and hints to help you solve them are available on our website:

www.studentxpress.ie

1. (a) Find the coefficient of xy in $(x \;\; y)\begin{pmatrix} 3 & 1 \\ 1 & 1 \end{pmatrix}\begin{pmatrix} x \\ y \end{pmatrix}$.

(b) If $X = \begin{pmatrix} p & 1+p \\ 1-p & -p \end{pmatrix}$ find (i) X^2, (ii) X^{-1}. For $p = -2$ find Y if

$X^{15}Y = \begin{pmatrix} -5 & 8 \\ -4 & 5 \end{pmatrix}$.

(c) If $M = \begin{pmatrix} 4 & 2 \\ -3 & -1 \end{pmatrix}$ and $A = \begin{pmatrix} 1 & 2 \\ -1 & -3 \end{pmatrix}$ evaluate $A^{-1}MA$. Prove

$(A^{-1}MA)^8 = A^{-1}M^8A$. Hence, evaluate M^8.

2 (a) Write $(x \;\; y)\begin{pmatrix} 5 & 8 \\ 8 & 13 \end{pmatrix}\begin{pmatrix} x \\ y \end{pmatrix}$ in the form $ax^2 + bxy + cy^2$.

(b) If $A = \begin{pmatrix} 2 & 1 \\ 2 & 2 \end{pmatrix}$ and $B = \begin{pmatrix} 2 & 1 \\ -2 & -1 \end{pmatrix}$ find C if $AB = CA$.

(c) If $M = \begin{pmatrix} 3 & 1 \\ 2 & 4 \end{pmatrix}$ and $A = \begin{pmatrix} 1 & 1 \\ 2 & -1 \end{pmatrix}$ find A^{-1} and evaluate

$A^{-1}MA$. Prove $(A^{-1}MA)^8 = A^{-1}M^8A$. Express M^8 in the form

ADA^{-1} where D is a diagonal matrix.

3 (a) Evaluate $\begin{pmatrix} 2 & -3 \\ 1 & -2 \end{pmatrix}^{10}$.

(b) For what value of $x \in R$ does $\begin{pmatrix} x^3 & x \\ 1 & 1 \end{pmatrix}$ have no inverse?

(c) If $M = \begin{pmatrix} 3 & 4 \\ -2 & -3 \end{pmatrix}$ find k, $l \in R$ such that $k\begin{pmatrix} 1 \\ -1 \end{pmatrix} = M\begin{pmatrix} 1 \\ -1 \end{pmatrix}$ and $l\begin{pmatrix} -2 \\ 1 \end{pmatrix} = M\begin{pmatrix} -2 \\ 1 \end{pmatrix}$. If $A = \begin{pmatrix} 1 & -2 \\ -1 & 1 \end{pmatrix}$ evaluate $A^{-1}MA$. Show that $(A^{-1}MA)^{100} = A^{-1}M^{100}A$. Hence evaluate M^{100}.

4. (a) If $A = \frac{1}{2}\begin{pmatrix} 1 & -\sqrt{3} \\ \sqrt{3} & 1 \end{pmatrix}$, $B = \frac{1}{\sqrt{2}}\begin{pmatrix} 1 & -1 \\ 1 & 1 \end{pmatrix}$ show $A^3 = B^4$.

(b) Evaluate $\begin{pmatrix} 1 & 1 \\ 1 & 4 \end{pmatrix}^{-1}\begin{pmatrix} 3 & 1 \\ -4 & 8 \end{pmatrix}\begin{pmatrix} 1 & 1 \\ 1 & 4 \end{pmatrix}$.

(c) $M = \begin{pmatrix} -3 & -2 \\ 8 & 7 \end{pmatrix}$. Let α, β be the roots of $x^2 - 4x - 5 = 0$, $\alpha > \beta$. If $M\begin{pmatrix} x \\ y \end{pmatrix} = \alpha\begin{pmatrix} x \\ y \end{pmatrix}$ find a relation between x and y and if $M\begin{pmatrix} w \\ z \end{pmatrix} = \beta\begin{pmatrix} w \\ z \end{pmatrix}$ find a relation between w and z. Verify $M^2 - 4M - 5I = 0$.

5 (a) If $X=\begin{pmatrix}1 & 0\\ 1 & 2\end{pmatrix}$ and $Y=\begin{pmatrix}-1 & 1\\ 0 & -2\end{pmatrix}$ show that

$(X+Y)^2 \neq X^2+2XY+Y^2$.

(b) $M=\begin{pmatrix}9 & -2\\ 8 & -1\end{pmatrix}$. If $M\begin{pmatrix}x\\ y\end{pmatrix}=\begin{pmatrix}x\\ y\end{pmatrix}$ find y in terms of x. Hence,

find $a, c \in R$ if $\begin{pmatrix}a & 1\\ c & 2\end{pmatrix}\begin{pmatrix}x\\ y\end{pmatrix}=\begin{pmatrix}0\\ 0\end{pmatrix}$, $x\neq 0$, $y\neq 0$.

(c) If $\begin{pmatrix}1 & 1\\ 4 & 1\end{pmatrix}\begin{pmatrix}\alpha\\ \beta\end{pmatrix}=\begin{pmatrix}x\\ y\end{pmatrix}$ write $y^2 - 5xy + 4x^2 = 0$ in terms of α and

β.

6. (a) $A=\begin{pmatrix}\frac{1}{2} & \frac{2}{3}\\ \frac{1}{2} & -\frac{2}{3}\end{pmatrix}$, $X=\begin{pmatrix}1 & 0\\ 0 & 0\end{pmatrix}$, $Y=\begin{pmatrix}0 & 1\\ 0 & 0\end{pmatrix}$, $Z=\begin{pmatrix}0 & 0\\ 1 & 0\end{pmatrix}$,

$W=\begin{pmatrix}1 & 1\\ 1 & 1\end{pmatrix}$. If $A=\alpha X+\beta Y+\gamma Z+\delta W$ find $\alpha,\beta,\gamma,\delta \in R$.

(b) If α,β are roots of $x^2 - 3x - 4 = 0$ where α is the positive root

show $\begin{pmatrix}2-\alpha & 3\\ 2 & 1-\alpha\end{pmatrix}\begin{pmatrix}\frac{1}{2}\\ \frac{1}{3}\end{pmatrix}=\begin{pmatrix}0\\ 0\end{pmatrix}$. Verify $\begin{pmatrix}2 & 3\\ 2 & 1\end{pmatrix}\begin{pmatrix}1\\ -1\end{pmatrix}=\beta\begin{pmatrix}1\\ -1\end{pmatrix}$.

7. (a) If $\begin{pmatrix}-6\\ 1\end{pmatrix}=a\begin{pmatrix}1\\ -3\end{pmatrix}+b\begin{pmatrix}-1\\ 2\end{pmatrix}$ find $a, b \in R$.

(b) Solve $2x - y = 7$; $4x + 3y = 9$ by matrices.

(c) If $M=\begin{pmatrix}4 & 1\\ 2 & 3\end{pmatrix}$, find y and z, if $M\begin{pmatrix}1\\ y\end{pmatrix}=5\begin{pmatrix}1\\ y\end{pmatrix}$ and

$M\begin{pmatrix}1\\z\end{pmatrix}=2\begin{pmatrix}1\\z\end{pmatrix}$. Let $A=\begin{pmatrix}1&1\\y&z\end{pmatrix}$. Evaluate $A^{-1}MA$.

8. (a) If $A=\begin{pmatrix}a&0\\0&b\end{pmatrix}$, show $A^{-1}=\begin{pmatrix}\frac{1}{a}&0\\0&\frac{1}{b}\end{pmatrix}$.

(b) Evaluate $\begin{pmatrix}2&1\\4&3\end{pmatrix}^{-1}\begin{pmatrix}2&1\\-6&7\end{pmatrix}\begin{pmatrix}2&1\\4&3\end{pmatrix}$.

(c) If $M=\begin{pmatrix}5&2\\3&4\end{pmatrix}$ and $A=\begin{pmatrix}1&-2\\1&3\end{pmatrix}$ evaluate $A^{-1}MA$. Show $(A^{-1}MA)^5=A^{-1}M^5A$. Hence find M^5.

9 (a) If $A=\begin{pmatrix}1&2\\-1&3\end{pmatrix}$ find a matrix B such that $AB=BA$.

(b) If $M=\begin{pmatrix}-1&2\\0&3\end{pmatrix}$ evaluate M^2-2M.

(c) If $M=\begin{pmatrix}-1&6\\-2&6\end{pmatrix}$ and $A=\begin{pmatrix}3&2\\2&1\end{pmatrix}$ show that $A^{-1}MA=\begin{pmatrix}3&0\\0&2\end{pmatrix}$.

Prove $(A^{-1}MA)^{20}=A^{-1}M^{20}A$. Evaluate M^{20}.

10. (a) Show that $X=\begin{pmatrix}2&-1\\3&0\end{pmatrix}$ is a solution of the equation

$X^2-2X+3I=O$ where $I=\begin{pmatrix}1&0\\0&1\end{pmatrix}$ and $O=\begin{pmatrix}0&0\\0&0\end{pmatrix}$.

(b) If $A=\begin{pmatrix}2 & 1\\ 0 & 1\end{pmatrix}$, $B=\begin{pmatrix}-1 & 3\\ 2 & 1\end{pmatrix}$ find C such that $AC = BA^{-1}$.

(c) If $M=\begin{pmatrix}1 & 4\\ 2 & 3\end{pmatrix}$ evaluate $A^{-1}MA$ where $A=\begin{pmatrix}1 & -2\\ 1 & 1\end{pmatrix}$. Hence evaluate M^{32}.

11 (a) (i) Solve $(x \quad y)\begin{pmatrix}2 & -1\\ 3 & 0\end{pmatrix} = (5 \quad 2)$ for x and y.

(ii) If $AB = B - I$ find B^{-1} if $A=\begin{pmatrix}-2 & 3\\ 10 & 1\end{pmatrix}$ and hence B where $I=\begin{pmatrix}1 & 0\\ 0 & 1\end{pmatrix}$.

(b) If $A=\begin{pmatrix}2 & 3\\ 3 & 5\end{pmatrix}$ show $A^2 = 7A - I$. Express A^3 in terms of A and I.

(c) If $B=\begin{pmatrix}2 & 1\\ 4 & 5\end{pmatrix}$ and $A=\begin{pmatrix}a & b\\ c & d\end{pmatrix}$ and $AB = BA$ show that $c = 4b$ and $d = a + 3b$. Hence, find one such matrix A.

12. (a) If $A=\begin{pmatrix}2 & -5\\ 3 & 1\end{pmatrix}$ and if $aI + bA + cA^2 = O$, $a, b, c \in R$, show that $a = 17c$ where $I=\begin{pmatrix}1 & 0\\ 0 & 1\end{pmatrix}$.

(b) If $X=\begin{pmatrix}a & b\\ c & d\end{pmatrix}$ and $X^2 = O$ where $O=\begin{pmatrix}0 & 0\\ 0 & 0\end{pmatrix}$ show $d = -a$,

$c = -\frac{a^2}{b}$ if $b \neq 0$. Hence, find one X.

(c) $M = \begin{pmatrix} 4 & 1 \\ 16 & -2 \end{pmatrix}$. If α, β are the roots of $x^2 - 2x - 24 = 0$ find α and β, $\alpha > \beta$. If $M\begin{pmatrix} 1 \\ k \end{pmatrix} = \alpha\begin{pmatrix} 1 \\ k \end{pmatrix}$ find k. If $M\begin{pmatrix} 1 \\ l \end{pmatrix} = \beta\begin{pmatrix} 1 \\ l \end{pmatrix}$ find l. If $B = \begin{pmatrix} 1 & 1 \\ k & l \end{pmatrix}$ show $B^{-1}MB = \begin{pmatrix} \alpha & 0 \\ 0 & \beta \end{pmatrix}$.

13 (a) Evaluate $\begin{pmatrix} \frac{\sqrt{3}}{2} & -\frac{1}{2} \\ \frac{1}{2} & \frac{\sqrt{3}}{2} \end{pmatrix}^6$.

(b) (i) If $(x \quad y)\begin{pmatrix} 3 & -1 \\ -1 & -2 \end{pmatrix}\begin{pmatrix} x \\ y \end{pmatrix} = 14$ find y when $x = 2$.

(ii) If $\begin{pmatrix} -6 \\ 1 \end{pmatrix} = a\begin{pmatrix} 1 \\ -3 \end{pmatrix} + b\begin{pmatrix} -1 \\ 2 \end{pmatrix}$ find $a, b \in R$.

(c) Express $2x - 3y = 7$

$4x + 7y = 1$

in matrix form. Hence, solve the simultaneous equations.

Answers and hints to Matrices Revision Questions available on: **www.studentxpress.ie**

ANSWERS

Exercise 1 [*Matrix Operations* (page **150**)]

1. (a) $\begin{pmatrix} -3 & -9 \\ -8 & \frac{13}{2} \end{pmatrix}$ (b) $\begin{pmatrix} -1 & 28 \\ -3 & -3 \end{pmatrix}$ (c) $\begin{pmatrix} -43 \\ 23 \end{pmatrix}$

2. (a) $\begin{pmatrix} 13 & 16 \\ 29 & 36 \end{pmatrix}$ (b) (-27) (c) $\begin{pmatrix} -20 \\ -3 \end{pmatrix}$ (d) $\begin{pmatrix} 16 \\ 17 \end{pmatrix}$

   (e) (11) (f) (-22) (g) (-3) (h) $\begin{pmatrix} 8 \\ 2 \end{pmatrix}$

   (i) $\begin{pmatrix} -5 \\ -9 \end{pmatrix}$ (j) $\begin{pmatrix} -4 \\ 6 \end{pmatrix}$

3. (a) $\begin{pmatrix} -4 & 3 \\ 0 & -6 \end{pmatrix}$ (b) $\begin{pmatrix} 20 & 0 \\ 22 & -6 \end{pmatrix}$ (c) $\begin{pmatrix} 1 \\ 0 \end{pmatrix}$ (d) $\begin{pmatrix} 3x^2+6xy \\ 6xy+2y^2 \end{pmatrix}$

4. $\begin{pmatrix} 1 & 0 \\ 0 & 4 \end{pmatrix}, \begin{pmatrix} 1 & 0 \\ 0 & 8 \end{pmatrix}, \begin{pmatrix} 4 & 0 \\ 2 & 0 \end{pmatrix}, \begin{pmatrix} 2 & 0 \\ 2 & 0 \end{pmatrix}, \begin{pmatrix} 2 & 0 \\ 1 & 0 \end{pmatrix}$

7. $\begin{pmatrix} 7 & 10 \\ 15 & 22 \end{pmatrix} \begin{pmatrix} 37 & 54 \\ 81 & 118 \end{pmatrix}$

8. (a) $\begin{pmatrix} 6 & -2 \\ -10 & 6 \end{pmatrix}$ (b) $\begin{pmatrix} 6 & -2 \\ -10 & 6 \end{pmatrix}$ (c) $\begin{pmatrix} 4 & 0 \\ -20 & 8 \end{pmatrix}$

9. $x = 3, y = 1$ 10. $ax^2 + 2bxy + cy^2$

Exercise 2 [*Matrix Algebra* (page **156**)]

1. $a = \frac{13}{3}$, $c = -\frac{1}{3}$ 2. $a = 2$ 4. $p = 2, q = -1$

5. $48A - 7I$ 7. $c = -\frac{4}{3}$

9. (a) $\begin{pmatrix} 2 & -3 \\ -1 & 2 \end{pmatrix}$ (b) $\begin{pmatrix} 1 & -1 \\ -2 & 3 \end{pmatrix}$ (c) $\begin{pmatrix} -1 & 0 \\ 0 & -1 \end{pmatrix}$ (d) $\begin{pmatrix} 1 & 0 \\ 0 & -1 \end{pmatrix}$

(e) $\begin{pmatrix} -1 & 0 \\ 0 & 1 \end{pmatrix}$ (f) $\begin{pmatrix} 1 & 0 \\ 0 & 1 \end{pmatrix}$ (g) $\frac{1}{14}\begin{pmatrix} 1 & 3 \\ 4 & -2 \end{pmatrix}$ (h) $\frac{1}{10}\begin{pmatrix} 1 & 2 \\ -3 & 4 \end{pmatrix}$

(i) $\frac{1}{2}\begin{pmatrix} 1 & -1 \\ -2 & 4 \end{pmatrix}$ (j) $\frac{1}{4}\begin{pmatrix} 1 & -1 \\ 0 & 2 \end{pmatrix}$

(k) $\begin{pmatrix} \cos A & \sin A \\ -\sin A & \cos A \end{pmatrix}$ (l) $\begin{pmatrix} \cos 2A & \sin 2A \\ \sin 2A & -\cos 2A \end{pmatrix}$

10. (a) $\begin{pmatrix} 2 & -3 \\ -3 & 5 \end{pmatrix}$ (b) $\begin{pmatrix} 0 & 1 \\ 1 & 0 \end{pmatrix}$ (c) $\begin{pmatrix} 3 & 5 \\ 2 & 3 \end{pmatrix}$ (d) $\begin{pmatrix} 3 & 2 \\ 5 & 3 \end{pmatrix}$

(e) $\begin{pmatrix} -3 & 5 \\ 2 & -3 \end{pmatrix}$ (f) $\begin{pmatrix} -3 & 5 \\ 2 & -3 \end{pmatrix}$ (g) $\begin{pmatrix} -3 & 2 \\ 5 & -3 \end{pmatrix}$ (h) $\begin{pmatrix} 1 & 0 \\ 0 & 1 \end{pmatrix}$

(i) $\begin{pmatrix} 5 & 3 \\ 3 & 2 \end{pmatrix}$ (j) $\begin{pmatrix} 13 & -21 \\ -21 & 34 \end{pmatrix}$ (k) $\begin{pmatrix} 19 & -12 \\ -30 & 19 \end{pmatrix}$

(l) $\begin{pmatrix} 1 & 0 \\ 0 & 1 \end{pmatrix}$ (m) $\begin{pmatrix} 5 & 3 \\ 3 & 2 \end{pmatrix}$ (n) $\begin{pmatrix} 0 & 1 \\ 1 & 0 \end{pmatrix}$

11. (a) ± 1 (b) 0, $\frac{1}{3}$, (c) $\frac{2}{3}$

Exercise 3 [*Equations* (page **162**)]

1. (a) (2, 1) (b) (1, 2) (c) (2, 3) (d) (1, 2)

(e) (4, 2) (f) (2, 1) (g) $\left(\frac{de-bf}{ad-bc}, \frac{af-ce}{ad-bc}\right)$ (h) (1, 3)

2. (i) $\begin{pmatrix} 2 & 2 \\ 2 & 2 \end{pmatrix}$ (ii) $\begin{pmatrix} 4 & 4 \\ 4 & 4 \end{pmatrix}$ (iii) $\begin{pmatrix} 512 & 512 \\ 512 & 512 \end{pmatrix}$

(iv) $\begin{pmatrix} 2^{n-1} & 2^{n-1} \\ 2^{n-1} & 2^{n-1} \end{pmatrix}$

3. $\begin{pmatrix} 1 & 0 \\ \sin 2A & \cos 2A \end{pmatrix}$

5. - 4

6. $c = -1$

7. $\alpha = 2, \beta = 5, x = -1, y = \frac{3}{2}$, $\begin{pmatrix} 2094 & 2062 \\ 1031 & 1063 \end{pmatrix}$

9. $x = -1$, $z = -2$; $x = -2$, $z = -1$

11. (i) $\alpha = 6, \beta = -4$, (ii) $z = 2$, $y = -8$

12. $z^2 - 4zy + 4y^2$

13. (i) $\begin{pmatrix} 1 & 0 \\ 4 & 1 \end{pmatrix}$ (ii) $\begin{pmatrix} 1 & 0 \\ 6 & 1 \end{pmatrix}$ (iii) $\begin{pmatrix} 1 & 0 \\ 20 & 1 \end{pmatrix}$ (iv) $\begin{pmatrix} 1 & 0 \\ 2n & 1 \end{pmatrix}$

14. $\begin{pmatrix} p + hkq & kq \\ qh & q \end{pmatrix}$

15. $\frac{1}{5}\begin{pmatrix} 4 & -1 \\ 8 & 3 \end{pmatrix}$

Sequences

1. SEQUENCES IN GENERAL

1.1 WHAT IS A SEQUENCE (PROGRESSION)?

It is a list of objects in a horizontal row with commas between them generated by plonking natural numbers into a function.

Example: $1, \frac{1}{2}, \frac{1}{3}, \frac{1}{4}, \frac{1}{5}$. This is a finite sequence because it stops.

Example: $1, \sin x, \sin^2 x, \sin^3 x, ...$ is an infinite sequence.

Each entry in the list is called a **term** and sequences are always read from left to right.

1.2 NOTATION (T AND S)

[A] T: Every term in a sequence is assigned a letter, usually T (sometimes u) with a subscript.

T_1 = First term
T_2 = Second term
T_{50} = 50th. term
T_n = nth. term

TRICK
T_{20} = Value of the object in the 20th. place in the list.

Example: 2, 4, 6, 8, 10, ...
$T_1 = 2, T_2 = 4, T_3 = 6, T_4 = 8, T_5 = 10$

Example: In the sequence $-1, -\frac{1}{2}, 0, \frac{1}{2}, 1, ...$, write down T_4.

T_4 = Value of the object in the 4th. place = $\frac{1}{2}$

The value of T can be anything. The subscripts must be whole positive numbers.

Example: In the sequence $\frac{x}{1-x}, \frac{x^2}{(1-x)^2}, \frac{x^3}{(1-x)^3}, \frac{x^4}{(1-x)^4}, ...$

$$T_3 = \frac{x^3}{(1-x)^3}$$

[B] S: This letter stands for sum. It is assigned a subscript to tell you how many terms to add. So

S_1 = Sum of first term = T_1

S_2 = Sum of first two terms = $T_1 + T_2$

S_{50} = Sum of first 50 terms = $T_1 + T_2 + ... + T_{50}$

S_n = Sum of first n terms = $T_1 + T_2 + ... + T_n$

Example 1: In the sequence -3, -1, 1, 3, 5, 7, 9, ... find S_5.

SOLUTION

-3, -1, 1, 3, 5, 7, 9, ...

$S_5 = -3 + (-1) + 1 + 3 + 5 = 5$

1.3 THE GENERAL TERM, T_n (the formula for a sequence)

TRICK

Given the general term T_n of a sequence every other term in the sequence can be generated by replacing n by the required value.

Example 2: For a sequence

$T_n = \dfrac{2^{n+1}}{n^2+2}$ find T_1, T_2, T_{15}, T_{n+1}, T_{2n+1}.

SOLUTION

$$T_n = \frac{2^{n+1}}{n^2+2} = \frac{2^{(n)+1}}{(n)^2+2}, \quad T_1 = \frac{2^{(1)+1}}{(1)^2+2} = \frac{4}{3}$$

$$T_2 = \frac{2^{(2)+1}}{(2)^2+2} = \frac{8}{6} = \frac{4}{3}, \quad T_{15} = \frac{2^{(15)+1}}{(15)^2+2} = \frac{2^{16}}{227}$$

$$T_{n+1} = \frac{2^{(n+1)+1}}{(n+1)^2+2} = \frac{2^{n+2}}{n^2+2n+3}$$

$$T_{2n+1} = \frac{2^{(2n+1)+1}}{(2n+1)^2+2} = \frac{2^{2n+2}}{4n^2+4n+3}$$

Danger!: Be careful. Make sure you know what the subscript is.

1. $T_{n^2} \neq T_n^2$ because $T_{n^2} = T_{(n^2)}$ but $T_n^2 = (T_n)^2$

2. $T_{n+1} \neq T_n + 1$ because $T_{n+1} = T_{(n+1)}$ but $T_n + 1 = (T_n) + 1$

Example 3: For a sequence $T_n = \frac{n}{2}(n+1)$, find T_{n+1}, $T_n + 1$, T_{n^2}, T_n^2, $T_{n+1} + T_n$, $T_{n+1} - T_n$

SOLUTION

$$T_n = \tfrac{n}{2}(n+1)$$

$$T_{n+1} = \frac{(n+1)}{2}((n+1)+1) = \frac{(n+1)(n+2)}{2}$$

$$(T_n)+1 = \tfrac{n}{2}(n+1)+1 = \frac{n(n+1)+2}{2} = \frac{n^2+n+2}{2}$$

$$T_{n^2} = \frac{(n)^2}{2}((n)^2+1) = \frac{n^2(n^2+1)}{2}$$

$$(T_n)^2 = (\tfrac{n}{2}(n+1))^2 = \tfrac{n^2}{4}(n+1)^2$$

$$T_{n+1} + T_n = \frac{(n+1)(n+2)}{2} + \frac{n}{2}(n+1) = \frac{(n+1)\{n+2+n\}}{2}$$

$$= (n+1)^2$$

$$T_{n+1} - T_n = \frac{(n+1)(n+2)}{2} - \frac{n}{2}(n+1) = \frac{(n+1)\{n+2-n\}}{2}$$

$$= (n+1)$$

T_n can be any function of n (Al, Expo, Trig, Log, Factorial). Don't be afraid!

Exercise 1 (Answers: page **212**)

Sequences

1. Write out the first 5 terms of the following sequences given the $n^{\text{th.}}$ term:

(a) $T_n = 5 + 2n$

(b) $T_n = 3 - \frac{1}{n}$

(c) $T_n = 5^n$

(d) $T_n = \dfrac{n!}{n+1}$

(e) $T_n = \frac{3}{n} + 2^n$

(f) $T_n = n^2 + n - 1$

(g) $T_n = \dfrac{1}{(n+1)^2}$

(h) $T_n = \cos n$

(i) $T_n = e^n$

(j) $T_n = \dfrac{n!}{2^n}$

2. For the following sequences find T_1, T_2, T_{20}, T_{n+2}, T_{n-1}, $(T_{n-1})^2$:

(a) $T_n = \dfrac{n-1}{n+2}$

(b) $T_n = \dfrac{2n-3}{n^2+1}$

(c) $T_n = \log_{10}\left(\dfrac{n+1}{n}\right)$

(d) $T_n = 2^n$

(e) $T_n = (n - 1)(n + 2)$

(f) $T_n = n^2 - 1$

(g) $T_n = 2n - 3$

(h) $T_n = \dfrac{n}{n+1}$

(i) $T_n = 2n^2 - 3n + 1$

(j) $T_n = \dfrac{2^n}{4^n+1}$

3. For the following sequences find S_1, S_3, S_7:

(a) $S_n = n + 2$

(b) $S_n = n^2 - 1$

(c) $S_n = 2^n - 1$

(d) $S_n = n^2 - 2n - 1$

(e) $S_n = (n - 2)^2$

(f) $S_n = \dfrac{n!}{n+2}$

(g) $S_n = 1 - \frac{1}{n}$

(h) $S_n = \log_2 (n + 1)$

(i) $S_n = 2^n - n$

(j) $S_n = \frac{2}{n} - 3$

1.4 SEQUENCE IDENTITIES

These involve proving identities which are sequences.
Show that the Left hand side (LHS) = Right hand side (RHS).

Example 4: If $T_n = (n + 2).n!$ show $(n + 1)T_n + (n + 1)! = T_{n+1}$.

SOLUTION

$T_n = (n + 2).n!$

LHS	*RHS*
$(n + 1)T_n + (n + 1)!$	T_{n+1}
$= (n + 1)(n + 2).n! + (n + 1)!$	$= (n + 1 + 2)(n + 1)!$
$= (n + 2)(n + 1)! + (n + 1)!$	$= (n + 3)(n + 1)!$
$= (n + 1)!(n + 2 + 1)$	
$= (n + 1)!(n + 3)$	

Example 5: If $T_n = (n - 20)2^n$ show $T_{n+2} - 4T_{n+1} + 4T_n = 0$.

SOLUTION

$T_n = (n - 20)2^n$

LHS	*RHS*
$T_{n+2} - 4T_{n+1} + 4T_n$	0
$= (n - 18)2^{n+2} - 4(n - 19)2^{n+1} + 4(n - 20)2^n$	
$= 2^n[4(n - 18) - 8(n - 19) + 4(n - 20)]$	
$= 4.2^n[n - 18 - 2n + 38 + n - 20]$	
$= 4.2^n[0]$	
$= 0$	

1.5 FINDING S_n FROM T_n

$S_n = T_1 + T_2 + ...+ T_n = \sum_{r=1}^{n} T_r$ (see later)

So S_n can be found by adding up the first n terms of a sequence.
This is treated in summation techniques in series.

1.6 FINDING T_n FROM S_n

There is a nifty trick to obtain T_n from S_n.

$S_n = T_1 + T_2 + ... + T_{n-1} + T_n$

$S_{n-1} = T_1 + T_2 + ... + T_{n-1}$

$\therefore S_n - S_{n-1} = T_n$ by subtraction

So $T_5 = S_5 - S_4$
and $T_{100} = S_{100} - S_{99}$

TRICK

T_n can be found from S_n using the formula
$T_n = S_n - S_{n-1}$

Don't be over impressed with this formula. It simply states that the sum of the first 50 terms minus the sum of the first 49 terms for example is the extra term T_{50}, etc...

Example 6: For a sequence $S_n = \log_{10}(n + 1)$, find T_n and T_{20}.

SOLUTION

$S_n = \log_{10}(n + 1)$

$S_{n-1} = \log_{10}(n)$

$S_n - S_{n-1} = \log_{10}(n + 1) - \log_{10}(n)$

$$\therefore T_n = \log_{10}\left(\frac{n+1}{n}\right)$$

$$\therefore T_{20} = \log_{10}\left(\frac{21}{20}\right)$$

Example 7: If $S_n = 2^n - 1$ find T_n and T_{10}.

SOLUTION

$S_n = 2^n - 1$

$S_{n-1} = 2^{n-1} - 1$

$T_n = 2^n - 2^{n-1} = 2^{n-1}(2 - 1) = 2^{n-1}$

$\therefore T_{10} = 2^9$

TRICK

To find S_{n-1} replace n by $n - 1$ in the S_n formula.

Example 8: If $S_n = \frac{2}{3}(4^n - 1)$ show $\frac{T_{n+1}}{T_n} = 4$.

SOLUTION

$S_n = \frac{2}{3}(4^n - 1)$

$S_{n-1} = \frac{2}{3}(4^{n-1} - 1)$

$T_n = \frac{2}{3}\{4^n - 1 - 4^{n-1} + 1\} = \frac{2}{3}\{4^n - 4^{n-1}\} = \frac{2}{3}4^{n-1}(4-1)$

$\therefore T_n = 2.4^{n-1}$

$\frac{T_{n+1}}{T_n} = \frac{2.4^n}{2.4^{n-1}} = 4$

Exercise 2 (Answers: page **213**)

Finding T_n from S_n and Sequence Identities

1. For the following sequences find S_{n-1}, T_n, T_1, T_2, T_8, T_{n-2}:

(a) $S_n = \frac{n}{2}(n+1)$

(b) $S_n = \frac{3n^2}{2} + \frac{n}{2}$

(c) $S_n = \log_{10}(n+1)$

(d) $S_n = 1 - (\frac{1}{2})^n$

(e) $S_n = 4n - n^2$

(f) $S_n = 3^n - 1$

(g) $S_n = \frac{n}{n+1}$

(h) $S_n = \frac{1}{2} - \frac{1}{n+2}$

(i) $S_n = \sqrt{n+1} - 1$

(j) $S_n = \frac{2}{3}(4^n - 1)$

---

2. If $T_n = 3^n - 1$ show $T_{n+1} = 3T_n + 2$.

3. If $S_n = 2(3^n + 1)$ show $\frac{T_{n+1}}{T_n} = 3$.

4. If $S_n = 2n^2 - 5n$ find T_n, T_{n+1}. Show $T_{n+1} - T_n = 4$.

5. If $T_n = 7 - 2(3)^n$ show that $T_{n+2} - 4T_{n+1} + 3T_n = 0$.

6. If $T_n = (5n - 3)2^n$ show that $T_{n+1} - 2T_n = 5.2^{n+1}$.

7. If $S_n = n(n + 1)$ find T_n. Hence, show
$T_{n+3}^2 - T_{n+1}^2 - T_{n+2}^2 + T_n^2 = 16$.

8. If $S_n = \log_{10}(n + 1)$ find T_n and T_{30}.

9. If $T_n = (n - 10)3^n$ show that $T_{n+2} - 6T_{n+1} + 9T_n = 0$.

10. If $T_n = 600(2)^n - 7(5)^n$ show that $T_{n+2} - 7T_{n+1} + 10T_n = 0$.
Find the least value of $n \in N_0$ if $T_n < 0$.

11. If $T_n = (n + 1)(n - 1)!$ show that $nT_n + n! = T_{n+1}$.

12. If $T_n = 5(3)^n + 7(2)^n$ show that $T_{n+2} - 5T_{n+1} + 6T_n = 0$.

1.7 CONVERGENCE/DIVERGENCE OF A SEQUENCE

[A] The Idea: Infinite sequences either approach a definite finite number as you look further and further down the list or they don't, i.e. they approach an infinite value. They are said to be convergent and divergent respectively.

Example: 1.9, 1.99, 1.999, 1.9999, ... gets closer and closer to 2. We say that it is convergent (CGT) to 2.
Example: 1, 3, 5, 7, 9, ... just gets bigger and bigger. We say it is divergent (DGT).

Test for convergence/divergence: Do $\lim_{n\to\infty} T_n$

If $\lim_{n\to\infty} T_n = L$ (Finite) ...CGT (Convergent)

If $\lim_{n\to\infty} T_n = \infty$ (Infinite) ...DGT (Divergent)

This is called taking an infinity limit.

[B] **Steps to taking an infinity limit:**

STEPS

1. Take out the highest power of the variable from each bracket on the top.
2. Do the same for the bottom.
3. Tidy up the takeouts.
4. Plonk in ∞ for the variable.

SOME IMPORTANT INFINITY LIMITS

1. $\lim\limits_{n\to\infty} \frac{\text{Number}}{n^p} = 0$, for p a whole positive number.

Example: $\lim\limits_{n\to\infty} \frac{8}{(n)^5} = 0$

---

2. $\lim\limits_{n\to\infty} (n)^p = \infty$, for p a whole positive number.

Example: $\lim\limits_{n\to\infty} (n)^3 = \infty$

---

3. $\lim\limits_{n\to\infty} r^n = 0$ for $-1 < r < 1$

Example: $\lim\limits_{n\to\infty} (\frac{3}{5})^n = 0$

---

4. $\lim\limits_{n\to\infty} r^n = \infty$ for $r > 1$, $r < -1$

Example: $\lim\limits_{n\to\infty} (\frac{3}{2})^n = \infty$

NOTES

1. $-1 < r < 1 \Leftrightarrow |r| < 1$
2. $r < -1, r > 1 \Leftrightarrow |r| > 1$

Example 9: Test the sequence $T_n = \dfrac{n^2-4n+7}{(2n+1)(n-3)}$ for convergence.

SOLUTION

$$\lim_{n\to\infty} T_n = \lim_{n\to\infty} \frac{n^2-4n+7}{(2n+1)(n-3)} = \lim_{n\to\infty} \frac{n^2(1-\frac{4}{n}+\frac{7}{n^2})}{n(2+\frac{1}{n})n(1-\frac{3}{n})}$$

$$= \lim_{n\to\infty} \frac{(1-\frac{4}{n}+\frac{7}{n^2})}{(2+\frac{1}{n})(1-\frac{3}{n})} = \frac{(1-0+0)}{(2+0)(1-0)} = \frac{1}{2} \Rightarrow \text{CGT to } \frac{1}{2}$$

Example 10: Test $T_n = \dfrac{(n-2)(5n^2+3n-2)}{(3n-1)(2n+4)}$ for convergence.

SOLUTION

$$\lim_{n\to\infty} T_n = \lim_{n\to\infty} \frac{(n-2)(5n^2+3n-2)}{(3n-1)(2n+4)} = \lim_{n\to\infty} \frac{n(1-\frac{2}{n})n^2(5+\frac{3}{n}-\frac{2}{n^2})}{n(3-\frac{1}{n})n(2+\frac{4}{n})}$$

$$= \lim_{n\to\infty} \frac{n(1-\frac{2}{n})(5+\frac{3}{n}-\frac{2}{n^2})}{(3-\frac{1}{n})(2+\frac{4}{n})} = \frac{\infty(1)(5)}{(3)(2)} = \infty \Rightarrow \text{DGT}$$

Example 11: Test $T_n = \dfrac{4^n}{4^n+5^n}$ for convergence.

SOLUTION

$$T_n = \frac{4^n}{4^n+5^n}$$

$$\lim_{n\to\infty} T_n = \lim_{n\to\infty} \frac{4^n}{5^n((\frac{4}{5})^n+1)} = \lim_{n\to\infty} \frac{(\frac{4}{5})^n}{(\frac{4}{5})^n+1} = \frac{0}{0+1} = 0$$

$\Rightarrow$ CGT to 0.

Exercise 3 (Answers: page **213**)

Convergence of Sequences

1. Test the following sequences for convergence:

(a) $T_n = n$

(b) $T_n = \frac{1}{n}$

(c) $T_n = \frac{1}{n^5}$

(d) $T_n = \frac{1}{n-1}$

(e) $T_n = \frac{1}{\sqrt{n}}$

(f) $T_n = \frac{n(n+1)}{2}$

(g) $T_n = \frac{n(n+1)(2n+1)}{6}$

(h) $T_n = a + (n - 1)d$

(i) $T_n = r^n$, $-1 < r < 1$

(j) $T_n = 2^n$

(k) $T_n = (\frac{1}{2})^n$

(l) $T_n = (-3)^n$

(m) $T_n = (-\frac{1}{2})^n$

(n) $T_n = r^n$, $r > 1$, $r < -1$

2. Test the following sequences for convergence:

(a) $T_n = \dfrac{n-1}{2n+1}$

(b) $T_n = \dfrac{n^2-2n}{n+1}$

(c) $T_n = \dfrac{n+1}{n^2-2n}$

(d) $T_n = \dfrac{2n^5+7n^2}{4n^5-3n^3+4}$

(e) $T_n = \dfrac{n}{\sqrt{n-1}}$

(f) $T_n = \dfrac{\sqrt{n+1}}{n}$

(g) $T_n = \sqrt{\dfrac{n-1}{4n+1}}$

(h) $T_n = \dfrac{(8n^3-1)^{\frac{1}{3}}}{(n^2+3)^{\frac{1}{2}}}$

(i) $T_n = \dfrac{(n-1)(n+1)n^2}{4n^4+2n^2-7}$

(j) $T_n = \dfrac{(2n-1)(n^2+1)}{4n^3+1}$

(k) $T_n = \dfrac{(n+1)(2n+3)}{(2n-1)n}$

(l) $T_n = \dfrac{(n+1)^2(n-1)}{(n^2+1)(n+2)}$

(m) $T_n = (\frac{2}{3})^n$

(n) $T_n = 3(\frac{1}{2})^n$

(o) $T_n = \dfrac{7^n}{7^n+6^n}$

2. ARITHMETIC SEQUENCES

2.1 THE IDEA

An arithmetic sequence is also called an arithmetic progression (AP). An AP is a sequence where you start with any object (number/function) and then keep on boringly adding any other object (number/function) you like.

Example: Start with $\frac{2}{3}$ say and keep on adding on $-\frac{1}{2}$.

AP: $\frac{2}{3}, \frac{1}{6}, -\frac{1}{3}, -\frac{5}{6}$

Example: Start with the function e^x and keep on adding 2

AP: $e^x, e^x + 2, e^x + 4, ...$

2.2 THE GENERAL AP

Start with a and keep on adding on the number d to generate the general AP: $a, a + d, a + 2d, a + 3d, ...$

So $T_1 = a$ = first term,

$T_2 = a + d$ = second term,

$T_3 = a + 2d$ = third term

$\therefore\ T_{37} = a + 36d$

TRICK

If you are told the 56[th.] term of an AP is -32 write

$T_{56} = a + 55d = -32$

The General Term (T_n)

Clearly:

$$T_n = a + (n - 1)d$$

d = Any term - Previous one = Constant = Common difference

Example 1: In an AP the fifth term is 7 and the thirteenth term is 17. Find the first term and the common difference.

SOLUTION

$T_5 = 7 \quad = a + 4d$

$T_{13} = 17 \quad = a + 12d$

$10 = \quad 8d \Rightarrow d = \frac{5}{4}$

$\therefore\ 7 = a + 5 \Rightarrow a = 2$

Example 2: Which term is 84 in the AP: 12, 15, 18, 21, ...

> **TRICK**
> If an AP is given always write down a and d.

SOLUTION

AP: 12, 15, 18, 21, ...

$\Rightarrow a = 12, d = 3$

$T_n = 84 = 12 + (n - 1)3$

$\therefore\ 72 = (n - 1)3$

$\Rightarrow 24 = n - 1$

$\therefore\ 25 = n$

> **TRICK**
> If you don't know which term a number is in a sequence call it T_n.

Example 3: If 5, x, y, 32 are consecutive terms of an AP find x, y.

SOLUTION

AP: 5, x, y, 32

$\Rightarrow a = 5, a + 3d = 32$

$\therefore\ d = 9$

AP: 5, 14, 23, 32 (keep adding on 9)

TEST FOR AN AP

A sequence is an AP if

Any term - Previous term = Constant for all $n \in N_0$

$$T_{n+1} - T_n = \text{Constant} = d \text{ for all } n \in N_0$$

Example 4: A sequence has $T_n = \frac{n}{2}(n+1)$. Is it an AP?

SOLUTION

$T_{n+1} = \frac{(n+1)}{2}(n+2)$

$T_n = \frac{n}{2}(n+1)$

$\therefore T_{n+1} - T_n = \frac{(n+1)}{2}\{n+2-n\} = n+1 \neq \text{const.}$

$\therefore$ It is not an AP.

Example 5: A sequence has $T_n = \frac{3n}{2} + 7$. Test to see if it is an AP.

SOLUTION

$T_{n+1} = \frac{3(n+1)}{2} + 7$

$T_n = \frac{3n}{2} + 7$

$T_{n+1} - T_n = \frac{3}{2}\{n+1-n\} = \frac{3}{2} = d$ (Constant)

$\therefore$ It is an AP.

2.3 THE SUM S_n OF AN AP

The formula for adding up the first n terms of an AP is given by

$$S_n = \tfrac{n}{2}\left[2a + (n-1)d\right]$$

The proof is not required.

Example 6: The sum of the first 15 terms of an AP is 600 and the common difference is 5. Find the first term.

SOLUTION

$S_{15} = 600,\ d = 5$

$S_{15} = \tfrac{15}{2}\left[2a + 14(5)\right] = 600$

$\Rightarrow a + 35 = 40$

$\therefore\ a = 5$

Example 7: How many terms of an AP 12, 16, 20, ... must be added to give 208.

SOLUTION

AP: 12, 16, 20, ...

$a = 12,\ d = 4$

$S_n = 208 = \tfrac{n}{2}\left[24 + (n-1)(4)\right] \Rightarrow 208 = 12n + 2n(n-1)$

$\Rightarrow n^2 + 5n - 104 = 0 \Rightarrow (n-8)(n+13) = 0$

$\Rightarrow n = 8$ (Ignore the negative solution)

Example 8: Find the sum of all even numbers from 156 to 430 inclusive.

SOLUTION

AP: 156, 158, ... , 428, 430

$a = 156,\ d = 2,\ T_n = 430 = 156 + (n - 1)2$

$\Rightarrow 274 = (n - 1)2 \Rightarrow 137 = n - 1 \Rightarrow 138 = n$

$\therefore S_{138} = \tfrac{138}{2}\left[2\times 156 + 137\times 2\right] = 40{,}434$

5 SYMBOLS OF THE AP

$a = T_1 = S_1$ = The value of the first term
d = Any term - Previous term = Common Difference
T_n = General term = $a + (n - 1)d$
= The value of the object in the $n^{th.}$ place.
n = The number of terms
S_n = The sum of first n terms = $\frac{n}{2}\left[2a+(n-1)d\right]$

Always put the right symbol on the given numbers.

Trick: If you know a and d for an AP you can find everything else.

2.4 THREE CONSECUTIVE TERMS IN AN AP

TRICKS

Trick 1. If you are asked to choose 3 consecutive terms in an AP choose them as: $a - d, a, a + d$

Example 9: Three consecutive terms in an AP add to 36. If their product is 1536 find them.

SOLUTION

Choose $a - d, a, a + d$
Sum: $3a = 36 \Rightarrow a = 12$
$12 - d, 12, 12 + d$
Product: $(12 - d)(12)(12 + d) = 1536$
$\Rightarrow 144 - d^2 = 128 \Rightarrow 16 = d^2 \Rightarrow d = \pm 4$
$d = +4$ gives 8, 12, 16
$d = -4$ gives 16, 12, 8

Trick 2. If you are told that a, c, b are consecutively in a AP write:

$$c - a = b - c$$
$$\Rightarrow 2c = a + b$$
$$\Rightarrow c = \frac{a+b}{2}$$

Example 10: If $\frac{1}{b+c}, \frac{1}{a+c}, \frac{1}{a+b}$ are consecutive terms of an AP show a^2, b^2, c^2 are also consecutive terms of an AP.

SOLUTION

AP: $\frac{1}{b+c}, \frac{1}{a+c}, \frac{1}{a+b}$

$$\Rightarrow \frac{1}{a+c} - \frac{1}{b+c} = \frac{1}{a+b} - \frac{1}{a+c} \Rightarrow \frac{b+c-a-c}{(a+c)(b+c)} = \frac{a+c-a-b}{(a+b)(a+c)}$$

$$\Rightarrow \frac{b-a}{b+c} = \frac{c-b}{b+a} \Rightarrow b^2 - a^2 = c^2 - b^2 \Rightarrow b^2 = \frac{a^2+c^2}{2}$$

$\therefore\ a^2, b^2, c^2$ are consecutive terms of an AP.

Trick 3. **The Arithmetic Mean** (AM)

Given 2 numbers, a and b, can you find a number between these so that all three are consecutively in an AP.

From Trick 2 $\Rightarrow c = \frac{a+b}{2}$

Example 11: The arithmetic mean of 2 numbers is $23\frac{1}{2}$. Their product is 510. Find them.

SOLUTION

The numbers are a, b

$\text{AM} = \frac{a+b}{2} = 23\frac{1}{2} \Rightarrow a + b = 47$

Product $= ab = 510$

$\Rightarrow a(47 - a) = 510 \Rightarrow a^2 - 47a + 510 = 0$

$\Rightarrow (a - 17)(a - 30) = 0$

$\therefore\ a = 17, b = 30$ or $a = 30, b = 17$

Exercise 4 (Answers: page **214**)

AP's

1. Test to see which of the following are AP's?
(a) $T_n = n - 1$
(b) $T_n = n^2 + n$
(c) $T_n = \frac{n}{3} - 5$
(d) $T_n = n!$
(e) $T_n = \frac{2}{n} - 3$
(f) $T_n = 2.3^n$

2. Which of the following are AP's?
(a) $S_n = 2^n$
(b) $S_n = n^2$
(c) $S_n = n^2 - 4n$
(d) $S_n = 2n^2 + 3n$
(e) $S_n = 3n^2 - 5n$
(f) $S_n = \frac{1}{n} - 3$

3. For each of the following AP's find (i) T_{10}, (ii) T_n, (iii) S_6, (iv) S_n:
(a) 2, 6, 10, 14, ...
(b) 4, 2, 0, -2, ...
(c) $3,\ 4\frac{1}{2},\ 6,\ 7\frac{1}{2}$, ...
(d) $0,\ -1\frac{1}{4},\ -2\frac{1}{2},\ -3\frac{3}{4}$, ...
(e) 2, 4, 6, 8, 10, ...

4. For each of the following find the indicated sum:
(a) S_{20} for $2,\ 3\frac{1}{4},\ 4\frac{1}{2}$, ...
(b) S_{50} for $\frac{6}{\sqrt{3}},\ 3\sqrt{3},\ \frac{12}{\sqrt{3}}$, ...
(c) S_{19} for $\frac{3}{4},\ \frac{2}{3},\ \frac{7}{12}$, ...
(d) S_n for 1, 2, 3, ...
(e) S_n for $\frac{1}{1+\sqrt{x}},\ \frac{1}{1-x},\ \frac{1}{1-\sqrt{x}}$, ...

5. The second term of an AP is 4 and the sixth term is 16. Find the first 4 terms.

6. In an AP the seventh term is 37 and the tenth term is 58. Find the first term and the common difference.

7. The fifth term of an AP is 20 and the ninth term is 8. Find the first 4 terms.

8. The third term of an AP is 2 and the fifth term is - 6. Find the first term and the common difference.

9. Which term is 50 in the AP 8, 11, 14, ...?

10. Is 243 a term of the AP 4, 7, 10, ...?

11. Find the fifteenth term of the AP 1, 8, 15, 22, ...

12. Is the sequence $T_n = 6n + 5$ an AP? Find T_3.

13. If $7\frac{1}{2}$, x, y, 12 are consecutive terms of an AP, find x and y.

14. In an AP the third term is four times the first term and the sixth term is 17. Find the AP.

15. The fourth term of an AP is 18 and the seventh term is 30. Find the first term.

16. The $54^{th.}$ term and $4^{th.}$ terms of an AP are - 61 and 64 respectively. Find the $23^{rd.}$ term.

17. The $p^{th.}$ term of an AP is q and the $q^{th.}$ term is p. Find the $m^{th.}$ term.

18. How many terms of the AP 8, 13, 18, ... must be added to give 426?

19. The sum of the first n terms of an AP is 950. Find the number of terms, n, if the common difference is 2 and the first term is -30.

20. Find the sum of all even numbers less than 100.

21. If $T_n = 2n + 3$ for a sequence show it is an AP and find S_n.

22. If $S_n = n^2 + 5n$ find T_n and hence show its AP. Find the first 3 terms.

23. If $S_7 = 49$ and $S_{17} = 289$ for an AP, find S_n.

24. Find the least number of terms of the AP 28, 25, 22,.... needed to give a negative sum.

25. The first term of an AP is 1 and the sum of the first 10 terms is 235. Find the common difference.

26. How many terms of the AP 2, 6, 10, ... make a total of 288?

27. The 11th. term of an AP is -12 and the sum of 11 terms is -22. Find the sequence.

28. How many terms of the AP 10, 13, 16, ... do you need to make the sum exceed 400?

29. Find the sum of all the odd numbers from 101 to 199 inclusive.

30. Find the sum of all even numbers from 52 to 100 inclusive.

31. Find the arithmetic mean (AM) of the following:
(a) 4, 6
(b) -7, 18
(c) a^2, b^2
(d) $x - 1$, $x + 1$

32. The AM of 2 numbers is 5. Their product is 21. Find them.

33. The AM of 2 numbers is 3. Their product is -7. Find them.

34. The sum of three consecutive numbers in an AP is 6. If their product is - 24, find them.

35. The sum of three consecutive numbers in an AP is 3. If the sum of their squares is 35, find them.

3. GEOMETRIC SEQUENCES

3.1 THE IDEA

A geometric sequence is also called a geometric progression (GP). A GP is a sequence where you start with any object (number/ function) and then keep on boringly multiplying by any other object (number/function) you like.

Example: Start with a number, $-\frac{1}{2}$, and keep multiplying by $-\frac{3}{4}$.

GP: $-\frac{1}{2}, \frac{3}{8}, -\frac{9}{32}, \frac{27}{128}, \ldots.$

Example: Start with the function ln x and keep multiplying by 5.

GP: ln x , 5 ln x, 25 ln x, 125 ln x, ...

3.2 THE GENERAL GP

Start with a and keep on multiplying by the number r to generate the general GP $a, ar, ar^2, ar^3, ar^4, \ldots$

So $T_1 = a =$ first term

$T_2 = ar =$ second term

$T_3 = ar^2 =$ third term...

$\therefore\ T_{45} = ar^{44}$

The general term, T_n

Clearly

TRICK

If they say that the forty-third term of a GP is 132 you go:

$T_{43} = 132 = ar^{42}$

$$T_n = ar^{n-1}$$

$r =$ Any term $\div$ Previous term = Constant = Common ratio

Example 1: The third term of a GP is 36 and the sixth term is $4\frac{1}{2}$. Find the first four terms.

SOLUTION

$$\frac{T_6 = ar^5 = \frac{9}{2}}{T_3 = ar^2 = 36} \Rightarrow r^3 = \frac{1}{8} \text{ by dividing } \therefore r = \frac{1}{2}$$

Substituting for $r \Rightarrow \frac{a}{4} = 36 \Rightarrow a = 144$

GP: 144, 72, 36, 18, ...

Trick: If a GP is given always write down a and r.

Example 2: Which term is 160 in the GP: 5, 10, 20, ...

SOLUTION

$a = 5$, $r = 2$, $T_n = 160$, $n = ?$

$T_n = 160 = 5.2^{n-1}$

$\Rightarrow 2^{n-1} = 32 = 2^5 \Rightarrow n - 1 = 5$

$\therefore n = 6$

TRICK
If you don't know which term a number is in a sequence call it T_n.

Example 3: If 2, x, 8, y are four consecutive terms of a GP find x and y.

SOLUTION

$a = 2 \Rightarrow 2r^2 = 8 \Rightarrow r = \pm 2$

$\therefore$ GP: 2, ± 4, 8, ± 16

$x = \pm 4$, $y = \pm 16$

TEST FOR GP

A sequence is a GP if

Any term $\div$ Previous term = Constant = r for all $n \in N_0$

$$\frac{T_{n+1}}{T_n} = \text{constant} = r \text{ for all } n \in N_0$$

Example 4: Test the sequence $T_n = 3(2)^{n+1}$ to see if it is a GP.

SOLUTION

$T_{n+1} = 3(2)^{n+2}$

$T_n = 3(2)^{n+1}$

Dividing $\Rightarrow \dfrac{T_{n+1}}{T_n} = \dfrac{2^{n+2}}{2^{n+1}} = 2 = r$

$\therefore$ It is a GP.

3.3 THE SUM S_n OF A GP

The formula for adding up the first n terms of a GP is given by:

$$S_n = \frac{a(1-r^n)}{1-r}$$

The proof is not required.

Example 5: How many terms of the GP: 8, 24, 72, ... must be added to give 968.

SOLUTION

$a = 8, r = 3, S_n = 968$

$$\Rightarrow S_n = 968 = \frac{8(1-3^n)}{1-3} = 4(3^n - 1)$$

$\Rightarrow 242 = 3^n - 1 \Rightarrow 3^n = 243 = 3^5$

$\therefore\ n = 5$

5 SYMBOLS OF THE GP

$a = T_1 = S_1$ = The value of the first term

r = Common ratio = Any term $\div$ Previous one

T_n = General term = ar^{n-1}
= Value of the object in the $n^{th.}$ place

n = The number of terms (the place in the list)

S_n = The sum of the first n terms = $\frac{a(1-r^n)}{1-r}$

Always put the right symbol on the given numbers.

Trick: If you know the first term, $T_1 = a$, of a GP and the common ratio, r, you can find everything else.

3.4 THREE CONSECUTIVE TERMS IN A GP

TRICKS

Trick 1. If you are asked to choose 3 consecutive terms in a GP then choose them as: $\frac{a}{r}, a, ar$

Example 6: Find 3 consecutive numbers in a GP whose sum is 38 and whose product is 1728.

SOLUTION

Choose the 3 numbers as: $\frac{a}{r}, a, ar$

Sum: $\frac{a}{r}+a+ar=38$

Product: $\frac{a}{r}\times a\times ar=1728 \Rightarrow a^3=1728 \Rightarrow a=12$

$\therefore \frac{12}{r}+12+12r=38 \Rightarrow 6r^2-13r+6=0$

$\Rightarrow (3r-2)(2r-3)=0 \Rightarrow r=\frac{2}{3}, \frac{3}{2}$

The numbers are: 8, 12, 18

Trick 2. If you are told that a, c, b are consecutively in a GP then simply write:

$$\frac{c}{a}=\frac{b}{c} \Rightarrow c^2=ab \Rightarrow c=\sqrt{ab}$$

Example 7: If $\frac{1}{y-x}, \frac{1}{2y}, \frac{1}{y-z}$ are consecutive terms of an AP show x, y, z are consecutive terms of a GP.

SOLUTION

AP: $\frac{1}{y-x}, \frac{1}{2y}, \frac{1}{y-z}$

$\Rightarrow \frac{1}{2y} - \frac{1}{y-x} = \frac{1}{y-z} - \frac{1}{2y} \Rightarrow \frac{y-x-2y}{2y(y-x)} = \frac{2y-y+z}{2y(y-z)}$

$\Rightarrow \frac{-(x+y)}{(y-x)} = \frac{(y+z)}{(y-z)} \Rightarrow -xy - y^2 + zx + zy = y^2 - xy + zy - xz$

$\Rightarrow 2xz = 2y^2 \Rightarrow y = \sqrt{xz}$

$\therefore$ x, y, z are consecutive terms of a GP.

Trick 3. **The Geometric Mean** (GM)

Given 2 numbers, a and b, can you find a number, c, between these so that all three are consecutively in a GP.

From **Trick** 2 the GM = $\sqrt{ab}$

Example 8: The arithmetic mean of 2 numbers x and y is 10. Their geometric mean is 8. Find x and y.

SOLUTION

AM: $\frac{x+y}{2} = 10 \Rightarrow x + y = 20$

GM: $\sqrt{xy} = 8 \Rightarrow xy = 64$

$\therefore$ $x(20 - x) = 64 \Rightarrow x^2 - 20x + 64 = 0$

$\Rightarrow (x - 16)(x - 4) = 0$

$\Rightarrow x = 16, x = 4$ and $y = 4, y = 16$

Exercise 5 (Answers: page **214**)
GP's

1. Test to see which of the following are GP's:
(a) $T_n = n - 1$
(b) $T_n = (\frac{3}{2})^{n-1}$
(c) $T_n = 2(\frac{1}{2})^{n-1}$
(d) $T_n = \dfrac{7^n}{7^{n+2}}$
(e) $T_n = \frac{1}{2}(3)^{n-2}$
(f) $T_n = n!$

2. For each of the following GP's find (i) T_6, (ii) T_n, (iii) S_6, (iv) S_n:
(a) 8, 12, 18, 27, ...
(b) 48, 36, 27, $20\frac{1}{4}$, ...
(c) 2, -6, 18, -54, ...
(d) 1, $\frac{1}{3}$, $\frac{1}{9}$, $\frac{1}{27}$, ...

3. Find the indicated sum for each of the following GP's:
(a) S_{12} for 1, 2, 4, ...
(b) S_8 for $\frac{3}{4}$, $\frac{3}{2}$, 3, ...
(c) S_p for 1, 5, 25, ...
(d) S_5 for $\frac{8}{5}$, -1, $\frac{5}{8}$, ...
(e) S_6 for 7, $\sqrt{42}$, 6, ...
(f) S_{10} for 2, $-\sqrt{2}$, 1, ...

4. Write down the $20^{th.}$ term of the GP 2, 10, 50, ...

5. What is the tenth term of the GP 1, -7, 49, ...?

6. Find the GP's whose fourth term is 4 and whose eighth term is 324.

7. If 5, x, y, 320 are consecutive numbers of a GP find x and y.

8. If 3, x, 48, y form a GP find x and y.

9. The third term of a GP is 81 and the second term is 24. Find the GP.

10. The sum of 3 consecutive numbers in a GP is 28 and their product is -1728. Find them.

11. Write down the $n^{th.}$ term of the GP 12, 6, 3, ...

12. If $\frac{1}{2^{14}}$ is a term of the GP 8, 4, 2, ... find which one it is.

13. Three consecutive numbers in a GP add to 21. If their product is 216, find them.

14. The lengths of the sides of a triangle are in a GP with the shortest side 3 cm. If the perimeter is 21 cm, find the other sides.

15. How many terms of a GP $\frac{3}{2}$, 3, 6, ... must be taken so that their sum is $94\frac{1}{2}$?

16. How many terms of the GP 2, 8, 32, ... are needed to give a sum greater than 1,000?

17. The $n^{th.}$ term of a sequence is 3.2^{n-1}. Prove it is a GP. Find S_n.

18. The first term of a GP is 5 and the sixth term is 160. Find S_6.

19. The first term of a GP is 8 and the seventh term is $\frac{1}{8}$. Find the common ratio and the sum of the first seven terms.

20. How many terms are there in the following GP's:
(a) 1, 3, 9, ... , 729
(b) 1, $\frac{1}{2}$, $\frac{1}{4}$, ... , $\frac{1}{64}$
(c) -3, 6, -12, ... , 384
(d) 81, 108, 144, ... , 256

21. The third term of a GP is 36 and the sixth term is $4\frac{1}{2}$. Find the common ratio.

22. How many terms of the GP 4, 12, 36, ... must be taken to total 1456?

23. Find the geometric mean (GM) of the following:
(a) 6, 15
(b) 1, 9
(c) -2, -8
(d) 5, 8
(e) c^2, d^2

24. The arithmetic mean of 2 numbers is $\frac{13}{2}$. Their GM is 6. Find them.

3.5 THE SUM TO INFINITY OF A GP, S_∞

The formula for adding up an infinite GP is given by

$$S_\infty = \frac{a}{1-r}, \quad -1 < r < 1$$

Example 9: Find the sum to infinity of the GP: 1, $\cos^2 x$, $\cos^4 x$, ... when $x = 30^\circ$

SOLUTION

GP: 1, $\cos^2 x$, $\cos^4 x$, ...

$a = 1$, $r = \cos^2 x$

$$S_\infty = \frac{a}{1-r} = \frac{1}{1-\cos^2 x} = \frac{1}{\sin^2 x}$$

When $x = 30^\circ$, $S_\infty = \dfrac{1}{(\sin 30^\circ)^2} = 4$

Example 10: The sum to infinity of the GP: a, ar, ar^2, ... is 15. The sum to infinity of the GP: a^2, a^2r^2, a^2r^4, ... is 45. Find a and r.

SOLUTION

GP: a, ar, ar^2,...

$$\Rightarrow S_\infty = \frac{a}{1-r} = 15 \Rightarrow a = 15(1-r)$$

GP: a^2, a^2r^2, a^2r^4, ...

$$\Rightarrow S_\infty = \frac{a^2}{1-r^2} = 45 \Rightarrow a^2 = 15(1-r^2)$$

$\therefore\ 225(1 - r)^2 = 45(1 - r^2)$

$\Rightarrow 5(1 - r)(1 - r) = (1 - r)(1 + r) \Rightarrow 5 - 5r = 1 + r$

$\therefore r = \frac{2}{3}, a = 5$

TRICK
The sum to infinity of a GP can be used to write a non-terminating recurring decimal as a rational (fraction).

Example 11: Write $0.2\dot{7}$ as a rational.

SOLUTION

$0.2\dot{7} = 0.2777777.... = \frac{2}{10} + \frac{7}{100} + \frac{7}{1000} + ..$

$= \frac{2}{10} + \frac{7}{100}(1 + \frac{1}{10} + \frac{1}{100} + ...)$

Consider the expression in the bracket:

$$a = 1, r = \tfrac{1}{10}, S_\infty = \frac{a}{1-r} = \frac{1}{1-\frac{1}{10}} = \frac{10}{9}$$

$$\Rightarrow 0.2\dot{7} = \frac{2}{10} + \frac{7}{100}\left(\frac{10}{9}\right)$$

$$= \frac{2}{10} + \frac{7}{90} = \frac{25}{90} = \frac{5}{18}$$

Exercise 6 (Answers: page **215**)

Sum to Infinity of GP's

1. Find the sum to infinity of GP's:

(a) 1, $\frac{1}{2}$, $\frac{1}{4}$, ...

(b) 2, $\frac{2}{3}$, $\frac{2}{9}$, ...

(c) 1, $-\frac{1}{2}$, $\frac{1}{4}$, ...

(d) 8, 6, $\frac{9}{2}$, ...

2. The first term of a GP is 100 and the third term is 4. Find the sum to infinity.

3. A GP starts with 96 and its sum to infinity is 128. Find the GP.

4. The common ratio of a GP is $\frac{2}{3}$ and the sum to infinity is 30. Find the first term.

5. How many terms of the GP 12, 6, 3, ... must be taken to differ from the sum to infinity by less than 0.02?

6. The second term of a GP is 20 and the fifth is 1.28. Find the sum to infinity.

7. Find the sum to infinity of the GP $1, \sin^2\theta, \sin^4\theta, \ldots..$ Evaluate it when $\theta = 45^{\circ}$.

8. The second term of a GP is 6 and the sum to infinity is 25. Find the first term.

9. How many terms of the GP 108, 36, 12, ... must be taken for the sum to differ from the sum to infinity by less than 0.05?

10. Find the sum to infinity of the GP $1, -\tan^2\theta, \tan^4\theta, \ldots$ for $0 < \theta < 45^{\circ}$ and its value when $\theta = 30^{\circ}$.

11. Express each of the following recurring non-terminating decimals in the form $\frac{a}{b}$ where $a, b, \in N_0$:

(a) $0.1\dot{7}$

(b) $0.\dot{2}\dot{3}$

(c) $3.\dot{4}\dot{7}$

(d) $0.\dot{1}\dot{2}\dot{3}$

(e) $6.\dot{3}$

(f) $1.\dot{1}\dot{9}$

(g) $2.\dot{2}$

(h) $0.\dot{1}\dot{9}\dot{2}\dot{4}$

12. The sum to infinity of a GP is 3 and the sum to infinity of the squares of the same GP is $\frac{9}{5}$. Find the GP.

4. ARITHMETIC GEOMETRIC SEQUENCES (AGP)

4.1 THE IDEA

An arithmetic geometric sequence (AGP) in one in which each term is the product of an AP term multiplied by the GP term.

Example: $1x, 2x^2, 3x^3, ...$
$1, 2, 3, ...$ AP ($a = 1, d = 1$)
$x, x^2, x^3, ..$ GP ($a = x, r = x$)

4.2 THE GENERAL AGP

T_n = General term of AP × General term of GP

Example 1: What is the general term of AGP $1, 3x, 5x^2, 7x^3, ...$

SOLUTION
AG: $1, 3x, 5x^2, 7x^3, ...$
AP: $1, 3, 5, 7, ...$
$a = 1, d = 2 \Rightarrow T_n = 1 + (n - 1)2 = 2n - 1$
GP: $1, x, x^2, ...$
$a = 1, r = x \Rightarrow T_n = 1.x^{n-1} = x^{n-1}$
$\therefore\ T_n = (2n - 1)x^{n-1}$ for AGP

4.3 SUM TO INFINITY OF AGP

Steps to finding the sum to infinity of an AGP:

STEPS

1. Write out list S_∞.
2. Multiply each term by common ratio, x, of GP and move each term one place to right.
3. Subtract $S_\infty - xS_\infty$ to reveal a GP.
4. Add GP using $S_\infty = \dfrac{a}{1-r}$.

Example 2: Find S_∞ for the AGP 3, $5x^2$, $7x^4$, ... ($|x| < 1$).

SOLUTION

$$S_\infty = 3 + 5x^2 + 7x^4 + \ldots$$

$$x^2 S_\infty = \quad 3x^2 + 5x^4 + \ldots$$

$$S_\infty - x^2 S_\infty = 3 + 2x^2 + 2x^4 + \ldots$$

$$\Rightarrow S_\infty(1 - x^2) = 3 + 2x^2(1 + x^2 + x^4 + \ldots)$$

The expression in the bracket is a GP: $a = 1$, $r = x^2$

$$\Rightarrow S_\infty(1-x^2) = 3 + 2x^2\left(\frac{1}{1-x^2}\right)$$

$$S_\infty = \frac{a}{1-r} = \frac{1}{1-x^2}$$

$$\Rightarrow S_\infty = \frac{3}{(1-x^2)} + \frac{2x^2}{(1-x^2)^2}$$

Exercise 7 (Answers: page **216**)

AGP's

Evaluate S_∞ for the following AGP's:

1. 1, $2x$, $3x^2$, $4x^3$, ... $|x| < 1$

2. 2, $3(\frac{1}{2})$, $4(\frac{1}{2})^2$, $5(\frac{1}{2})^3$, ...

3. 2, $4(\frac{1}{3})$, $6(\frac{1}{3})^2$, $8(\frac{1}{3})^3$, ...

4. x, $2x^2$, $3x^3$, ... $|x| < 1$

SEQUENCES REVISION QUESTIONS

These 3 part questions are similar to the questions on the LC paper. The answers to these questions and hints to help you solve them are available on our website:

www.studentxpress.ie

1. (a) Find the sum to infinity of the GP $1, \frac{1}{3}, \frac{1}{9}, \frac{1}{27}, \ldots$

(b) The sum of 3 consecutive numbers in an AP is 27 and the sum of their squares is 293. Find them.

(c) Show that $T_n = 2(4^n - (-1)^n)$ is a solution of

$T_{n+2} - 3T_{n+1} - 4T_n = 0$.

2. (a) Evaluate $\lim_{n\to\infty} \frac{1}{n}\sqrt{2n^2 + n}$.

(b) (i) If $2\sin\theta$, $2\cos\theta$, $3\cos\theta$ are consecutive terms of a GP, find $\tan\theta$ and the 3 terms.

(ii) If $S_n = \log_{10}(n+1)$, find T_n and test the sequence for convergence.

(c) The first, third and ninth terms of an AP form the consecutive terms of a GP. Find the common ratio of the GP.

3. (a) Evaluate $\lim_{n\to\infty} \dfrac{4^n}{3^n + 4^n}$.

(b) Show that the sequence with $S_n = pn^2 + qn$ is an AP. Find the first term and the common difference in terms of p and q.

(c) Prove that if 3 numbers are consecutive terms of a GP then their logs are consecutive terms of an AP. Find S_n for the AP if a is the first term and r, the common ratio of the GP.

4. (a) Find the sum of the first 10 terms of the AP 3, 7, 11, ... What is the sum of the second ten terms?
(b) For a sequence, $S_n = n(n - 1)$, find T_n, T_{n+1}, T_{n-1}.
(c) The second, fourth and eighth terms of an AP form consecutive terms of a GP. Find the common ratio of the GP.

5. (a) In what term will you find 243 in
(i) the sequence $T_n = n^2 - n + 3$,
(ii) the sequence $T_n = 3^{n-1}$.
(b) If $S_6 = 9S_3$ for a GP, find the common ratio, r.
(c) If a, b, na are consecutive terms of an AP show that a, b, $\frac{1}{2}(n+1)b$ are consecutive terms of a GP.

6. (a) If $T_r = 3T_{r-1} + 4T_{r-2}$ show that $T_4 = 13T_2 + 12T_1$. Express T_5 in terms of T_1 and T_2.
(b) The first 3 terms of a GP are a, a^2, b. The first 3 terms of an AP are a, b, a^2. Show that $a = -\frac{1}{2}$. Find S_∞ for the GP.
(c) 100 g of a substance is left to evaporate. Each day it loses one-tenth of its weight at the beginning of that day. How many days elapse before it is less than half its original mass.

7. (a) By writing $0.\dot{3}\dot{7}$ as a GP, express it as a rational.
(b) In a GP, the sum of the first and third terms is 52. The sum of the second and fourth terms is 78. Find the first term and the common ratio.
(c) The corresponding terms of the AP: a, $a + 2$, $a + 4$, ... and the GP: b, $2b$, $4b$, ... are added. If the first and fifth terms of the new sequence are 8 and 91 respectively, find the first term of the AP and GP.

8. (a) How many terms of the AP: 10, 13, 16, ... must be added to give a sum greater than 400.

(b) If $k = \lim_{n\to\infty} \frac{3n+1}{n+2}$ find k. Find the least $n \in N_0$ for which

$k - \frac{3n+1}{n+2} < \frac{1}{1000}$.

(c) If $T_n = n!(n+2)$, show that $(n+2)T_{n+1} + (n+2)! = T_{n+2}$.

9. (a) Express $1.\dot{7}$ as a rational using the sum to infinity of a GP.

(b) (i) How many terms of the GP: 2, 3, $4\frac{1}{2}$, ... add up to $\frac{665}{16}$?

(ii) Find S_∞ for the GP: 1, $\tan^2\theta$, $\tan^4\theta$, ... , $0^\circ < \theta < 45^\circ$ and its value when $\theta = 30^\circ$.

(c) The shortest side of a triangle has a length of 6 cm. If all 3 lengths are consecutively in a GP, find the length of each side if the perimeter is $28\frac{1}{2}$ cm.

10. (a) If $T_n = \frac{(8n^3-6)^{\frac{1}{3}}}{\sqrt{4n^2+2}}$ find $\lim_{n\to\infty} T_n$.

(b) For a sequence $S_n = n^2 - 2n$, deduce it is an AP.

(c) 120° is the largest angle in a triangle. $3l$ is the largest side. The sides are consecutive terms of an AP. Use the Cosine rule to find the length of each side in terms of l.

11. (a) Find the sum of all even numbers from 42 to 100 inclusive.

(b) (i) 1, x, y are the first 3 terms of an AP. 1, x, $-y$ are the first 3 terms of a GP. Find x and y.

(ii) Three consecutive terms in a GP add to - 14. If their product is 216 find them.

(c) The sum to infinity of a GP is $13\frac{1}{2}$. The sum to infinity of the squares of the terms of the GP is $\frac{729}{8}$. Find the first term and the common ratio of the GP.

12. (a) $S_{20} = 45$ and $S_{40} = 290$ for an AP. Find the first 3 terms.
(b) For the GP: $a, ar, ar^2, \ldots$ find S_{2n}.

For the GP: $b, br^2, br^4, \ldots$ find S_n. If $S_{2n} = S_n$ show $r = \frac{b}{a} - 1$.
(c) If a, b, c, d are consecutive terms of a GP prove
$(b - c)^2 + (c - a)^2 + (d - b)^2 = (a - d)^2$.

13. (a) For a sequence $4T_n = [1 + (-1)^n][1 + i^n]$ ($i = \sqrt{-1}$). Write out the first 4 terms and find S_{100}.

(b) (i) Write $1.4\dot{7}$ as a rational using the sum to infinity of a GP.
(ii) For a sequence $S_n = n(n - 1)$, find T_n. Show

$(T_{n+3}^2 - T_{n+1}^2) - (T_{n+2}^2 - T_n^2) = 16$.

(c) Show that $T_n = A(\frac{1}{2})^n + B(-\frac{4}{3})^n$ is a solution of the equation
$6T_{n+2} + 5T_{n+1} - 4T_n = 0$.

14. (a) The first 3 terms of an AP are $\log_a p^2$, $2\log_a pq$,

$2\log_a pq^2$. If $pq^2 = a$ find S_5.

(b) (i) Evaluate $1 + \cos^2 x + \cos^4 x + \ldots$ when $x = \frac{\pi}{6}$.

(ii) Find S_∞ for the AGP $3, 4x, 5x^2, 6x^3, \ldots$ for $|x| < 1$.
(c) For a sequence $T_1, T_2, T_3, \ldots$ the product of the first n terms equals the sum of the first n terms. Express T_{n+1} in terms of S_n.

15. (a) How many terms of the GP $5, \frac{5}{2}, \frac{5}{4}, \ldots$ must be added so that its sum differs from its sum to infinity by less than 0.01.
(b) Find 3 consecutive terms of an AP whose sum is 3 and whose product is - 8.
(c) The arithmetic mean of 2 numbers, x and y, is 10 and their geometric mean is $4\sqrt{6}$. Find x and y.

Answers and hints to Sequence Revision Questions available on: **www.studentxpress.ie**

ANSWERS

Exercise 1 [*Sequences* (page **179**)]

1. (a) 7, 9, 11, 13, 15 (b) 2, $2\frac{1}{2}$, $2\frac{2}{3}$, $2\frac{3}{4}$, $2\frac{4}{5}$

(c) 5, 25, 125, 625, 3125 (d) $\frac{1}{2}$, $\frac{2}{3}$, $\frac{3}{2}$, $\frac{24}{5}$, 20

(e) 5, $5\frac{1}{2}$, 9, $16\frac{3}{4}$, $32\frac{2}{5}$ (f) 1, 5, 11, 19, 29

(g) $\frac{1}{4}$, $\frac{1}{9}$, $\frac{1}{16}$, $\frac{1}{25}$, $\frac{1}{36}$ (h) cos 1, cos 2, cos 3, cos 4, cos 5

(i) e^1, e^2, e^3, e^4, e^5 (j) $\frac{1}{2}$, $\frac{1}{2}$, $\frac{3}{4}$, $\frac{3}{2}$, $\frac{15}{4}$

2. (a) 0, $\frac{1}{3}$, $\frac{19}{22}$, $\frac{n+1}{n+4}$, $\frac{n-2}{n+1}$, $\frac{n^2-4n+4}{n^2+2n+1}$

(b) $-\frac{1}{2}$, $\frac{1}{5}$, $\frac{37}{401}$, $\frac{2n+1}{n^2+4n+5}$, $\frac{2n-5}{n^2+2n+2}$, $(\frac{2n-5}{n^2+2n+2})^2$

(c) $\log_{10} 2$, $\log_{10}(\frac{3}{2})$, $\log_{10}(\frac{21}{20})$, $\log_{10}(\frac{n+3}{n+2})$, $\log_{10}(\frac{n}{n-1})$,

$(\log_{10}(\frac{n}{n-1}))^2$

(d) 2, 4, 2^{20}, 2^{n+2}, 2^{n-1}, 2^{2n-2}

(e) 0, 4, 418, $(n + 1)(n + 4)$, $(n - 2)(n + 1)$, $(n - 2)^2(n + 1)^2$

(f) 0, 3, 399, $n^2 + 4n + 3$, $n^2 - 2n$, $n^2(n - 2)^2$

(g) -1, 1, 37, $2n + 1$, $2n - 5$, $(2n - 5)^2$

(h) $\frac{1}{2}$, $\frac{2}{3}$, $\frac{20}{21}$, $\frac{n+2}{n+3}$, $\frac{n-1}{n}$, $(\frac{n-1}{n})^2$

(i) 0, 3, 741, $2n^2 + 5n + 3$, $2n^2 - 7n + 6$, $(2n^2 - 7n + 6)^2$

(j) $\frac{2}{5}$, $\frac{4}{17}$, $\frac{2^{20}}{4^{20}+1}$, $\frac{2^{n+2}}{4^{n+2}+1}$, $\frac{2^{n-1}}{4^{n-1}+1}$, $\frac{2^{2n-2}}{(4^{n-1}+1)^2}$

3. (a) 3, 5, 9 (b) 0, 8, 48

(c) 1, 7, 127 (d) -2, 2, 34

(e) 1, 1, 25 (f) $\frac{1}{3}$, $\frac{6}{5}$, 560

(g) 0, $\frac{2}{3}$, $\frac{6}{7}$ (h) 1, 2, 3

(i) 1, 5, 121 (j) -1, $-\frac{7}{3}$, $-\frac{19}{7}$

Exercise 2 [*Finding T_n from S_n and Sequence Identities* (page **182**)]

1. (a) $\frac{(n-1)n}{2}$, n, 1, 2, 8, n - 2

   (b) $\frac{(n-1)(3n-2)}{2}$, $3n$ - 1, 2, 5, 23, $3n$ - 7

   (c) $\log_{10} n$, $\log_{10}(\frac{n+1}{n})$, $\log_{10} 2$, $\log_{10}(\frac{3}{2})$, $\log_{10}(\frac{9}{8})$, $\log_{10}(\frac{n-1}{n-2})$

   (d) $1-(\frac{1}{2})^{n-1}$, $(\frac{1}{2})^n$, $\frac{1}{2}$, $\frac{1}{4}$, $\frac{1}{256}$, $(\frac{1}{2})^{n-2}$

   (e) $(n - 1)(5 - n)$, $5 - 2n$, 3, 1, -11, $9 - 2n$

   (f) $3^{n-1} - 1$, $2.\ 3^{n-1}$, 2, 6, 4374, 2.3^{n-3}

   (g) $\frac{n-1}{n}$, $\frac{1}{n(n+1)}$, $\frac{1}{2}$, $\frac{1}{6}$, $\frac{1}{72}$, $\frac{1}{(n-2)(n-1)}$

   (h) $\frac{1}{2}-\frac{1}{n+1}$, $\frac{1}{(n+1)(n+2)}$, $\frac{1}{6}$, $\frac{1}{12}$, $\frac{1}{90}$, $\frac{1}{n(n-1)}$

   (i) $\sqrt{n}-1$, $\sqrt{n+1}-\sqrt{n}$, $\sqrt{2}-1$, $\sqrt{3}-\sqrt{2}$, $3-2\sqrt{2}$, $\sqrt{n-1}-\sqrt{n-2}$

   (j) $\frac{2}{3}(4^{n-1}-1)$, 2.4^{n-1}, 2, 8, 2.4^7, 2.4^{n-3}

4. $T_n = 4n - 7$, $T_{n+1} = 4n - 3$

7. $T_n = 2n$

8. $\log_{10}(\frac{n+1}{n})$, $\log_{10}(\frac{31}{30})$

10. 5

Exercise 3 [*Convergence of Sequences* (page **186**)]

1. (a) DGT (b) CGT to 0 (c) CGT to 0 (d) CGT to 0
   (e) CGT to 0 (f) DGT (g) DGT (h) DGT
   (i) CGT to 0 (j) DGT (k) CGT to 0 (l) DGT
   (m) CGT to 0 (n) DGT

2. (a) CGT to $\frac{1}{2}$ (b) DGT (c) CGT to 0 (d) CGT to $\frac{1}{2}$
   (e) DGT (f) CGT to 0 (g) CGT to $\frac{1}{2}$ (h) CGT to 2
   (i) CGT to $\frac{1}{4}$ (j) CGT to $\frac{1}{2}$ (k) CGT to 1 (l) CGT to 1
   (m) CGT to 0 (n) CGT to 0 (o) CGT to 1

Exercise 4 [*AP's* (page **193**)]

1. (a) Yes (b) No (c) Yes (d) No
   (e) No (f) No

2. (a) No (b) Yes (c) Yes (d) Yes
   (e) Yes (f) No

3. (a) 38, $2(2n - 1)$, 72, $2n^2$ (b) -14, $2(3 - n)$, -6, $n(5 - n)$
   (c) $16\frac{1}{2}$, $\frac{3}{2}(n+1)$, $40\frac{1}{2}$, $\frac{3n}{4}(n+3)$
   (d) $-11\frac{1}{4}$, $\frac{5}{4}(1-n)$, $-18\frac{3}{4}$, $\frac{5n}{8}(1-n)$
   (e) 20, $2n$, 42, $n(n + 1)$

4. (a) $\frac{555}{2}$ (b) $1325\sqrt{3}$ (c) 0 (d) $\frac{n}{2}(n+1)$
   (e) $\frac{n}{2(1-x)}(\sqrt{x}(n-3)+2)$

5. 1, 4, 7, 10
6. -5, 7
7. 32, 29, 26, 23
8. 10, -4
9. $15^{th.}$
10. No
11. 99
12. Yes, 23
13. 9, $10\frac{1}{2}$
14. 2, 5, 8, 11
15. 6
16. $\frac{33}{2}$
17. $p + q - m$
18. 12
19. 50
20. 2,450
21. $n(4 + n)$
22. $2(n + 2)$; 6, 8, 10
23. n^2
24. 20
25. 5
26. 12
27. 8, 6, 4, ...
28. 14
29. 7,500
30. 1,900
31. (a) 5, (b) $\frac{11}{2}$, (c) $\frac{a^2+b^2}{2}$, (d) x
32. 7, 3
33. -1, 7
34. -2, 2, 6
35. -3, 1, 5

Exercise 5 [*GP's* (page **201**)]

1. (a) No (b) Yes (c) Yes (d) Yes
   (e) Yes (f) No

2. (a) (i) $\frac{243}{4}$ (ii) $8(\frac{3}{2})^{n-1}$ (iii) $\frac{665}{4}$ (iv) $16((\frac{3}{2})^n - 1)$

(b) (i) $\frac{729}{64}$ (ii) $48(\frac{3}{4})^{n-1}$ (iii) $\frac{10101}{64}$ (iv) $192(1-(\frac{3}{4})^{n})$

(c) (i) -486 (ii) $2(-3)^{n-1}$ (iii) -364 (iv) $\frac{1}{2}(1-(-3)^{n})$

(d) (i) $\frac{1}{243}$ (ii) $(\frac{1}{3})^{n-1}$ (iii) $\frac{364}{243}$ (iv) $\frac{3}{2}(1-(\frac{1}{3})^{n})$

3. (a) 4,095 (b) $\frac{765}{4}$ (c) $\frac{5^{p}-1}{4}$

(d) $\frac{64}{65}(1+(\frac{5}{8})^{5})$ (e) $\frac{127}{49}(7+\sqrt{42})$ (f) $\frac{31(2-\sqrt{2})}{16}$

4. 2.5^{19} 5. -7^{9}

6. $\frac{4}{27}, \frac{4}{9}, \frac{4}{3}$ and $-\frac{4}{27}, \frac{4}{9}, -\frac{4}{3}$

7. 20, 80 8. ± 12, ± 192 9. $\frac{64}{9}$, 24, 81

10. 4, -12, 36 11. 3.2^{3-n} 12. 18th.

13. 3, 6, 12 14. 3, 6, 12 15. 6

16. 6 17. $3(2^{n} - 1)$ 18. 315

19. $\pm\frac{1}{2}$, $15\frac{7}{8}$, $5\frac{3}{8}$

20. (a) 7, (b) 7, (c) 8, (d) 5

21. $\frac{1}{2}$ 22. 6

23. (a) $3\sqrt{10}$, (b) 3, (c) 4, (d) $2\sqrt{10}$, (e) cd 24. 9, 4

Exercise 6 [*Sum to Infinity of GP's* (page **204**)]

1. (a) 2, (b) 3, (c) $\frac{2}{3}$, (d) 32

2. 125 or $\frac{250}{3}$ 3. 96, 24, 6, ... 4. 10

5. 11 6. $83\frac{1}{3}$ 7. $\sec^2\theta$, 2

8. 10 or 15 9. 8 10. $\cos^2\theta$, $\frac{3}{4}$

11. (a) $\frac{8}{45}$ (b) $\frac{23}{99}$ (c) $\frac{344}{99}$

(d) $\frac{123}{999}$ (e) $\frac{57}{9}$ (f) $\frac{118}{99}$

(g) $\frac{20}{9}$ (h) $\frac{1924}{9999}$

12. 1, $\frac{2}{3}$, $\frac{4}{9}$, ...

Exercise 7 [*AGP's* (page **207**)]

1. $\frac{1}{(1-x)^2}$ 2. 6 3. $\frac{9}{2}$ 4. $\frac{x}{(1-x)^2}$

Series

1. WORKING WITH A SERIES

1.1 WHAT IS A SERIES?

A **series** is the sum of the terms of a sequence.

For the **Sequence**: 1, $\frac{1}{2}$, $\frac{1}{4}$, $\frac{1}{8}$, ... the corresponding

Series is: $1+\frac{1}{2}+\frac{1}{4}+\frac{1}{8}+....$

i.e. the commas are replaced by $\pm$ signs.

Example:

Sequence: 1, 3, 7, 11,......

$T_1\ T_2\ T_3\ T_4$

Series: 1 + 3 + 7 + 11,....

$T_1 + T_2 + T_3 + T_4$

TRICK

The notation for sequences and series is the same.

T_5 = 5th. term of a sequence/series

S_5 = Sum of the first five terms

$= T_1 + T_2 + T_3 + T_4 + T_5$

1.2 THE SHORTHAND Σ NOTATION (sigma notation)

A series can be written in one of 2 ways:

1. **Listdot**: 3 + 5 + 7 + 9 + ... *OR*

2. Sigma: $\sum_{r=1}^{\infty}(2r+1)$

Understanding the Σ notation

End *Variable*

$$\sum_{r=1}^{n} f(r) = f(1)+f(2)+f(3)+....+f(n)$$

Start *Function*

NOTES

1. Every Σ notation has a function *f* of any variable (dummy). The variable can be any letter. There is nothing special about *r*.
2. **Start value**: A whole positive number, usually 1, but not always.
3. **End value**: A whole positive number or a letter or ∞.

Trick: To convert the Σ notation into listdot simply fill in the value of the variable r into the function beginning at the start value and stopping at the end value increasing the value of r by 1 each time and putting + between each term.

End — *Variable*

Example 1: $\sum_{r=1}^{3}(4r-1)^2 = (4.1-1)^2 + (4.2-1)^2 + (4.3-1)^2$

Start — *Function*

Example 2: $\sum_{p=1}^{n}\cos^3 p = \cos^3 1 + \cos^3 2 + \cos^3 3 + \ldots\ldots + \cos^3 n$

Example 3: $\sum_{r=1}^{\infty}\frac{3}{r+2} = \frac{3}{1+2} + \frac{3}{2+2} + \frac{3}{3+2} + \ldots..$

NOTES CONTINUED

4. Function $f(r)$ can be anything.
5. $f(r)$ determines each term and so is the general term, T_r

$$f(n) = T_n,\ f(p) = T_p$$

Trick: $S_n = \sum_{r=1}^{n} T_r = T_1 + T_2 + .. + T_n$. The yoke beside the Σ sign is the general term. If they use the variable r call it T_r, if they use p call it T_p etc....

EXAMPLES

$S_7 = \sum_{n=1}^{7}\frac{n-1}{n+1}$, i.e. add up 7 terms — $T_n = f(n)$

$S_n = \sum_{l=1}^{n} e^l = e^1 + e^2 + \ldots. + e^n$ — $T_l = e^l = f(l)$

$\sum_{r=1}^{\infty}\log(r+1) = S_\infty$ — $T_r = f(r)$

Trick: $S_\infty = \lim_{n\to\infty} S_n$

1.3 RULES FOR MANIPULATING $\sum$

[A] **Split trick**

$$S_4 = \sum_{r=1}^{4}(r^2 + r) = (1^2 + 1) + (2^2 + 2) + (3^2 + 3) + (4^2 + 4)$$

$$= (1^2 + 2^2 + 3^2 + 4^2) + (1 + 2 + 3 + 4) = \sum_{r=1}^{4} r^2 + \sum_{r=1}^{4} r$$

Trick: You can split a function which is a sum into individual sums.

[B] **Factor trick**

$$S_5 = \sum_{r=1}^{5} 3r^2 = 3.1^2 + 3.2^2 + 3.3^2 + 3.4^2 + 3.5^2$$

$$= 3(1^2 + 2^2 + 3^2 + 4^2 + 5^2) = 3\sum_{r=1}^{5} r^2$$

Trick: You can take out constants out of $\sum$ signs.

[C] **The One trick**

$$S_n = \sum_{r=1}^{n} 1 = \sum_{r=1}^{n} r^0 = 1^0 + 2^0 + ... + n^0 = 1 + 1 + ... + 1 = n$$

Trick: $\sum_{r=1}^{n} 1$ means add 1 to itself n times = n.

Danger!!!: Just be a little careful with the start value if it's not 1.

Example: $S_n = \sum_{r=4}^{22} f(r) \neq S_{22} = S_{22} - S_3$

Using these tricks a series can be written as individual $\sum$'s:

Example: $\sum_{r=1}^{n}(r-1)^2 = S_n = \sum_{r=1}^{n}(r^2 - 2r + 1) = \sum_{r=1}^{n} r^2 - 2\sum_{r=1}^{n} r + \sum_{r=1}^{n} 1$

Example: $\sum_{r=1}^{n}(2r+3) = S_n = 2\sum_{r=1}^{n} r + 3\sum_{r=1}^{n} 1$

Series can now be treated in 2 sections: **Summation techniques** and **Binomial series**.

Exercise 1 (Answers: page **251**)

Series: The Σ Notation

1. Write out the following Σ's in listdot form:

(a) $\sum_{r=1}^{\infty}(r-2)^2$

(b) $\sum_{r=3}^{10}2r+5$

(c) $\sum_{r=1}^{\infty}(\frac{3}{2})^r$

(d) $\sum_{r=2}^{n}\frac{r-1}{r+2}$

(e) $\sum_{r=0}^{n}(\frac{1}{2})^r-2r$

(f) $\sum_{l=1}^{\infty}(\frac{3}{4})^l$

(g) $\sum_{r=3}^{20}\frac{1}{2^{r-1}}$

(h) $\sum_{r=1}^{n}2r^2+\frac{5}{r}$

2. Write out the following Listdot series in Σ form by finding T_r:

(a) $1^2+2^2+3^2+4^2+\ldots+20^2$

(b) $1+3+5+7+\ldots.+19$

(c) $4+8+12+16+\ldots+100$

(d) $1+\frac{1}{2}+\frac{1}{3}+\ldots\ldots\ldots+\frac{1}{n}$

(e) $1+\frac{1}{2}+\frac{1}{6}+\frac{1}{24}+\ldots\ldots\ldots+\frac{1}{n!}$

(f) $1.2+2.3+3.4+\ldots+50.51$

(g) $\frac{1}{3.5}+\frac{1}{4.6}+\frac{1}{5.7}+\ldots\ldots\ldots+\frac{1}{20.22}$

(h) $\frac{1}{3}+\frac{1}{9}+\frac{1}{27}+\frac{1}{81}+\ldots\ldots\ldots$

3. For each of the following series find T_n:

(a) $\sum_{r=1}^{n}\frac{1}{(2r-1)(2r+1)}$

(b) $\sum_{r=1}^{\infty}\frac{5r-1}{2r+1}$

(c) $\sum_{r=1}^{20}r(r+1)$

(d) $\sum_{n=1}^{50}(n+2)(n+4)$

(e) $\sum_{s=1}^{n}\frac{s^2-1}{2s+3}$

(f) $\sum_{r=1}^{\infty}\frac{r+1}{r+3}$

(g) $1+2+3+\ldots\ldots$

(h) $1+\frac{1}{2}+\frac{1}{4}+\frac{1}{8}\ldots\ldots.$

2. Summation Techniques

2.1 The Idea

Adding up lots of numbers is very difficult and we have not done it yet. On the LC course summation techniques can be divided up into 2 sections: **Memory Series** and **Method of Differences**.

2.2 Memory Series

There are 4 formulae for series to remember.

Series Formulae

[A] **Arithmetic Series** (AS):

$$S_n = \tfrac{n}{2}\left[2a + (n-1)d\right]$$

[B] **Geometric Series** (GS):

$$S_n = \frac{a(1-r^n)}{1-r}\ ;\ S_\infty = \frac{a}{1-r} \text{ iff } -1 < r < 1$$

[C] $\sum_{r=1}^{n} r = S_n = 1 + 2 + ... + n = \tfrac{n}{2}(n+1)$

[D] $\sum_{r=1}^{n} r^2 = S_n = 1^2 + 2^2 + ... + n^2 = \tfrac{n}{6}(n+1)(2n+1)$

You must remember these.

Notes

1. $\sum_{r=1}^{n} r = 1 + 2 + ... + n$ is an AS with $a = 1$, $d = 1$ and so is a special case of [A].

2. $\sum_{r=1}^{n} r^2 = \tfrac{n}{6}(n+1)(2n+1)$ is proved by induction (page 425).

3. You may be asked to do a combination of [A] to [D].
4. The hardest series to recognise from its Σ notation is a GS.

TRICK

If you see a series with a variable power it's a GS so $\sum_{r=1}^{n}(\text{Yoke})^r$ is a GS. Write it out and find a and r.

Steps for evaluating Σ memory:

STEPS

1. Call it S_n no matter what the end number is.
2. Simplify using the rules.
3. Recognise each part as [A] to [D].
4. Fill in formula for each part.
5. Plonk in value for n, e.g. 23, ∞.

Example 1: Evaluate $\sum_{r=1}^{30}(2r-3)^2$.

SOLUTION

$$\sum_{r=1}^{30}(2r-3)^2 = S_{30}$$

$$S_n = \sum_{r=1}^{n}(2r-3)^2 = \sum_{r=1}^{n}(4r^2-12r+9) = 4\sum_{r=1}^{n}r^2 - 12\sum_{r=1}^{n}r + 9\sum_{r=1}^{n}1$$

$$\Rightarrow S_n = 4\tfrac{n}{6}(n+1)(2n+1) - 12\tfrac{n}{2}(n+1) + 9n$$

$$\therefore S_{30} = 4.5(31)(61) - 6.30(31) + 9.30 = 32{,}510$$

Example 2: Evaluate $\sum_{r=1}^{n}(r-2^r)$.

SOLUTION

$$S_n = \sum_{r=1}^{n}(r-2^r) = \sum_{r=1}^{n} r - \sum_{r=1}^{n} 2^r$$

$$= \tfrac{n}{2}(n+1) - \{2+4+8+.....2^n\}$$

$$= \tfrac{n}{2}(n+1) - 2(2^n - 1)$$

$\{2+4+8+.....2^n\}$ is S_n for a GS with $a = 2$ and $r = 2$

$$S_n = \frac{2(1-2^n)}{1-2} = 2(2^n - 1)$$

Example 3: Evaluate $\sum_{r=10}^{20}(r^2 - 3r)$.

SOLUTION

$$\sum_{r=10}^{20}(r^2 - 3r) = S_{20} - S_9$$

$$S_n = \sum_{r=1}^{n}(r^2 - 3r) = \sum_{r=1}^{n} r^2 - 3\sum_{r=1}^{n} r$$

$$\Rightarrow S_n = \tfrac{n}{6}(n+1)(2n+1) - 3\tfrac{n}{2}(n+1)$$

$$\therefore S_{20} = \tfrac{20}{6}(21)(41) - 3\tfrac{20}{2}(21) = 2{,}240$$

$$\therefore S_9 = \tfrac{9}{6}(10)(19) - 3\tfrac{9}{2}(10) = 150$$

$$\therefore S_{20} - S_9 = 2{,}240 - 150 = 2{,}090$$

Example 4: Evaluate $\sum_{r=0}^{\infty}\cos^{2r} x$ when $x = \frac{\pi}{6}$.

SOLUTION

Look out for S_∞ of GS

$$S_\infty = \sum_{r=0}^{\infty}\cos^{2r} x \;\therefore S_\infty = 1 + \cos^2 x + \cos^4 x + ...$$

This is a GS with $a = 1$ and $r = \cos^2 x$

$$\therefore S_\infty = \frac{1}{1-\cos^2 x} = \frac{1}{\sin^2 x}, \; S_\infty = \frac{1}{(\frac{1}{2})^2} = 4 \text{ at } x = \tfrac{\pi}{6}$$

Exercise 2 (Answers: page **252**)
(Answers: page 252)

Memory Summation Techniques

1. Evaluate

(a) $\sum_{r=1}^{4}(r-2)^2$

(b) $\sum_{r=1}^{9}(r+1)^2$

(c) $\sum_{r=2}^{7}(r^2+1)$

(d) $\sum_{r=1}^{n}(r-1)^2$

(e) $\sum_{r=1}^{n}(r^2+2r)$

(f) $\sum_{r=1}^{n}(r^2+2r+1)$

(g) $\sum_{r=1}^{20}(r^2+3r)$

(h) $\sum_{r=1}^{40}(r^2-2r+7)$

(i) $\sum_{r=1}^{30}(r-1)^2$

(j) $\sum_{r=2}^{20}(r^2+3r+1)$

(k) $\sum_{r=1}^{10}(\frac{1}{2})^r$

(l) $\sum_{r=0}^{\infty}(\frac{2}{5})^r$

(m) $\sum_{r=0}^{n}(\frac{1}{2})^r$

(n) $\sum_{r=1}^{n}4(\frac{1}{3})^r$

(o) $\sum_{r=0}^{\infty}3(\frac{2}{3})^r$

(p) $\sum_{r=1}^{10}((\frac{1}{2})^r+r)$

(q) $\sum_{r=7}^{15}(r^2-r)$

(r) $\sum_{r=10}^{20}(r^2+3r+1)$

2. Find T_n and hence find S_n:

(a) $1^2 + 2^2 + 3^2 + ...$

(b) $1^2 + 3^2 + 5^2 + 7^2 + ...$

(c) 1.3 + 3.5 + 5.7 + ...

(d) 2.1 + 3.2 + 4.3 + ...

3. (a) Show that

$$\sum_{1}^{n}(2+3r) = \sum_{1}^{3n}(1+\tfrac{r}{3})$$

(b) Find a if $\sum_{1}^{10}(a+2r) = 250$

(c) Find n if $\sum_{1}^{n}(4r-1) = 300$

2.3 THE METHOD OF DIFFERENCES (MOD)

This method is used for all other sums, i.e. fractions, surds, logs, factorials and others.

Trick: The MOD depends on splitting up the general term into a difference and constructing a sum table.

[A] **Fractions** (one overs): A fraction can be split up into its partial fractions (PF) which is an identical way of writing a single fraction (SF).

Example: $\frac{1}{6} = \frac{1}{2.3} = \frac{1}{2} - \frac{1}{3}$ (PF)

Example 5: Split $\frac{4}{(x+3)(2x-1)}$ into its partial fractions.

SOLUTION

$$\frac{4}{(x+3)(2x-1)} = \frac{A}{(x+3)} + \frac{B}{(2x-1)} \text{ (Identity)}$$

$\Rightarrow 4 = A(2x - 1) + B(x + 3)$

This is an identity so you can choose any values you like. So suit yourself.

$x = -3 \Rightarrow 4 = -7A \therefore A = -\frac{4}{7}$

$x = \frac{1}{2} \Rightarrow 4 = \frac{7}{2}B \therefore B = \frac{8}{7}$

$$\therefore \frac{4}{(x+3)(2x-1)} = \frac{-4}{7(x+3)} + \frac{8}{7(2x-1)} = \frac{8}{7(2x-1)} - \frac{4}{7(x+3)}$$

Steps for adding fractions (one overs):

STEPS

1. Write general term as its PF.
2. Build a sum table (ST).

Example 6: Evaluate $\displaystyle\sum_{r=1}^{n} \frac{5}{(2r-1)(2r+1)}$.

Hence find $\displaystyle\sum_{r=1}^{\infty} \frac{5}{(2r-1)(2r+1)}$.

SOLUTION

$$S_n = \sum_{r=1}^{n} \frac{5}{(2r-1)(2r+1)} = 5\sum_{r=1}^{n} \frac{1}{(2r-1)(2r+1)}$$

PF (i): $T_r = \dfrac{1}{(2r-1)(2r+1)} = \dfrac{A}{(2r-1)} + \dfrac{B}{(2r+1)}$

$\Rightarrow 1 = A(2r+1) + B(2r-1)$

$r = \frac{1}{2} : 1 = 2A \Rightarrow A = \frac{1}{2}$

$r = -\frac{1}{2} : 1 = -2B \Rightarrow B = -\frac{1}{2}$

$$\therefore \quad T_r = \frac{1}{2(2r-1)} - \frac{1}{2(2r+1)}$$

ST (ii): $T_1 = \dfrac{1}{2.1} - \dfrac{1}{2.3}$

One line cancellation gives 1 number at start and 1 at the end.

$T_2 = \dfrac{1}{2.3} - \dfrac{1}{2.5}$

•
•
•
•

$T_{n-1} = \dfrac{1}{2(2n-3)} - \dfrac{1}{2(2n-1)}$

$T_n = \dfrac{1}{2(2n-1)} - \dfrac{1}{2(2n+1)}$

$$\therefore S_n = 5\left(\frac{1}{2} - \frac{1}{2(2n+1)}\right)$$

As $n \to \infty, S_n \to S_\infty = 5(\frac{1}{2} - 0) = \frac{5}{2}$

Example 7: Evaluate $\sum_{n=1}^{\infty} \frac{1}{(n+2)(n+4)}$.

SOLUTION

$$S_n = \sum_{n=1}^{\infty} \frac{1}{(n+2)(n+4)}$$

PF (i): $T_n = \frac{1}{(n+2)(n+4)} = \frac{A}{n+2} + \frac{B}{n+4}$

$\Rightarrow 1 = A(n+4) + B(n+2)$

$n = -2$: $1 = 2A \Rightarrow A = \frac{1}{2}$

$n = -4$: $1 = -2B \Rightarrow B = -\frac{1}{2}$

$$\therefore\ T_n = \frac{1}{2(n+2)} - \frac{1}{2(n+4)}$$

ST (ii):

$$T_1 = \frac{1}{2.3} - \frac{1}{2.5}$$

$$T_2 = \frac{1}{2.4} - \frac{1}{2.6}$$

$$T_3 = \frac{1}{2.5} - \frac{1}{2.7}$$

$$T_{n-1} = \frac{1}{2(n+1)} - \frac{1}{2(n+3)}$$

$$T_n = \frac{1}{2(n+2)} - \frac{1}{2(n+4)}$$

Two line cancellation gives 2 numbers at start and 2 at the end.

$$S_n = \frac{1}{6} + \frac{1}{8} - \frac{1}{2(n+3)} - \frac{1}{2(n+4)}$$

Cont.....

$$\therefore S_n = \frac{7}{24} - \frac{1}{2(n+3)} - \frac{1}{2(n+4)}$$

$$S_\infty = \lim_{n\to\infty} S_n = \frac{7}{24}$$

Example 8: Evaluate S_n for the series $\frac{1}{4.5} + \frac{1}{5.6} + \frac{1}{6.7} + ...$

SOLUTION

This is tricky because you don't have the general term.

$$\frac{1}{4.5} + \frac{1}{5.6} + \frac{1}{6.7} + ...$$

AP: 4, 5, 6 with $T_n = 4 + (n - 1)1 = (n + 3)$

AP: 5, 6, 7 with $T_n = 5 + (n - 1)1 = (n + 4)$

$\therefore T_n = \frac{1}{(n+3)(n+4)}$ for the series.

Now split T_n up into its PF and hence do the ST to find S_n.

[B] **Surds**

Example 9: Evaluate $\sum_{n=1}^{n} \frac{1}{\sqrt{n+1}+\sqrt{n}}$.

TRICK

Rationalizing (**R**) the denominator gives a difference.

SOLUTION

$$S_n = \sum_{n=1}^{n} \frac{1}{\sqrt{n+1}+\sqrt{n}}$$

R (i): $T_n = \frac{1}{\sqrt{n+1}+\sqrt{n}} = \frac{1}{\sqrt{n+1}+\sqrt{n}} \times \frac{\sqrt{n+1}-\sqrt{n}}{\sqrt{n+1}-\sqrt{n}}$

$\Rightarrow T_n = \sqrt{n+1} - \sqrt{n}$

Cont.....

ST (ii): $T_1 = \sqrt{2} - \sqrt{1}$

$T_2 = \sqrt{3} - \sqrt{2}$

⋮

$T_{n-1} = \sqrt{n} - \sqrt{n-1}$

$T_n = \sqrt{n+1} - \sqrt{n}$

$S_n = \sqrt{n+1} - 1$

[C] **Logs**

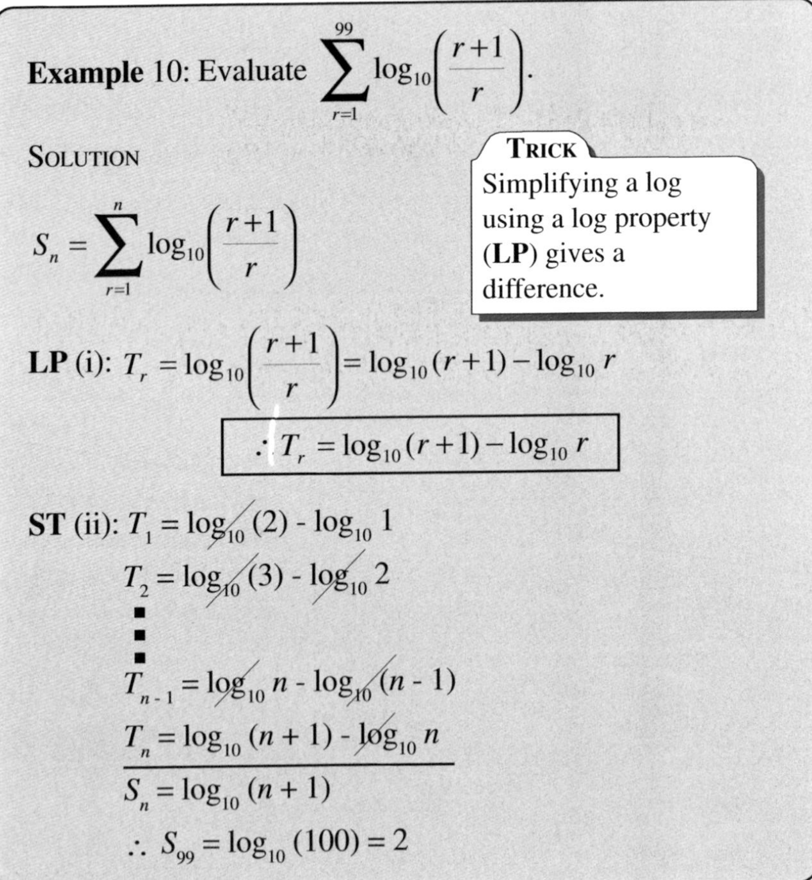

Example 10: Evaluate $\displaystyle\sum_{r=1}^{99} \log_{10}\left(\frac{r+1}{r}\right)$.

SOLUTION

TRICK
Simplifying a log using a log property (**LP**) gives a difference.

$$S_n = \sum_{r=1}^{n} \log_{10}\left(\frac{r+1}{r}\right)$$

LP (i): $T_r = \log_{10}\left(\frac{r+1}{r}\right) = \log_{10}(r+1) - \log_{10} r$

$$\therefore T_r = \log_{10}(r+1) - \log_{10} r$$

ST (ii): $T_1 = \log_{10}(2) - \log_{10} 1$

$T_2 = \log_{10}(3) - \log_{10} 2$

⋮

$T_{n-1} = \log_{10} n - \log_{10}(n-1)$

$T_n = \log_{10}(n+1) - \log_{10} n$

$S_n = \log_{10}(n+1)$

$\therefore S_{99} = \log_{10}(100) = 2$

[D] **Factorial**

Example 11: Show $\frac{1}{n!}-\frac{1}{(n+1)!}=\frac{n}{(n+1)!}$. Hence evaluate $\sum_{n=1}^{n}\frac{n}{(n+1)!}$

TRICK
If this question is set you will be asked to prove a factorial result (**FR**) first.

SOLUTION

FR (i): $\frac{1}{n!}-\frac{1}{(n+1)!}=\frac{(n+1)-1}{(n+1)!}=\frac{n}{(n+1)!}$

$$\therefore T_n=\frac{1}{n!}-\frac{1}{(n+1)!}$$

ST (ii): $T_1=\frac{1}{1!}-\frac{1}{2!}$

$T_2=\frac{1}{2!}-\frac{1}{3!}$

•
•
•
•

$T_{n-1}=\frac{1}{(n-1)!}-\frac{1}{n!}$

$T_n=\frac{1}{n!}-\frac{1}{(n+1)!}$

$S_n=1-\frac{1}{(n+1)!}$

[E] **Other**

Example 12: If $f(r)=\frac{1}{r^2}$ show $f(r)-f(r+1)=\frac{2r+1}{r^2(r+1)^2}$.

Hence find $\sum_{r=1}^{n}\frac{2r+1}{r^2(r+1)^2}$.

SOLUTION

R (i): $f(r)-f(r+1)=\frac{1}{r^2}-\frac{1}{(r+1)^2}=\frac{(r+1)^2-r^2}{r^2(r+1)^2}$

$=\frac{r^2+2r+1-r^2}{r^2(r+1)^2}=\frac{2r+1}{r^2(r+1)^2}$

TRICK
You will be asked to prove a result (**R**) first.

ST (ii): $S_n=\sum_{r=1}^{n}\frac{2r+1}{r^2(r+1)^2}$

$T_r=\frac{2r+1}{r^2(r+1)^2}=\frac{1}{r^2}-\frac{1}{(r+1)^2}$

$\therefore T_r=\frac{1}{r^2}-\frac{1}{(r+1)^2}$

$T_1=\frac{1}{1^2}-\frac{1}{2^2}$

$T_2=\frac{1}{2^2}-\frac{1}{3^2}$

•
•
•
•

$T_{n-1}=\frac{1}{(n-1)^2}-\frac{1}{n^2}$

$T_n=\frac{1}{n^2}-\frac{1}{(n+1)^2}$

$S_n=1-\frac{1}{(n+1)^2}$

2.4 ARITHMETIC GEOMETRIC SERIES (AGS)

An arithmetic geometric series has been dealt with in the section on sequences. It is necessary to be able to find S_∞ using the technique described there.

Trick: Recognition of an AGS from its Σ notation is hard.

$$\Sigma\,(\text{Variable})(\text{Yoke})^{\text{Variable}}$$

Example: $\sum_{r=1}^{\infty}(2r-1)3^r$, $\sum_{r=0}^{\infty} rx^r$ are AGS's.

So write them out as a list and do S_∞ using the steps in sequences.

Exercise 3 (Answers: page **252**)

MOD's & AG's

1. Evaluate

(a) $\sum_{r=1}^{n}\frac{1}{r(r+1)}$

(b) $\sum_{r=1}^{n}\frac{1}{(2r-1)(2r+1)}$

(c) $\sum_{r=1}^{n}\frac{1}{(r+3)(r+5)}$

(d) $\sum_{r=1}^{n}\frac{1}{(r+1)(r+3)}$

(e) $\sum_{r=1}^{20}\frac{1}{(r+4)(r+5)}$

2. Evaluate

(a) $\sum_{r=1}^{n}(\sqrt{r+1}-\sqrt{r})$

(b) $\sum_{r=1}^{n}\frac{1}{\sqrt{r+1}+\sqrt{r}}$

(c) $\sum_{r=1}^{n}\log\left(\frac{r+1}{r}\right)$

(d) $\sum_{r=1}^{n}\frac{1}{\sqrt{r}}-\frac{1}{\sqrt{r+1}}$

3. Find S_n and S_∞ for the following GS's:

(a) $10+5+\frac{5}{2}+.......$

(b) $\frac{1}{8}+\frac{1}{4}+\frac{1}{2}+.......$

(c) $\sum_{l=1}^{\infty}(\frac{1}{4})^l$

(d) $\sum_{r=1}^{\infty}(-\frac{2}{3})^r$

(e) $\sum_{n=1}^{\infty}3(\frac{1}{2})^n$

(f) $\frac{1}{3}+\frac{4}{3}+\frac{16}{3}+.......$

(g) $2-\frac{1}{2}+\frac{1}{8}-\frac{1}{32}+.......$

(h) 4 - 12 + 36 - .....

(i) $\frac{1}{2}+\frac{1}{3}+\frac{2}{9}+.......$

4. Find S_∞ for the GS's:

(a) $\sum_{r=1}^{\infty}(\frac{1}{2})^r$

(b) $\sum_{n=1}^{\infty}(\sin^2 x)^n$

(c) $\sum_{n=1}^{\infty}\left(\frac{x}{x+1}\right)^n, x>0$

(d) $\sum_{n=1}^{\infty}(\frac{2}{3})^n$

(e) $\sum_{n=1}^{\infty}2^r$

5. Find S_∞ for the following AGS's:

(a) $\sum_{n=1}^{\infty}nx^n$, $|x|<1$

(b) $\sum_{n=1}^{\infty}(n+1)(\frac{1}{2})^n$

(c) $\sum_{n=1}^{\infty}(n+2)(\frac{1}{3})^n$

(d) $\sum_{r=1}^{\infty}r(\frac{1}{2})^r$

3. THE BINOMIAL SERIES

3.1 THE IDEA

This is a method of expanding out brackets with 2 entries quickly.

Statement for the Binomial Series for $n \in N_0$:

$$(x+y)^n = \binom{n}{0}(x)^n(y)^0 + \binom{n}{1}(x)^{n-1}(y)^1 + \binom{n}{2}(x)^{n-2}(y)^2 + \dots\dots + \binom{n}{n}(x)^0(y)^n$$

NOTES

1. It is an identity so terms must line up.

2. FP = First placeholder = (x) and SP = Second placeholder = (y). x and y can be anything.

3. The list of terms is called a finite series and there are (n + 1) terms.

4. Power of FP decreases from n to 0 in steps of 1.
Power of SP increases from 0 to n in steps of 1.
Therefore, sum of powers of FP and SP is n.

5. **General term**: $T_{r+1} = {}^nC_r(x)^{n-r}(y)^r = \binom{n}{r}(x)^{n-r}(y)^r$

6. Every term consists of 3 bits multiplied together.

$$T_{r+1} = \underbrace{{}^nC_r}_{\text{BC}}\underbrace{(x)^{n-r}}_{\text{FP}}\underbrace{(y)^r}_{\text{SP}} = \binom{n}{r}(x)^{n-r}(y)^r$$

If you know any of these bits you can work out the others because:
(a) Power of SP = Subscript of BC (Binomial coefficient)
(b) Power of FP = Superscript - Subscript of BC

TRICK 1: Picking out terms

To pick out a term: Use the general term $T_{r+1} = \binom{n}{r}(x)^{n-r}(y)^r$

To pick out the middle term: Just half the bracket power, then work back from the subscript to get the term.

$$\text{Middle term} = {}^nC_{\frac{n}{2}}(x)^{\frac{n}{2}}(y)^{\frac{n}{2}}$$

NOTES: 1. Independent of x means x^0.
2. Coefficient of x^3 means everything else except x^3.

TRICK 2: You should remember the BC's for:

$(x+y)^3$		1	3	3	1	
$(x+y)^4$		1	4	6	4	1
$(x+y)^5$	1	5	10	10	5	1

TRICK 3: $\sum$ Notation

$$(x+y)^n = \sum_{r=0}^{n}\binom{n}{r}x^{n-r}y^r$$

$$= \binom{n}{0}(x)^n(y)^0 + \binom{n}{1}(x)^{n-1}(y)^1 + \binom{n}{2}(x)^{n-2}(y)^2 + ... + \binom{n}{n}(x)^0(y)^n$$

TRICK 4: Properties of Binomial Coefficients

Putting values into the above expansion gives an interesting result:

1. $x = 1, y = 1 \Rightarrow 2^n = \binom{n}{0} + \binom{n}{1} + ... + \binom{n}{n} = \sum_{r=0}^{n}\binom{n}{r}$

2. $x = 1, y = -1 \Rightarrow 0 = \binom{n}{0} - \binom{n}{1} + \binom{n}{2} - \binom{n}{3} + ...$

$$\Rightarrow \binom{n}{0} + \binom{n}{2} + \binom{n}{4} + ... = \binom{n}{1} + \binom{n}{3} + \binom{n}{5} + ...$$

3.2 PROBLEMS ON THE BINOMIAL

[A] EXPANDING BRACKETS (TYPE 1)

Example 1: Expand out $(x - 2y)^4$.

SOLUTION

$(x - 2y)^4$ [FP = (x), SP = $(-2y)$]

$(x - 2y)^4$

$= 1(x)^4(-2y)^0 + 4(x)^3(-2y)^1 + 6(x)^2(-2y)^2 + 4(x)1(-2y)^3 + 1(x)^0(-2y)^4$

$= x^4 - 8x^3y + 24x^2y^2 - 32xy^3 + 16y^4$

Example 2: Expand out $(\cos A + i\sin A)^3$ where $i = \sqrt{-1}$.

SOLUTION

$(\cos A + i\sin A)^3$ [FP = $(\cos A)$, SP = $(i\sin A)$]

$= 1(\cos A)^3(i\sin A)^0 + 3(\cos A)^2(i\sin A)^1 + 3(\cos A)^1(i\sin A)^2$

$+ 1(\cos A)^0(i\sin A)^3$

$= \cos^3 A + 3i\cos^2 A\sin A - 3\cos A\sin^2 A - i\sin^3 A$

Example 3: Write out the first 3 terms and the last 3 terms of $(x + \frac{1}{x})^{20}$.

SOLUTION

$(x + \frac{1}{x})^{20}$ [FP = (x), SP = $(\frac{1}{x})$]

$$= \binom{20}{0}(x)^{20}(\tfrac{1}{x})^0 + \binom{20}{1}(x)^{19}(\tfrac{1}{x})^1 + \binom{20}{2}(x)^{18}(\tfrac{1}{x})^2 \ldots\ldots\ldots\ldots$$

$$\ldots\ldots\ldots\ldots \binom{20}{18}(x)^2(\tfrac{1}{x})^{18} + \binom{20}{19}(x)^1(\tfrac{1}{x})^{19} + \binom{20}{20}(x)^0(\tfrac{1}{x})^{20}$$

$$= x^{20} + 20x^{18} + 190x^{16} + \ldots\ldots\ldots\ldots + \frac{190}{x^{16}} + \frac{20}{x^{18}} + \frac{1}{x^{20}}$$

Trick: Add before simplifying because + terms cancel with - terms.

Example 4: Show $(2+\sqrt{3})^5+(2-\sqrt{3})^5=724$.

SOLUTION

$(2+\sqrt{3})^5=1(2)^5(\sqrt{3})^0+5(2)^4(\sqrt{3})^1+10(2)^3(\sqrt{3})^2$

$+10(2)^2(\sqrt{3})^3+5(2)^1(\sqrt{3})^4+1(2)^0(\sqrt{3})^5$

$(2-\sqrt{3})^5=1(2)^5(-\sqrt{3})^0+5(2)^4(-\sqrt{3})^1+10(2)^3(-\sqrt{3})^2$

$+10(2)^2(-\sqrt{3})^3+5(2)^1(-\sqrt{3})^4+1(2)^0(-\sqrt{3})^5$

$(2+\sqrt{3})^5+(2-\sqrt{3})^5=2(2)^5+2.10(2)^3(\sqrt{3})^2+2.5(2)(\sqrt{3})^4$

$= 64 + 480 + 180 = 724$

[B] **FINDING COEFFICIENTS GIVEN THE BINOMIAL SERIES (Type 2)**

Example 5: If $1+6x+\frac{33x^2}{2}$ are the first 3 terms of the binomial series of $(1 + ax)^n$ find $a, n \in N_0$.

SOLUTION

$$(1+ax)^n=\binom{n}{0}(1)^n(ax)^0+\binom{n}{1}(1)^{n-1}(ax)^1+\binom{n}{2}(1)^{n-2}(ax)^2+...$$

$$=1+nax+\frac{n(n-1)}{2}a^2x^2=1+6x+\frac{33x^2}{2}$$

Lining up the coefficients:

x: $na=6 \Rightarrow a=\frac{6}{n}$

x^2: $\frac{n(n-1)a^2}{2}=\frac{33}{2} \Rightarrow \frac{n(n-1)36}{n^2}=33$

$\Rightarrow (n - 1)12 = 11n \Rightarrow 12n - 12 = 11n$

$\Rightarrow n = 12$ and $a=\frac{1}{2}$

TRICK
Expand out and line up the coefficients as the binomial is an identity.

[C] PICKING OUT TERMS (Type 3)

Trick: Use the general term $T_{r+1} = \binom{n}{r}(x)^{n-r}(y)^r$

Example 6: Find the seventh term in $(1+\frac{a}{b})^{12}$.

SOLUTION

$(1+\frac{a}{b})^{12}$ [FP = (1), SP = $(\frac{a}{b})$, n =12]

$$T_7 = \binom{12}{6}(1)^6\left(\frac{a}{b}\right)^6 = 924\frac{a^6}{b^6}$$

Trick: Once you know one bit of the general term, you can work out the other two.

Example 7: Find the fourteenth term in $(2y+\frac{1}{y})^{17}$.

SOLUTION

$(2y+\frac{1}{y})^{17}$ [FP = (2y), SP = $(\frac{1}{y})$, n = 17]

$$T_{14} = \binom{17}{13}(2y)^4\left(\frac{1}{y}\right)^{13} = \frac{2380\times16}{y^9} = \frac{38080}{y^9}$$

Example 8: Find the term with x^{10} in $(2x^2 - \frac{3}{x})^{11}$.

SOLUTION

$(2x^2 - \frac{3}{x})^{11}$ [FP = (2x^2), SP = $(-\frac{3}{x})$, n = 11]

$$T_{r+1} = \binom{11}{r}(2x^2)^{11-r}(-\tfrac{3}{x})^r$$

Tidy up the Algebra isolating the x stuff.

$$T_{r+1} = \binom{11}{r}(2)^{11-r}(-3)^r\frac{x^{22-2r}}{x^r} = \binom{11}{r}(2)^{11-r}(-3)^r x^{22-3r}$$

Power of x: 22 - 3r = 10 (Given) $\Rightarrow r = 4$

$$\therefore T_5 = \binom{11}{4}2^7(-3)^4x^{10} = 330\times128\times81\times x^{10} = 3{,}421{,}440x^{10}$$

Example 9: Find the term independent of x in $(3x-\frac{2}{x^2})^{15}$.

SOLUTION

$(3x-\frac{2}{x^2})^{15}$ [FP = $(3x)$, SP = $(-\frac{2}{x^2})$, n = 15]

$$T_{r+1}=\binom{15}{r}(3x)^{15-r}(-\tfrac{2}{x^2})^r=\binom{15}{r}3^{15-r}(-2)^r\frac{x^{15-r}}{x^{2r}}$$

$$=\binom{15}{r}3^{15-r}(-2)^r x^{15-3r}$$

Independent of $x \Rightarrow$ Power of $x = 0$

$\therefore$ $15 - 3r = 0 \Rightarrow r = 5$

$$\therefore T_6=\binom{15}{5}3^{10}(-2)^5x^0=3003\times 59{,}049\times(-32)$$

$$=-5{,}674{,}372{,}704$$

Example 10: Find n and the coefficient of x^3y^4 in $(2x - y)^n$

SOLUTION

$(2x - y)^n$ [FP = $(2x)$, SP = $(-y)$, $n = n$]

$$T_{r+1}=\binom{n}{r}(2x)^{n-r}(-y)^r=\binom{n}{r}2^{n-r}(-1)^r x^{n-r}y^r$$

Power of $x = 3 \Rightarrow n - r = 3$

Power of $y = 4 \Rightarrow r = 4$ $\therefore$ $n = 7$

$$\therefore T_5=\binom{7}{4}2^3(-1)^4x^3y^4=35\times 8x^3y^4=280x^3y^4$$

Therefore coefficient of x^3y^4 is 280.

Example 11: Find the middle term in $(2x-\frac{1}{x^2})^{12}$.

SOLUTION

$(2x-\frac{1}{x^2})^{12}$ [FP = (2x), SP = $(\frac{1}{x^2})$, $n = 12$, $\frac{n}{2} = 6$]

$$\therefore \text{ Middle term is } \binom{12}{6}(2x)^6(-\frac{1}{x^2})^6 = T_7$$

$$\therefore T_7 = 924 \times 64\left(\frac{x^6}{x^{12}}\right) = \frac{59{,}136}{x^6}$$

TRICK

Middle term = $\binom{n}{\frac{n}{2}} x^{\frac{n}{2}} y^{\frac{n}{2}}$

and work backwards.

[D] **HARD QUESTIONS (Type 4)**

These will usually involve $T_{r+1} = \binom{n}{r}(x)^{n-r}(y)^r$

Example 12: In the expansion of $(2 + 3x)^n$ the coefficient of the third term is half the coefficient of the next term. Find n.

SOLUTION

$(2 + 3x)^n$ [FP = (2), SP = (3x), $n = n$]

$$T_3 = \binom{n}{2}(2)^{n-2}(3x)^2 = \binom{n}{2}(2^{n-2})(9x^2)$$

$$T_4 = \binom{n}{3}(2)^{n-3}(3x)^3 = \binom{n}{3}(2^{n-3})(27x^3)$$

$$\therefore \binom{n}{2}(2^{n-2})(9) = \frac{1}{2}\binom{n}{3}(2^{n-3})(27)$$

$$\Rightarrow \frac{n(n-1)}{2}2 = \frac{1}{2}\frac{n(n-1)(n-2)}{6}3 \Rightarrow 4 = n-2 \Rightarrow n = 6$$

Example 13: Find n if the coefficients of x, x^2, x^3 in the expansion of $(1 + x)^n$ are consecutively in an AP.

SOLUTION

$(1 + x)^n$ [FP = (1), SP = (x), $n = n$]

$$T_{r+1} = \binom{n}{r}(1)^{n-r}(x)^r = \binom{n}{r}x^r$$

$$x^1: r = 1 \Rightarrow T_2 = \binom{n}{1}x^1$$

$$x^2: r = 2 \Rightarrow T_3 = \binom{n}{2}x^2$$

$$x^3: r = 3 \Rightarrow T_4 = \binom{n}{3}x^3$$

Coeffs: $\binom{n}{1}, \binom{n}{2}, \binom{n}{3}$

Consecutive in AP $\Rightarrow \binom{n}{2} - \binom{n}{1} = \binom{n}{3} - \binom{n}{2}$

$$\Rightarrow \frac{n(n-1)}{2} - \frac{n}{1} = \frac{n(n-1)(n-2)}{6} - \frac{n(n-1)}{2}$$

$\Rightarrow 3(n - 1) - 6 = (n - 1)(n - 2) - 3(n - 1)$

$\Rightarrow 3n - 9 = n^2 - 3n + 2 - 3n + 3$

$\Rightarrow 0 = n^2 - 9n + 14$

$\Rightarrow 0 = (n - 7)(n - 2)$

$\therefore n = 7, 2$

2 is rejected as $T_4 = \binom{2}{3}$ does not exist.

Exercise 4 (Answers: page **253**)
Binomials

1. Expand out fully and simplify:
(a) $(1 + x)^5$
(b) $(c - d)^6$
(c) $(2 + 3x)^4$
(d) $(2x - \frac{1}{x})^3$
(e) $(x - \frac{1}{y})^4$
(f) $(3x - \frac{1}{x^2})^5$
(g) $(\frac{5}{a} - \frac{b}{3})^4$

2. Write out the first 3 terms and the last 3 terms of:
(a) $(1 + x)^{10}$
(b) $(2 - 3x)^7$
(c) $(x - 1)^{20}$
(d) $(2x - 1)^{12}$
(e) $(x - y)^8$
(f) $(1 + z^2)^{14}$

3. Show
(a) $(1+\sqrt{3})^4 = 28+16\sqrt{3}$
(b) $(1+\sqrt{3})^4 + (1-\sqrt{3})^4 = 56$
(c) $(1-\sqrt{2})^5 = 41-29\sqrt{2}$
(d) $(1+x)^5 + (1-x)^5 = 2+20x^2+10x^4$

4. Find
(a) the 5th. term in $(x^3 - \frac{1}{2x})^6$
(b) the 4th. term in $(2x + \frac{3}{x})^7$
(c) the 16th. term in $(x^2 - \frac{1}{x^3})^{20}$

5. Find
(a) T_5 in $(x - y)^4$
(b) T_7 in $(2 - x)^{13}$
(c) T_5 in $(x - \frac{1}{x})^9$
(d) T_{11} in $(3 - \frac{x}{2})^{15}$
(e) T_8 in $(x - \frac{y}{2})^{11}$
(f) T_3 in $(a^2 + \frac{2}{a^2})^7$

6. Find the middle terms in:
(a) $(x - \frac{1}{x})^8$
(b) $(2x - y^2)^{10}$
(c) $(y + \frac{1}{y^2})^{12}$
(d) $(2 + \frac{a}{2})^8$
(e) $(2a - 3b)^{10}$
(f) $(x^2 - \sqrt{y})^8$

7. Find the term with
(a) a^7 in $(2a - 3b)^9$
(b) x^3 in $(2x - y)^7$
(c) x^7 in $(3x - 2y)^{10}$
(d) x^{14} in $(2x^2 - 3y)^{12}$
(e) a^5 in $(2a - 3)^{11}$
(f) b^4 in $(a - b)^{17}$

8. (a) If $(1+bx)^p = 1+14x+84x^2+\ldots$ find $b, p \in N_0$.

(b) If $(a+x)^n = \frac{243}{32} + \frac{405}{16}x + \ldots$ find $a, n \in N_0$.

(c) If $(1-\frac{a}{x})^n = 1 - \frac{20}{x} + \frac{180}{x^2} + \ldots$ find $a, n \in N_0$.

9. Find the

(a) term independent of x in $(x - \frac{1}{3x})^{18}$

(b) term with x^{-3} in $(x + \frac{1}{x^2})^{12}$

(c) constant term in $(2x^3 - \frac{1}{x})^{12}$

(d) term with x^3 in $(2x + \frac{1}{2x})^{11}$

(e) coefficient of x^9 in $(5x^2 - 4x^3)^4$

(f) coefficient of x^7 in $(2x^2 - \frac{1}{4x})^{11}$

(g) term with $\frac{\sqrt{y}}{x^5}$ in $(\frac{y\sqrt{x}}{3} - \frac{3}{x\sqrt{y}})^{11}$

(h) constant term in $(\sqrt{x} - \frac{2}{x^2})^{10}$

(i) term with a^{12} in $(a^2 + \frac{2}{a})^9$

(j) term with x in $(x^2 + \frac{1}{x})^5$

(k) term with x^{18} in $(x^2 + \frac{3}{x})^{15}$

(l) term independent of x in $(x - \frac{1}{x^2})^{15}$

(m) term with x^{-20} in $(x^2 + \frac{3}{x^3})^{10}$

(n) term with x^8 in $(x^3 - \frac{1}{x})^{12}$

10. (a) Find n and the coefficient of x^3y^4 in $(2x - y)^n$
(b) Find n and the coefficient of x^4y^6 in $(3x^2 + 4y)^{2n}$
(c) Find n and the coefficient of x^6y^{12} in $(x^2 - y^3)^{2n}$

11. In the expansion of $(1 + 2ax)^{15}$ the coefficient of x^2 is $\frac{28}{15}$. Find a, $a > 0$, and the coefficient of x^3.

12. Write the first 3 terms of x in the expansion of $(x + \frac{1}{x})^{12}$, $x > 0$. If $T_6 > T_5$ show $x < \sqrt{\frac{8}{5}}$.

13. Evaluate $5^{10} - \binom{10}{1}5^9\,3^1 + \binom{10}{2}5^8\,3^2 - \ldots\ldots\ldots + 3^{10}$

14. Find the 2 middle terms in the expansion of $\left(x^{\frac{1}{2}} - \frac{y^2}{x^{\frac{1}{3}}}\right)^{11}$.

15. Find n in the expansion of $(a + b)^n$
(i) if the coefficients of the 5th. and 11th. terms are equal,
(ii) if the 9th. and 10th. terms are the middle terms.

16. In the expansion of $(3 + \frac{x}{2})^n$ the coefficients of x^7 and x^8 are equal. Find n.

17. Show $(\sqrt{x^2 + a^2} + x)^5 - (\sqrt{x^2 + a^2} - x)^5$
$= 2x(16x^4 + 20a^2x^2 + 5a^4)$.

18. Prove that the coefficient of x^n in the expansion of $(1 + x)^{2n}$ is twice the coefficient of x^n in the expansion of $(1 + x)^{2n - 1}$.

19. Evaluate (i) $\binom{40}{0} + \binom{40}{1} + \binom{40}{2} + \ldots\ldots\ldots + \binom{40}{40}$

(ii) $\binom{40}{0}-\binom{40}{1}+\binom{40}{2}-\dots\dots\dots+\binom{40}{40}$.

20. Evaluate (i) $\sum_{r=0}^{30}\binom{30}{r}\left(\frac{3}{4}\right)^{r}\left(\frac{1}{4}\right)^{30-r}$,

(ii) $3^8-\binom{8}{1}3^7(2)+\binom{8}{2}3^6(2)^2-\dots\dots\dots+(2)^8$.

21. Expand $(x + y)^5$. By choosing $x = 1$, $y = -1$ show that
${}^5C_0+{}^5C_2+{}^5C_4={}^5C_1+{}^5C_3+{}^5C_5$.

22. Find $a > 0$ which will make the coefficient of x^5 equal to that of x^{15} in $(2x^2 + \frac{a}{x^3})^{10}$.

23. The first 3 terms of $(a-\frac{x}{3})^6$ are $64 - 64x + bx^2$. Find a, b.

24. Expand out $(1 + x)^n$.

(i) By putting $x = 1$ show $\sum_{r=0}^{n} {}^nC_r = 2^n$,

(ii) By putting $x = -1$ show ${}^nC_0+{}^nC_2+\dots\dots = {}^nC_1+{}^nC_3\dots\dots$
i.e. the sum of even BC's = sum of odd BC's.

Use (i) and (ii) to evaluate $\sum_{r=0}^{10}\binom{20}{2r}$.

25. Evaluate (i) $\sum_{r=0}^{8} {}^8C_r(2)^{8-r}$, (ii) $\sum_{r=0}^{10}\binom{10}{r}\left(\frac{1}{4}\right)^{10-r}\left(\frac{3}{4}\right)^{r}$.

SERIES REVISION QUESTIONS

These 3 part questions are similar to the questions on the LC paper. The answers to these questions and hints to help you solve them are available on our website:

www.studentxpress.ie

1 (a) Express $(1+x+x^2+....+x^{n-1})+\dfrac{x^n}{1-x}$ as a single fraction.

(b) Find the term independent of x in $(2x+\frac{1}{x^3})^{12}$.

(c) Show that $\dfrac{1}{(n+1)(n+2)}=\dfrac{1}{n+1}-\dfrac{1}{n+2}$. Hence evaluate

$$\sum_{n=1}^{\infty}\frac{1}{(n+1)(n+2)}.$$

2. (a) Find S_n if $T_n = 3(3n + 1)$.
(b) For series 2.5 + 5.9 + 8.13 + ... find T_n and S_n.

(c) For a geometric series show $\dfrac{S_{2n}-S_n}{S_n}=r^n$.

3. (a) Find S_∞ for GP 1, $\sin^2\theta$, $\sin^4\theta$, ... when $\theta = 60^\circ$.

(b) For series $\dfrac{1}{1.2}+\dfrac{1}{2.3}+\dfrac{1}{3.4}$ find T_n and hence S_n.

(c) (i) Find term with x^{-5} in the expansion of $(2x+\frac{1}{x})^7$,

(ii) Find middle term in $(x-\frac{1}{x})^{10}$.

4. (a) Find the sum of all even numbers between 96 and 180 inclusive divisible by 3.

(b) Show $\frac{1}{(r+2)(r+4)} = \frac{1}{2(r+2)} - \frac{1}{2(r+4)}$ and hence evaluate

$$\sum_{r=1}^{\infty} \frac{1}{(r+2)(r+4)}.$$

(c) Write out the first 4 terms in the binomial expansion $(1 + ax)^n$.

Show that the ratio of the coefficient of x^{r+1} to that of x^r is $\frac{a(n-r)}{(r+1)}$.

5. (a) For series $1 + (1 + 2) + (1 + 2 + 3) + ... + (1 + 2 + ... + n)$ find T_n.
(b) In (a) find S_n.

(c) Evaluate $\sum_{r=1}^{\infty} r(\frac{1}{3})^r$.

6. (a) For series $5 + 55 + 555 + ... = 5 + (5 + 50) + (5 + 50 + 500) + ..$, find T_n.
(b) In (a) find S_n.

(c) Evaluate $\sum_{r=2}^{n} \frac{1}{r^2 - 1}$.

7. If $T_n = (n - 1)^2$, find S_{20}.
(b) Find T_n for the series: $1.3 + 2.5 + 3.7 + ...$
Hence find S_n and S_{20}.
(c) Find n if the coefficients of x^4, x^5 and x^6 in the expansion of $(1 + x)^n$ are consecutively in an AP.

8. (a) Evaluate $\sum_{r=0}^{20}\binom{20}{r}\left(\frac{1}{2}\right)^{20-r}\left(\frac{1}{2}\right)^{r}$.

(b) Evaluate $\sum_{r=0}^{\infty}\left(\frac{x}{1+x}\right)^{r}$ if $x > 0$.

(c) Find the sum of the GS $1 + x + x^2 + ...$ for $|x| < 1$.
By differentiation with respect to x find the sum of the AG:
$1 + 2x + 3x^2 + ...$ for $|x| < 1$.

Deduce the sum of $1 + 2(\frac{1}{2}) + 3(\frac{1}{4}) + ...$

9. (a) Find T_r for the series $1.1 + 2.3 + 3.5 + ...$

Hence show that $\sum_{r=1}^{n} T_r = \frac{1}{6}n(n+1)(4n-1)$.

(b) Find T_r for the series $\frac{1}{2.4} + \frac{1}{3.5} + \frac{1}{4.6} + ...$

Deduce $\sum_{r=1}^{n} T_r = \frac{1}{2}\left(\frac{5}{6} - \frac{1}{n+2} - \frac{1}{n+3}\right)$. Find $\lim_{n\to\infty} S_n$.

(c) Show that $\frac{1}{(n-1)!} - \frac{1}{n!} = \frac{n-1}{n!}$. Hence evaluate $\sum_{n=1}^{n}\left(\frac{n-1}{n!}\right)$.

10. (a) The $n^{\text{th.}}$ term of a series is $n(n + 1)$. Find S_{20}.
(b) (i) The sum of the first 11 terms of an AS is 0. If -10 is the first term, find the sum of the next 11 terms.

(ii) Express $\frac{2}{(n+2)(n+3)}$ in the form $\frac{A}{n+2} + \frac{B}{n+3}$.

Hence evaluate $\sum_{n=1}^{\infty} \frac{2}{(n+2)(n+3)}$.

(c) If a^2, x, b^2 are consecutive terms of an AS, express x in terms of a and b. If a^2, y, b^2 are consecutive terms of a GS, express y in terms of a and b ($y > 0$). Show $x \geq y$.

11. (a) Write $0.\dot{2}\dot{7}$ as an infinite GS and hence as a fraction.
(b) If $T_n = n - n^2$ show $T_{n+1} - T_n = -2n$.

(c) Show $\frac{1}{n^2 + 2n} = \frac{1}{2}\left(\frac{1}{n} - \frac{1}{n+2}\right)$. Hence evaluate $\sum_{r=1}^{n} \frac{1}{r^2 + 2r}$.

Find $\lim_{n \to \infty} S_n$.

12. (a) Evaluate $\sum_{r=0}^{10} \binom{10}{r} \left(\frac{2}{3}\right)^r \left(\frac{4}{3}\right)^{10-r}$.

(b) If $T_n = 3n(4n^2 - 1)$ show $\frac{T_{n+1} - 2T_n + T_{n-1}}{9} = 8n$.

(c) Show $\frac{1}{(n+4)(n+6)} = \frac{1}{2(n+4)} - \frac{1}{2(n+6)}$.

Hence evaluate $\sum_{r=1}^{n} \frac{1}{(r+4)(r+6)}$.

Answers and hints to Series Revision Questions available on:
www.studentxpress.ie

ANSWERS

Exercise 1 [*Series: The* Σ *Notation* (page **221**)]

1 (a) $(1 - 2)^2 + (2 - 2)^2 + (3 - 2)^2 + ... + (n - 2)^2 + ...$

(b) $(2.3 + 5) + (2.4 + 5) + (2.5 + 5) + ... + (2.10 + 5)$

(c) $(\frac{3}{2})^1 + (\frac{3}{2})^2 + (\frac{3}{2})^3 + ... (\frac{3}{2})^n + ...$

(d) $\frac{2-1}{2+2} + \frac{3-1}{3+2} + \frac{4-1}{4+2} + ... + \frac{n-1}{n+2}$

(e) $((\frac{1}{2})^0 - 0) + ((\frac{1}{2})^1 - 2.1) + ((\frac{1}{2})^2 - 2.2) + ... + ((\frac{1}{2})^n - 2n)$

(f) $(\frac{3}{4})^1 + (\frac{3}{4})^2 + (\frac{3}{4})^3 + ...$

(g) $\frac{1}{2^{3-1}} + \frac{1}{2^{3-1}} + ... + \frac{1}{2^{20-1}}$

(h) $(2.1^2 + \frac{5}{1}) + (2.2^2 + \frac{5}{2}) + ... + (2n^2 + \frac{5}{n})$

2. (a) $\sum_{r=1}^{20} r^2$ (b) $\sum_{r=1}^{10} (2r-1)$ (c) $\sum_{r=1}^{25} 4r$

(d) $\sum_{r=1}^{n} \frac{1}{r}$ (e) $\sum_{r=1}^{n} \frac{1}{r!}$ (f) $\sum_{r=1}^{50} r(r+1)$

(g) $\sum_{r=1}^{18} \frac{1}{(r+2)(r+4)}$ (h) $\sum_{r=1}^{\infty} \left(\frac{1}{3}\right)^r$

3. (a) $T_n = \frac{1}{(2n-1)(2n+1)}$ (b) $T_n = \frac{5n-1}{2n-1}$

(c) $T_n = n(n+1)$ (d) $T_n = (n+2)(n+4)$

(e) $T_n = \frac{n^2 - 1}{2n+3}$ (f) $T_n = \frac{n+1}{n+3}$

(g) $T_n = n$ (h) $T_n = (\frac{1}{2})^{n-1}$

Exercise 2 [*Summation Techniques* (page **225**)]

1. (a) 6 (b) 384 (c) 145
   (d) $\frac{n}{6}(2n-1)(n-1)$ (e) $\frac{n}{6}(2n+7)(n+1)$ (f) $\frac{n}{6}(2n^2+9n+13)$
   (g) 3,500 (h) 20,780 (i) 8,555
   (j) 3,515 (k) $1-\frac{1}{2^{10}}$ (l) $\frac{5}{3}$
   (m) $2(1-\frac{1}{2^{n+1}})$ (n) $2(1-\frac{1}{3^n})$ (o) 9
   (p) $56-\frac{1}{2^{10}}$ (q) 1,050 (r) 3,091

2. (a) $T_n = n^2$, $S_n = \frac{n}{6}(n+1)(2n+1)$
   (b) $T_n = (2n-1)^2$, $S_n = \frac{n}{3}(2n-1)(2n+1)$
   (c) $T_n = (2n-1)(2n+1)$, $S_n = \frac{n}{3}(4n^2+6n-1)$
   (d) $T_n = (n+1)n$, $S_n = \frac{n}{3}(n+2)(n+1)$

3. (b) 14 (c) 12

Exercise 3 [*MOD's & AG's* (page **233**)]

1. (a) $1-\frac{1}{n+1}$ (b) $\frac{1}{2}-\frac{1}{2(2n+1)}$ (c) $\frac{9}{40}-\frac{1}{2}(\frac{1}{n+4}+\frac{1}{n+5})$
   (d) $\frac{5}{12}-\frac{1}{2}(\frac{1}{n+2}+\frac{1}{n+3})$ (e) $\frac{4}{25}$

2. (a) $\sqrt{n+1}-1$ (b) $\sqrt{n+1}-1$ (c) log (n + 1)
   (d) $1-\frac{1}{\sqrt{n+1}}$

3. (a) $20(1-\frac{1}{2^n})$, 20 (b) $\frac{1}{8}(2^n-1)$, $\frac{1}{4}$ (c) $\frac{1}{3}(1-\frac{1}{4^l})$, $\frac{1}{3}$
   (d) $\frac{2}{5}((-\frac{2}{3})^n-1)$, $-\frac{2}{5}$ (e) $3(1-\frac{1}{2^n})$, 3 (f) $\frac{1}{9}(4^n-1)$, ∞
   (g) $\frac{8}{5}(1-(-\frac{1}{4})^n)$, $\frac{8}{5}$ (h) $1-(-3)^n$, ∞ (i) $\frac{3}{2}(1-(\frac{2}{3})^n)$, $\frac{3}{2}$

4. (a) 1 (b) $\tan^2 x$ (c) x
(d) 2 (e) ∞

5. (a) $\frac{x}{(1-x)^2}$ (b) 3 (c) $\frac{7}{4}$
(d) 2

Exercise 4 [*Binomials* (page **243**)]

1. (a) $1 + 5x + 10x^2 + 10x^3 + 5x^4 + x^5$
(b) $c^6 - 6c^5d^4 + 15c^4d^2 - 20c^3d^3 + 15c^2d^4 - 6cd^5 + d^6$
(c) $16 + 96x + 216x^2 + 216x^3 + 81x^4$
(d) $8x^3 - 12x + \frac{6}{x} - \frac{1}{x^3}$
(e) $x^4 - \frac{4x^3}{y} + \frac{6x^2}{y^2} - \frac{4x}{y^3} + \frac{1}{y^4}$
(f) $243x^5 - 405x^2 + \frac{270}{x} - \frac{90}{x^4} + \frac{15}{x^7} - \frac{1}{x^{10}}$
(g) $\frac{625}{a^4} - \frac{500b}{3a^3} + \frac{50b^2}{3a^2} - \frac{20b^3}{27a} + \frac{b^4}{81}$

2. (a) $1 + 10x + 45x^2 + ... + 45x^8 + 10x^9 + x^{10}$
(b) $128 - 1344x + 6048x^2 + ... - 20412x^5 + 10206x^6 - 2187x^7$
(c) $x^{20} - 20x^{19} + 190x^{18} + ... + 190x^2 - 20x + 1$
(d) $4096x^{12} - 24576x^{11} + 67584x^{10} - ... + 264x^2 - 24x + 1$
(e) $x^8 - 8x^7y + 28x^6y^2 - ... + 28x^2y^6 - 8xy^7 + y^8$
(f) $1 + 14z^2 + 91z^4 + ... + 91z^{24} + 14z^{26} + z^{28}$

4. (a) $\frac{15x^2}{16}$ (b) $15120x$ (c) $-\frac{15504}{x^{35}}$

5. (a) y^4 (b) $219648x^6$ (c) $126x$
(d) $\frac{729729}{1024}x^{10}$ (e) $-\frac{165}{64}x^4y^7$ (f) $84a^6$

6. (a) 70 (b) $-8064x^5y^{10}$ (c) $\frac{924}{y^6}$
(d) $70a^4$ (e) $-1959552a^5b^5$ (f) $70x^8y^2$

7. (a) $41472a^7b^2$ (b) $280x^3y^4$ (c) $-2099520x^7y^3$
(d) $-792\times128\times243x^{14}y^5$ (e) $462\times32\times729a^5$
(f) $2380a^{13}b^4$

8. (a) $p = 7, b = 2$ (b) $n = 5,\ a = \frac{3}{2}$ (c) $n = 10, a = 2$

9. (a) $-\frac{48620}{19683}$ (b) $792x^{-3}$ (c) -1760
(d) $2640x^{3}$ (e) $-2000x^{9}$ (f) $-\frac{231}{8}x^{7}$
(g) $-8910\frac{\sqrt{y}}{x^5}$ (h) 180 (i) $144a^{12}$
(j) $10x$ (k) $110565x^{18}$ (l) -3003
(m) $295245x^{-20}$ (n) $-792x^{8}$

10. (a) $n = 9$; -2016 (b) $n = 4$; 1032192 (c) $n = \frac{7}{2}$; 35

11. $a = \frac{1}{15}$, $\frac{728}{675}$

12. $x^{12} + 12x^{10} + 66x^{8}$

13. 2^{10}

14. $T_6 = -462x^{\frac{4}{3}}y^{10}$; $T_7 = 462x^{\frac{1}{2}}y^{12}$

15. (i) 14, (ii) 17

16. 55

19. (i) 2^{40}, (ii) 0

20. (i) 1, (ii) 1

22. $\frac{1}{\sqrt{3}}$

23. $a = 2,\ b = \frac{80}{3}$

24. $1+\binom{n}{1}x+\binom{n}{2}x^2+\ldots+\binom{n}{n}x^n$, 2^{19}

25. (i) 6561, (ii) 1

DIFFERENTIATION

1. UNDERSTANDING DIFFERENTIATION

1.1 THE IDEA

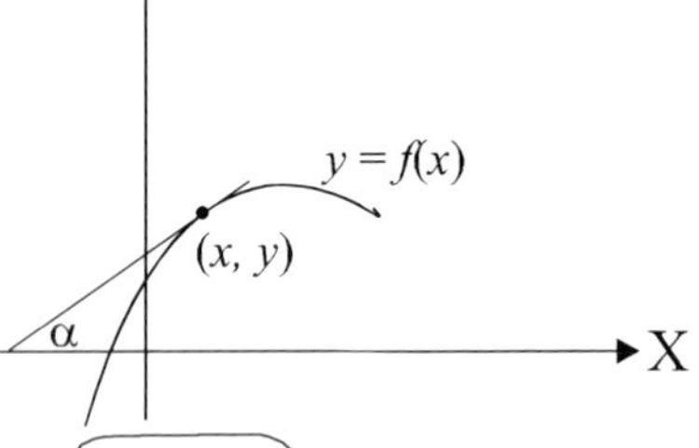

Diffo can be viewed in 2 ways:

[A] **Geometrical**: The slope of the curve changes from point to point.

$\frac{dy}{dx} = f'(x) = \tan\alpha = m =$ slope of tangent to the curve at the point (x, y)

Note: All functions on the LC course are curves.

TRICK

If a point is on a curve, it satisfies the equation of the curve and the equation of the tangent. So plonk it into both equations.

Example 1: If $(t, 2)$ is on the curve $y = \frac{x-1}{x+3}$ find t.

SOLUTION

$$y = \frac{x-1}{x+3}$$

Plonk in $(t, 2)$: $2 = \frac{t-1}{t+3} \Rightarrow 2t + 6 = t - 1 \Rightarrow t = -7$

Example 2: If $f(x) = x^2 - 2x + 1$ find (i) $f(1)$, (ii) $f(a)$, (iii) $f(t - 2)$, (iv) $f(x + 1)$, (v) $f(x + h)$, (vi) $f(x + \Delta x)$

SOLUTION

$f(x) = x^2 - 2x + 1$

(i) $f(1) = (1)^2 - 2(1) + 1 = 0$

(ii) $f(a) = a^2 - 2a + 1$

(iii) $f(t - 2) = (t - 2)^2 - 2(t - 2) + 1 = t^2 - 6t + 9$

(iv) $f(x + 1) = (x + 1)^2 - 2(x + 1) + 1 = x^2$

(v) $f(x + h) = (x + h)^2 - 2(x + h) + 1 = x^2 + 2xh + h^2 - 2x - 2h + 1$

(vi) $f(x + \Delta x) = (x + \Delta x)^2 - 2(x + \Delta x) + 1$

$= x^2 + 2x\Delta x + (\Delta x)^2 - 2x - 2\Delta x + 1$

In **Example** 2 we calculated all y co-ordinates on the curve $y = f(x)$ corresponding to the x co-ordinate.

$y = f(x) = x^2 - 2x + 1$

$(t - 2, t^2 - 6t + 9)$

> **TRICK**
>
> To find the y co-ordinate of a point on a curve corresponding to the x co-ordinate, simply plonk the x co-ordinate into the equation.

So for $x = t - 2$, $y = f(t - 2) = t^2 - 6t + 9$

[B] **Rate of Change** (ROC)

$\frac{dy}{dx}$ is the end result in a limiting process of calculating:

$$\frac{\text{Change in } y}{\text{Change in } x} = \frac{\Delta y}{\Delta x}$$

$\frac{dy}{dx} = 3 \Rightarrow \frac{\Delta y}{\Delta x} \approx 3$, i.e. $\Delta y \approx 3\Delta x$,

i.e. y is changing 3 times as fast as x at a particular point on the curve. $\frac{dy}{dx} = 3$ means the rate of change of y with respect to (wrt) x at a particular point on the curve is 3.

1.2 DIFFERENTIATION FROM FIRST PRINCIPLES (FP)

This is the starting point of learning how to diffo. It leads on to developing the rules of diffo.

[A] **Slope of a straight line**

Trick: To find the slope of a straight line you need 2 points.

(1, 4) (3, 7)

$$\text{Slope } m = \frac{\text{Change in } y}{\text{Change in } x} = \frac{\Delta y}{\Delta x} = \frac{7-4}{3-1} = \frac{3}{2}$$

[B] **Slope of a tangent to a curve** $y = f(x)$ at a point (x, y) on the curve.

Δx = Change in x

Δy = Change in y

$$\text{Slope of L} = \frac{\Delta y}{\Delta x} = \frac{f(x+\Delta x) - f(x)}{\Delta x}$$

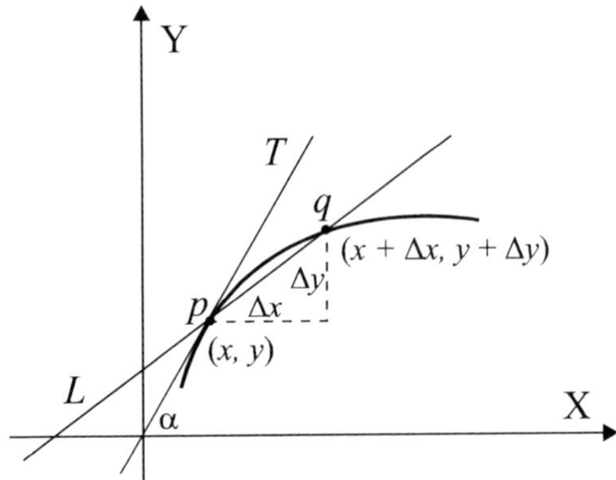

Now let q slide along the curve towards p, i.e. $\Delta x \to 0$ and $\Delta y \to 0$.

Evaluating $\frac{\Delta y}{\Delta x}$ each time, each answer gets closer and closer to the slope of T. $\frac{dy}{dx} = f'(x)$ is the end of this process.

$$f'(x) = \frac{dy}{dx} = \tan\alpha = m = \lim_{\Delta x \to 0} \frac{\Delta y}{\Delta x} = \lim_{\Delta x \to 0} \frac{f(x+\Delta x) - f(x)}{\Delta x}$$

$\Delta x \to 0$ and $\Delta y \to 0$ is a mathematical way of saying q slides down the curve to p.

Example 3: Find $\frac{dy}{dx}$ for $y = x^2$ from first principles.

SOLUTION

$y = f(x) = x^2$ is guiding formula.

$$
\begin{aligned}
y + \Delta y &= (x + \Delta x)^2 = x^2 + 2x\Delta x + (\Delta x)^2 \\
y &= x^2 \qquad\qquad\;\; = x^2 \\
\hline
\Delta y &= 2x\Delta x + (\Delta x)^2 \text{ by subtraction}
\end{aligned}
$$

$$\therefore \frac{\Delta y}{\Delta x} = 2x + \Delta x$$

$$\therefore \frac{dy}{dx} = \lim_{\Delta x \to 0} \frac{\Delta y}{\Delta x} = 2x$$

(x + Δx, y + Δy)
(x, y)

So for the curve $y = x^2 \Rightarrow \frac{dy}{dx} = 2x$

This is a very powerful result as you can now find the slope of the tangent to the curve $y = x^2$ at any point.

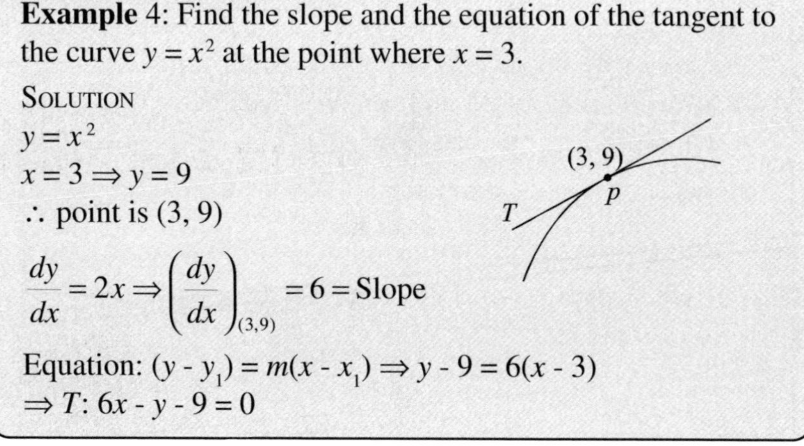

Example 4: Find the slope and the equation of the tangent to the curve $y = x^2$ at the point where $x = 3$.

SOLUTION

$y = x^2$

$x = 3 \Rightarrow y = 9$

$\therefore$ point is $(3, 9)$

$$\frac{dy}{dx} = 2x \Rightarrow \left(\frac{dy}{dx}\right)_{(3,9)} = 6 = \text{Slope}$$

Equation: $(y - y_1) = m(x - x_1) \Rightarrow y - 9 = 6(x - 3)$

$\Rightarrow T: 6x - y - 9 = 0$

Trick: In all questions on curves always draw a rough squiggle. Draw a tangent and mark the point of intersection p. The function is the curve.

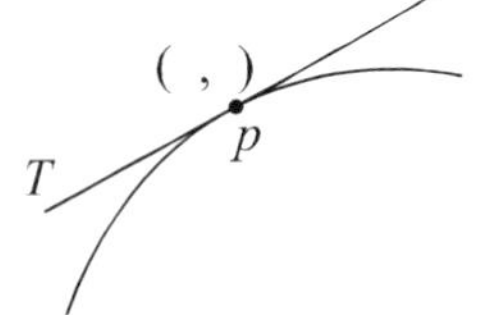

[C] **Types of functions to be differentiated from first principles**

There are only 7 to be diffed by FP:

1. $y = x$ (Easy: Do it yourself; Ans: $\frac{dy}{dx} = 1$)
2. $y = x^2$ (Already done: Example 3)
3. $y = x^3$ [**Trick**: Expand out brackets]
4. $y = \frac{1}{x}$ [**Trick**: Get a common denominator]
5. $y = \sqrt{x}$ [**Trick**: Rationalise the numerator]
6. $y = \cos x$ [**Trick**: page 9 of tables (Sumprods)]
7. $y = \sin x$ [**Trick**: page 9 of tables (Sumprods)]

[D] **Steps for FP:**

STEPS

1. Write down the function $y = f(x)$.
2. Replace y by $y + \Delta y$ and x by $x + \Delta x$ in the function $f(x)$.
3. Subtract y from $y + \Delta y$ and simplify by either:
   (i) Expanding brackets (x, x^2, x^3),
   (ii) Common denominator $(\frac{1}{x})$,
   (iii) Getting rid of surd in numerator $(\sqrt{x})$,
   (iv) Changing sums into products ($\sin x$, $\cos x$).
4. Divide Δy by Δx and take $\lim_{\Delta x \to 0} \frac{\Delta y}{\Delta x} = \frac{dy}{dx}$.

Example 5: Differentiate $y = x^3$ from first principles.

SOLUTION

$y = x^3$ (Guiding Function)

$$y + \Delta y = (x + \Delta x)^3 = x^3 + 3x^2\Delta x + 3x(\Delta x)^2 + (\Delta x)^3$$

$$y = x^3$$

$$\Delta y = 3x^2\Delta x + 3x(\Delta x)^2 + (\Delta x)^3$$

$$\therefore \frac{\Delta y}{\Delta x} = 3x^2 + 3x\Delta x + (\Delta x)^2$$

$$\therefore \frac{dy}{dx} = \lim_{\Delta x \to 0} \frac{\Delta y}{\Delta x} = 3x^2$$

Example 6: Differentiate $y = \frac{1}{x}$ from first principles.

SOLUTION

$y = \frac{1}{x}$ (Guiding Function)

$$y + \Delta y = \frac{1}{x + \Delta x}$$

$$y = \frac{1}{x}$$

$$\Delta y = \frac{1}{x + \Delta x} - \frac{1}{x} = \frac{x - x - \Delta x}{x(x + \Delta x)} = \frac{-\Delta x}{x(x + \Delta x)}$$

$$\therefore \frac{\Delta y}{\Delta x} = -\frac{1}{x(x + \Delta x)}$$

$$\therefore \frac{dy}{dx} = \lim_{\Delta x \to 0} \frac{\Delta y}{\Delta x} = -\frac{1}{x^2}$$

Example 7: Differentiate $y = \sqrt{x}$ from first principles.

SOLUTION

$y = f(x) = \sqrt{x}$ (Guiding function)

$y + \Delta y = \sqrt{x + \Delta x}$

$y = \sqrt{x}$

$$\therefore \Delta y = \sqrt{x+\Delta x} - \sqrt{x} = \frac{\sqrt{x+\Delta x} - \sqrt{x}}{1} \times \frac{\sqrt{x+\Delta x} + \sqrt{x}}{\sqrt{x+\Delta x} + \sqrt{x}}$$

$$\therefore \Delta y = \frac{x + \Delta x - x}{\sqrt{x+\Delta x} - \sqrt{x}} = \frac{\Delta x}{\sqrt{x+\Delta x} - \sqrt{x}}$$

$$\therefore \frac{\Delta y}{\Delta x} = \frac{1}{\sqrt{x+\Delta x} - \sqrt{x}}$$

$$\therefore \frac{dy}{dx} = \lim_{\Delta x \to 0} \frac{\Delta y}{\Delta x} = \frac{1}{2\sqrt{x}}$$

Example 8: Differentiate from first principles $y = \cos x$.

SOLUTION

$y = f(x) = \cos x$ (Guiding function)

$y + \Delta y \quad = \cos(x + \Delta x)$

$y \quad = \cos x$

$$\therefore \Delta y = \cos(x+\Delta x) - \cos x = -2\sin(x + \tfrac{\Delta x}{2})\sin(\tfrac{\Delta x}{2})$$

$$\therefore \frac{\Delta y}{\Delta x} = -\sin(x + \tfrac{\Delta x}{2})\frac{\sin(\frac{\Delta x}{2})}{(\frac{\Delta x}{2})}$$

$$\therefore \frac{dy}{dx} = \lim_{\Delta x \to 0} \frac{\Delta y}{\Delta x} = -\sin x \,.\, 1 \;(\lim_{\theta \to 0} \frac{\sin\theta}{\theta} = 1)$$

$= -\sin x$

Example 9: Differentiate from first principles $y = \sin x$.

SOLUTION

$y = \sin x$

$y + \Delta y = \sin(x + \Delta x)$

$y = \sin x$

$$\therefore \Delta y = \sin(x+\Delta x) - \sin x = 2\cos(x+\tfrac{\Delta x}{2})\sin(\tfrac{\Delta x}{2})$$

$$\therefore \frac{\Delta y}{\Delta x} = \cos(x+\tfrac{\Delta x}{2})\frac{\sin(\frac{\Delta x}{2})}{(\frac{\Delta x}{2})}$$

$$\therefore \frac{dy}{dx} = \lim_{\Delta x \to 0}\frac{\Delta y}{\Delta x} = \cos x \,.\, 1 \ (\lim_{\theta \to 0}\frac{\sin\theta}{\theta} = 1)$$

$= \cos x$

2. HOW TO DIFFERENTIATE

Diffo from FP is very tedious. From it, however, general rules of diffo have been developed that apply to all functions.

2.1 RULES OF DIFFERENTIATION (u and v are functions of x)

R1: THE SUM RULE

If $y = u + v$ then $\dfrac{dy}{dx} = \dfrac{du}{dx} + \dfrac{dv}{dx}$

TRICK

If y = sum of functions just diff each one individually.

R2: THE CONSTANT RULE

If $y = c$ (constant) then $\dfrac{dy}{dx} = 0$

$\Rightarrow$ Slope $= \dfrac{dy}{dx} = 0$

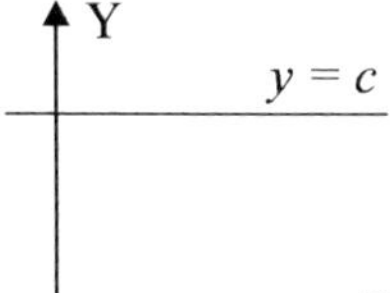

Graph is dead flat

R3: **THE MULTIPLICATION BY A CONSTANT RULE**

If $y = cu$ then $\frac{dy}{dx} = c\frac{du}{dx}$,

c is a constant.

TRICK

Just write down the constant again and multiply it by the function differentiated.

R4: **THE PRODUCT RULE**

If $y = u.v$ then $\frac{dy}{dx} = u\frac{dv}{dx} + v\frac{du}{dx}$

Trick: Remember it as (1st.)(Diff 2nd.) + (2nd.)(Diff 1st.)

R5: **THE QUOTIENT RULE**

If $y = \frac{u}{v}$ then $\frac{dy}{dx} = \frac{v\frac{du}{dx} - u\frac{dv}{dx}}{v^2}$

Trick: Remember it as

$$\frac{\text{(Bottom)(Diff Top) - (Top)(Diff Bottom)}}{\text{(Bottom)}^2}$$

R6: **THE CHAIN RULE**

If y is a function of u and u is a function of x then

$$\frac{dy}{dx} = \frac{dy}{du} \times \frac{du}{dx}$$

Notes on the Chain Rule:

1. This is the most powerful of all the 6 rules and is used to differentiate functions like $(x^2 - 1)^{\frac{1}{2}}$, sin $(2x^2 - 3)$ and e^{4x^3-2}.

2. This chain rule is like any other chain rule involving 3 quantities: $y \to u \to x$. The letter u is the link in the chain.
If A runs 3 times as fast as B and B runs 4 times as fast as C then A runs 12 times as fast as C.
Mathematically:

$$\text{If } \frac{dA}{dB} = 3 \text{ and } \frac{dB}{dC} = 4 \text{ then } \frac{dA}{dC} = \frac{dA}{dB} \times \frac{dB}{dC} = 3 \times 4 = 12.$$

2.2 DIFFERENTIATING FUNCTIONS

There are 5 different types of function to be differentiated on the LC course. They all have their basic x variable result on page 41 of the tables. You must be able to adapt this for $f(x)$.

[A] Algebraic (**Al**) Functions,
[B] Trigonometric (**Trig**) Functions,
[C] Exponential (**Expo**) Functions,
[D] Logarithmic (**Log**) Functions,
[E] Inverse Trigonometric (**IT**) Functions.

STEPS FOR DIFFO:

STEPS

1. Tidy up the algebra if possible.
2. Look at the function and decide on a rule.
3. Other rules may have to be used as you go along.
4. Diffo and tidy up the algebra.
5. Tidy up at the end.

[A] **Differentiating Algebraic (Al) Functions**

$$y = x^p \Rightarrow \frac{dy}{dx} = px^{p-1}$$

$$y = [f(x)]^p \Rightarrow \frac{dy}{dx} = p[f(x)]^{p-1} \times f'(x)$$

TRICK
When x is replaced by $f(x)$, you do the basic rule on the function and then multiply by $f'(x)$. This is the chain rule.

Example 1: Differentiate $y = x^4$.

SOLUTION

$$y = x^4 \Rightarrow \frac{dy}{dx} = 4x^3$$

TRICK

Slide the power down in front of the variable and take 1 away from the power.

Example 2: Differentiate $y = x^{\frac{3}{2}}$.

SOLUTION

$$y = x^{\frac{3}{2}} \Rightarrow \frac{dy}{dx} = \tfrac{3}{2}x^{\frac{1}{2}}$$

Example 3: Differentiate $y = (2x-1)^5$.

SOLUTION

$$y = (2x-1)^5 \Rightarrow \frac{dy}{dx} = 5(2x-1)^4 \times 2 = 10(2x-1)^4$$

Example 4: Differentiate $y = \dfrac{4x^2-1}{7}$.

SOLUTION

$$y = \frac{4x^2-1}{7} \Rightarrow y = \tfrac{1}{7}(4x^2-1)$$

$$\therefore \frac{dy}{dx} = \tfrac{1}{7}(8x) = \tfrac{8x}{7}$$

Example 5: Differentiate $y = \frac{2}{x} - \frac{1}{3x^2}$.

SOLUTION

$$y = \tfrac{2}{x} - \tfrac{1}{3x^2} \Rightarrow y = 2x^{-1} - \tfrac{1}{3}x^{-2}$$

$$\therefore \frac{dy}{dx} = -2x^{-2} + \tfrac{2}{3}x^{-3} = -\tfrac{2}{x^2} + \tfrac{2}{3x^3}$$

Example 6: Differentiate $y=\dfrac{2x}{\sqrt{1-x^2}}$.

SOLUTION

Start with the quotient rule.

$$y=\frac{2x}{(1-x^2)^{\frac{1}{2}}}$$

$$y=\frac{2x}{\sqrt{1-x^2}}\Rightarrow\frac{dy}{dx}=\frac{(1-x^2)^{\frac{1}{2}}(2)-2x.\frac{1}{2}(1-x^2)^{-\frac{1}{2}}(-2x)}{(1-x^2)}$$

Tidy up:

$$\Rightarrow\frac{dy}{dx}=\frac{2(1-x^2)^{\frac{1}{2}}+2x^2(1-x^2)^{-\frac{1}{2}}}{(1-x^2)}.\frac{(1-x^2)^{\frac{1}{2}}}{(1-x^2)^{\frac{1}{2}}}$$

$$=\frac{2(1-x^2)+2x^2}{(1-x^2)^{\frac{3}{2}}}=\frac{2(1-x^2+x^2)}{(1-x^2)^{\frac{3}{2}}}=\frac{2}{(1-x^2)^{\frac{3}{2}}}$$

Example 7: Differentiate $y=\left(\dfrac{2-x^2}{2+x^2}\right)^{\frac{1}{3}}$.

SOLUTION

$$\frac{dy}{dx}=\frac{1}{3}\left(\frac{2-x^2}{2+x^2}\right)^{-\frac{2}{3}}\left\{\frac{(2+x^2)(-2x)-(2-x^2)(2x)}{(2+x^2)^2}\right\}$$

$$=\frac{1}{3}\left(\frac{2+x^2}{2-x^2}\right)^{\frac{2}{3}}\frac{2x(-2-x^2-2+x^2)}{(2+x^2)^2}=\frac{-8x}{3(2-x^2)^{\frac{2}{3}}(2+x^2)^{\frac{4}{3}}}$$

Exercise 1 (Answers: page **300**)
Algebraic Differentiation

1. Differentiate with respect to x:
(a) x^4
(b) $-x$
(c) $\frac{1}{3}x^3$
(d) $6\sqrt{x}$
(e) $2x^2 - 5$
(f) $\frac{5}{x}$
(g) $x + \frac{1}{x}$
(h) $\frac{2}{x} - \sqrt{x}$
(i) $\frac{1}{5x}$
(j) $\frac{x^3-3}{x}$
(k) $(x - 1)(x^2 - 2)$
(l) $(2x^2 + 5)^2$
(m) $\sqrt{x}(x^2 + 2x + 3)$
(n) $\frac{x^2-5}{\sqrt{x}}$
(o) $\frac{x^n+1}{x}$
(p) $\dfrac{x^4 + 6x - 3}{x^{\frac{1}{3}}}$
(q) $ax^4 - cx^2$
(r) $ax^7 - 4bx^3$
(s) $2x^{\frac{4}{3}} - 3x^{\frac{2}{3}}$
(t) $\frac{\sqrt{x}}{2} + \frac{3}{\sqrt{x}}$
(u) $(4 - \frac{3}{x^2})^3$

2. Differentiate with respect to x:
(a) $x^2(2x - 1)$
(b) $x(3x - 2)$
(c) $(2x + 3)(4x - 5)$
(d) $(x^2 - 3)^3$
(e) $(x + 5)(x - 3)(x - 7)$
(f) $(x^2 - x + 6)(x^3 - x^2)$
(g) $(x + \sqrt{x})(x - \sqrt{x})$
(h) $(5 - \frac{2}{x})(4x - \frac{3}{\sqrt{x}})$

3. Differentiate with respect to x:
(a) $\frac{5x}{x-2}$
(b) $\frac{x-1}{x+1}$
(c) $\frac{4x^2}{7x^3-5}$
(d) $\frac{x^2+4x-3}{2x^2-3x+1}$
(e) $\frac{(x-1)^2}{2x+3}$
(f) $\frac{c-x}{a+x}$, a, c constants
(g) $\frac{ax^2+bx+c}{dx+g}$, a, b, c, d, g constants

(h) $\frac{4-x^2}{4+x^2}$

(i) $\frac{\sqrt{x}-1}{\sqrt{x}+1}$

(j) $\dfrac{x^{\frac{2}{3}}-6}{x^{\frac{1}{3}}+1}$

4. Differentiate with respect to x:
(a) $(3x^2 - 5)^3$
(b) $(6x^2 + 5)^{48}$
(c) $(1-\frac{1}{x})^3$
(d) $(3\sqrt{x}-2x)^{12}$
(e) $(x-\frac{1}{x})^{\frac{1}{2}}$
(f) $(\frac{2}{\sqrt{x}}+1)^{-1}$
(g) $\frac{1}{(3x^2+2)}$
(h) $\frac{1}{1+\sqrt{x}}$
(i) $(7x^2-4)^{\frac{1}{3}}$
(j) $(1-\sqrt{x})^{\frac{1}{3}}$

5. Differentiate with respect to x:
(a) $x^2(2x - 1)^4$
(b) $x(3x - 2)^3$
(c) $(2x - 1)^2(3x + 1)^3$
(d) $(3-2x)\sqrt{x}$
(e) $x\sqrt{x+1}$
(f) $(2+x^2)\sqrt{3-2x}$
(g) $x^2\sqrt{a^2-x^2}$, a constant
(h) $x^2\sqrt{x-1}$
(i) $(2x+3)\sqrt{x^2+4}$
(j) $(x^4-\frac{1}{x^2})^3$
(k) $\frac{1}{\sqrt{1+x}}$
(l) $\frac{1}{(2-5x^3)^2}$
(m) $x^n(1+x^n)$

6. Differentiate with respect to x:
(a) $\dfrac{x}{(1-x)^3}$
(b) $\dfrac{3x+1}{(3x-1)^2}$
(c) $\dfrac{(x+1)^2}{x-1}$
(d) $\dfrac{x^2+x+1}{(x^2-x+1)^2}$
(e) $\dfrac{\sqrt{a^2-x^2}}{x}$
(f) $\dfrac{\sqrt{a}+\sqrt{x}}{\sqrt{a}-\sqrt{x}}$, a constant
(g) $\left(\dfrac{2x-3}{3x+2}\right)^3$

(h) $\left(\frac{1+2x}{1-2x}\right)^{\frac{1}{2}}$

(i) $\left(\frac{ax+b}{cx+d}\right)^{n}$, a, b, c, d constants

(j) $\frac{x^2}{(1+x^2)^{\frac{3}{2}}}$

(k) $\left(1+\frac{1}{x^2}\right)^{\frac{3}{2}}$

(l) $\frac{x^{\frac{3}{2}}}{(1+x)^{\frac{1}{2}}}$

(m) $\left(\frac{1-x}{1+x}\right)^{\frac{5}{2}}$

(n) $\frac{1}{3(2-3x)^3}$

(o) $\frac{1}{\sqrt{2ax-x^2}}$, a constant

(p) $\left(\sqrt{x}-\frac{1}{\sqrt{x}}\right)^2$

(q) $\sqrt{\frac{1-cx}{1+cx}}$

(r) $\left(\frac{2-5x}{2+5x}\right)^{\frac{1}{3}}$

(s) $\frac{\sqrt{1-3x}}{(1+2x)^{\frac{1}{3}}}$

(t) $\frac{2}{x+2\sqrt{x}}$

7. Find $\frac{dy}{dx}$ if:

(a) $y=x^{\frac{2}{3}}-a^{\frac{2}{3}}$, a constant

(b) $y=\frac{a+bx+cx^2}{x}$, a, b, c constants

(c) $y=\frac{\sqrt{x}}{2}-\frac{2}{\sqrt{x}}$

(d) $y=\frac{a+bx+cx^2}{\sqrt{x}}$, a, b, c constants

(e) $y=\sqrt{1-2x}$

(f) $y=\left(a-\frac{b}{x}\right)^2$, a, b constants

(g) $y=x\sqrt{a+bx}$, a, b constants

(h) $y=x\sqrt{x^2+9}$

(i) $y=\frac{9+x^2}{9-x^2}$

(j) $y=\frac{x^3}{\sqrt{a^2-x^2}}$, a constant

(k) $y=\sqrt{\frac{1-3x}{1+3x}}$

(l) $y=x(2+3x)^{\frac{1}{3}}$

(m) $y=\left(\frac{2+3x}{2-3x}\right)^{\frac{1}{4}}$

(n) $y=\frac{(a+bx)^{\frac{1}{3}}}{x}$, a, b constants

(o) $y=2^3$

(p) $y=5\sqrt{a^2-x^2}$, a constant

(q) $y=(a^{\frac{3}{5}}-x^{\frac{3}{5}})^{\frac{5}{3}}$, a constant

(r) $y=(x+2)^2\sqrt{x^2+2}$

(s) $y=\left(\frac{x^2+2}{x^2+1}\right)^5$

(t) $y=(x^5-x^{10})^{20}$

[B] Differentiating Trigonometric (Trig) Functions

TABLE OF DIFFERENTIATION OF TRIG FUNCTIONS

Sin: $y = \sin x \Rightarrow \frac{dy}{dx} = \cos x$

$y = \sin f(x) \Rightarrow \frac{dy}{dx} = \cos f(x) \times f'(x)$

Cos: $y = \cos x \Rightarrow \frac{dy}{dx} = -\sin x$

$y = \cos f(x) \Rightarrow \frac{dy}{dx} = -\sin f(x) \times f'(x)$

Tan: $y = \tan x \Rightarrow \frac{dy}{dx} = \sec^2 x$

$y = \tan f(x) \Rightarrow \frac{dy}{dx} = \sec^2 f(x) \times f'(x)$

Cosec: $y = \operatorname{cosec} x \Rightarrow \frac{dy}{dx} = -\operatorname{cosec} x \cot x$

$y = \operatorname{cosec} f(x) \Rightarrow \frac{dy}{dx} = -\operatorname{cosec} f(x) \cot f(x) \times f'(x)$

Sec: $y = \sec x \Rightarrow \frac{dy}{dx} = \sec x \tan x$

$y = \sec f(x) \Rightarrow \frac{dy}{dx} = \sec f(x) \tan f(x) \times f'(x)$

Cot: $y = \cot x \Rightarrow \frac{dy}{dx} = -\operatorname{cosec}^2 x$

$y = \cot f(x) \Rightarrow \frac{dy}{dx} = -\operatorname{cosec}^2 f(x) \times f'(x)$

TRICK

When x is replaced by $f(x)$, do the basic trig diffo rule on the function and then multiply by $f'(x)$. This is the chain rule.

Trigonometric Algebra

TrigAl is on page 9 of the tables. However, some results should be noted.

$$\sin^2 x + \cos^2 x = 1$$
$$\sin 2x = 2\sin x \cos x$$
$$\cos 2x = \cos^2 x - \sin^2 x$$
Change products into sums

Example 8: If $y = \cos^2 3x - \sin^2 3x$ find $\frac{dy}{dx}$.

SOLUTION

$y = \cos^2 3x - \sin^2 3x = \cos 6x$

$\frac{dy}{dx} = -6\sin 6x$

Example 9: Differentiate $y = \tan\left(\frac{x}{4}\right)$.

SOLUTION

$y = \tan\left(\frac{x}{4}\right) = \tan\left(\frac{1}{4}x\right) \Rightarrow \frac{dy}{dx} = \frac{1}{4}\sec^2\left(\frac{1}{4}x\right)$

Example 10: Differentiate $y = \cos(x^2 + 3)$

SOLUTION

$y = \cos(x^2 + 3) \Rightarrow \frac{dy}{dx} = -\sin(x^2 + 3) \times 2x \;= -2x\sin(x^2 + 3)$

Example 11: Differentiate $y = \frac{\sin 3x}{7}$.

SOLUTION

$y = \frac{\sin 3x}{7} = \frac{1}{7}\sin 3x$

$\Rightarrow \frac{dy}{dx} = \frac{1}{7}\cos 3x.3 = \frac{3}{7}\cos 3x$

Example 12: Differentiate $y = \sec(5x^2 - 1)$.

SOLUTION

$$y = \sec(5x^2 - 1)$$

$$\frac{dy}{dx} = \sec(5x^2 - 1)\tan(5x^2 - 1).10x$$

$$= 10x\sec(5x^2 - 1)\tan(5x^2 - 1)$$

Example 13: Differentiate $y = \sec^3(5x^2 - 1)$.

SOLUTION

$$y = [\sec(5x^2 - 1)]^3$$

$$\frac{dy}{dx} = 3[\text{Yoke}]^2 \times \text{Differentiation of the Yoke in its own right}$$

$$= 3[\sec(5x^2 - 1)]^2 \times \sec(5x^2 - 1)\tan(5x^2 - 1).10x$$

$$= 30x\sec^3(5x^2 - 1)\tan(5x^2 - 1)$$

TRICK

The angle stays the same from the start of the differentiation to the end.

Example 14: If $y = \dfrac{2\sin 3x}{\sec 2x}$.

SOLUTION

$$y = \frac{2\sin 3x}{\sec 2x} = 2\sin 3x\cos 2x = \sin 5x + \sin x$$

$$\Rightarrow \frac{dy}{dx} = 5\cos 5x + \cos x$$

Trick: All trig diffo is done in radians because the diffo of sin x and cos x depend on the result $\lim_{\theta \to 0} \dfrac{\sin\theta}{\theta} = 1$ which only works iff θ is in radians.

Example 15: Find $\frac{dy}{dx}$ at $x = \frac{\pi}{6}$ if $y = \sin^3 2x$.

SOLUTION

$$y = (\sin 2x)^3 \Rightarrow \frac{dy}{dx} = 3(\sin 2x)^2.\cos 2x.2$$

$$= 6(\sin 2x)^2(\cos 2x)$$

$$\therefore \left(\frac{dy}{dx}\right)_{\frac{\pi}{6}} = 6(\sin \tfrac{\pi}{3})^2 \cos \tfrac{\pi}{3} = 6.\tfrac{3}{4}.\tfrac{1}{2} = \tfrac{9}{4}$$

Example 16: Find the equation of the tangent to the curve $y = \sin^2 3x$ at $x = \frac{\pi}{12}$.

SOLUTION

$$y = (\sin 3x)^2$$

$$\frac{dy}{dx} = 2(\sin 3x).\cos 3x.3 = 3\sin 6x$$

$$\left(\frac{dy}{dx}\right)_{x=\frac{\pi}{12}} = 3\sin 6(\tfrac{\pi}{12}) = 3$$

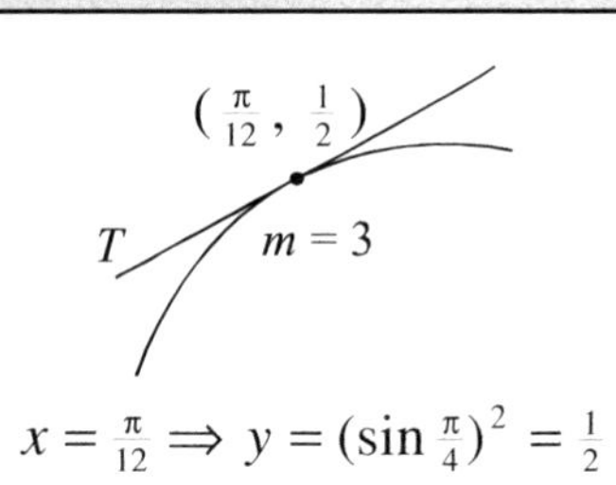

$$T\text{: } y - \tfrac{1}{2} = 3(x - \tfrac{\pi}{12})$$

$$\Rightarrow 36x - 12y + 6 - \pi = 0$$

Exercise 2 (Answers: page **303**)

Trigonometric Differentiation

I. Differentiate the following by rule:

1. $\tan x$
2. $\sec x$
3. $\operatorname{cosec} x$
4. $\cot x$
5. $\sin 5x$
6. $\cos(\frac{x}{3})$
7. $\tan 7x^2$
8. $\sec(3x^2 - 2x + 1)$
9. $\sin^3 2x$
10. $\tan^4(\frac{x}{4})$
11. $\operatorname{cosec}^3(\frac{x^2}{3})$
12. $\cot\sqrt{x^2 - 1}$
13. $\sqrt{\dfrac{1-\sin x}{1+\sin x}}$
14. $\cos 2x + \cos 4x$
15. $3\sin x \cos 2x$
16. $\dfrac{\sin 3x}{\sec 2x}$
17. $\dfrac{2\sin x}{\cos x}$
18. $2\sin x \cos x$
19. $\sin^2 x$
20. $\sin x^2$
21. $x^2 \cos x^3$
22. $x^2 \cot x - x \operatorname{cosec} x$
23. $(1 - \sin^2 x)^{\frac{1}{2}}$
24. $\dfrac{\sin x}{\cos(x+2)}$
25. $\dfrac{x \sin x}{1 + \cos x}$
26. $\sin(\cos x)$
27. $\sin^m x \cos^n x$
28. $\sin\sqrt{x}$
29. $\cot(\sin 3x)$
30. $\cos(\frac{2}{x})$
31. $\sqrt{\cos^3 x}$
32. $\dfrac{\sin x + \cos x}{\sin x - \cos x}$

II. Evaluate the following:

1. $\dfrac{dy}{dx}$ at $x = \frac{\pi}{6}$ if $y = \sin 3x$
2. $\dfrac{dy}{dx}$ at $x = \frac{\pi}{4}$ if $y = \cos^2 x$
3. $\dfrac{dy}{dx}$ at $x = -2$ if $y = \sin^2(x+2)$
4. $\dfrac{dy}{dx}$ at $x = \frac{\pi}{9}$ if $y = \sqrt{\cos 3x}$

[C] Differentiating Exponential (Expo) Functions

$$y = e^x \Rightarrow \frac{dy}{dx} = e^x$$

$$y = e^{f(x)} \Rightarrow \frac{dy}{dx} = e^{f(x)} \times f'(x)$$

TRICK

To diff an expofn, $y = e^{f(x)}$:
Repeat the whole function
× Diff of the power.

Example 17: Differentiate $y = \frac{e^{\frac{1}{x}}}{4}$.

SOLUTION

$$y = \frac{e^{\frac{1}{x}}}{4} = \tfrac{1}{4}e^{x^{-1}} \Rightarrow \frac{dy}{dx} = \tfrac{1}{4}e^{\frac{1}{x}}(-\tfrac{1}{x^2}) = -\frac{e^{\frac{1}{x}}}{4x^2}$$

Example 18: Differentiate $y = e^{2x^2}$.

SOLUTION

$$y = e^{2x^2} \Rightarrow \frac{dy}{dx} = e^{2x^2}.4x = 4xe^{2x^2}$$

Exponential Algebra

POWER RULES

1. $a^m.a^n = a^{m+n}$
2. $\frac{a^m}{a^n} = a^{m-n}$
3. $a^0 = 1$
4. $a^{-n} = \frac{1}{a^n}$
5. $(a^m)^n = a^{mn}$
6. $(a^m b^n)^p = a^{mp}b^{np}$
7. $\left(\frac{a^m}{b^n}\right)^p = \frac{a^{mp}}{b^{np}}$
8. $\left(\frac{a^m}{b^n}\right)^{-p} = \left(\frac{b^n}{a^m}\right)^p$

Note: $e \cong 2.7 > 0$

Example 19: If $y=\frac{(e^{x})^{2}e^{x^{3}-1}}{\sqrt{e^{x-3}}}$ find $\frac{dy}{dx}$.

SOLUTION

$$y=\frac{(e^{x})^{2}e^{x^{3}-1}}{\sqrt{e^{x-3}}}=\frac{e^{2x}e^{x^{3}-1}}{e^{\frac{1}{2}x-\frac{3}{2}}}=e^{x^{3}+\frac{3}{2}x+\frac{1}{2}}$$

$$\Rightarrow \frac{dy}{dx}=e^{x^{3}+\frac{3}{2}x+\frac{1}{2}}(3x^{2}+\tfrac{3}{2})$$

Example 20: If $y=\frac{x^{2}e^{x}}{e^{3x}}$ find $\frac{dy}{dx}$.

SOLUTION

$$y=\frac{x^{2}e^{x}}{e^{3x}}=x^{2}.e^{-2x}$$

Product rule: $\frac{dy}{dx}=x^{2}.e^{-2x}(-2)+e^{-2x}.2x=2xe^{-2x}(-x+1)$

$$=\frac{(1-x)2x}{e^{2x}}$$

Example 21: Differentiate $y=\frac{e^{\cos^{2}x}}{e^{\sin^{2}x}}$.

SOLUTION

$$y=\frac{e^{\cos^{2}x}}{e^{\sin^{2}x}}=e^{\cos^{2}x-\sin^{2}x}=e^{\cos 2x}$$

$$\therefore \frac{dy}{dx}=e^{\cos 2x}.-\sin 2x.2=-2\sin 2xe^{\cos 2x}$$

Example 22: Differentiate $y = \sqrt{\dfrac{1-e^x}{1+e^x}}$.

SOLUTION

$$y = \left(\frac{1-e^x}{1+e^x}\right)^{\frac{1}{2}}$$

$$\therefore \frac{dy}{dx} = \frac{1}{2}\left(\frac{1-e^x}{1+e^x}\right)^{-\frac{1}{2}} \left\{\frac{(1+e^x)(-e^x)-(1-e^x)e^x}{(1+e^x)^2}\right\}$$

$$= \frac{1}{2}\left(\frac{1+e^x}{1-e^x}\right)^{\frac{1}{2}} \frac{e^x(-1-e^x-1+e^x)}{(1+e^x)^2} = \frac{-e^x}{(1-e^x)^{\frac{1}{2}}(1+e^x)^{\frac{3}{2}}}$$

Exercise 3 (Answers: page **305**)

Exponential Differentiation

Differentiate the following with respect to x:

1. e^{-x}
2. e^{3x}
3. e^{x^2}
4. e^{x^5-3x}
5. $e^{\sqrt{x-1}}$
6. e^{x^3}
7. $e^{\frac{1}{x}}$
8. $e^x + e^{-x}$
9. $e^{\tan x}$
10. e^2
11. e^{ax+b}
12. $e^{(x-2)^5}$
13. $e^{\sqrt{1-x^2}}$
14. $e^{\frac{x^2}{3}+4}$
15. $e^{(\frac{x-1}{4})^2}$
16. $e^{x^{\frac{1}{3}}}$
17. $e^{x^{\frac{5}{2}}-1}$
18. $e^{\sin^2 x}$
19. x^2e^{2x}
20. $e^x(x-1)$
21. $x^n e^{ax}$
22. $5e^{3x}$
23. $e^x \sin x$
24. e^{e^x}
25. $e^{3x\sin x}$
26. $\dfrac{x^2+2x}{e^x}$
27. $\dfrac{e^x-e^{-x}}{e^x+e^{-x}}$
28. $\dfrac{\tan x}{e^x}$
29. $\dfrac{e^x}{\sin x}$
30. $\frac{1}{e^{2x}} - \frac{2}{e^{3x}}$
31. $\dfrac{e^{2x+1}}{x}$
32. xe^{x^2}
33. $\left(\dfrac{1-e^x}{1+e^x}\right)^{\frac{1}{3}}$

34. $e^{-x}\cos x$ 35. $e^{-x}\sin x$ 36. $\dfrac{e^x}{x\sin x}$	37. $\tan xe^{\sin x}$ 38. $\dfrac{e^{ax}-e^{bx}}{e^{ax}+e^{bx}}$ 39. $e^{\sqrt{x}+1}$	40. $e^{\cos^2 x}.e^{\sin^2 x}$

[D] **Differentiating Logarithmic (Log) Functions**

$$y = \ln x \Rightarrow \frac{dy}{dx} = \frac{1}{x}$$

$$y = \ln f(x) \Rightarrow \frac{dy}{dx} = \frac{1}{f(x)} \times f'(x)$$

TRICK

To diff a logfn, $y = \ln f(x)$:
One over the function inside the log
× Diff of the function.

Example 23: $y = \ln(\sec x) \Rightarrow \dfrac{dy}{dx} = \dfrac{1}{\sec x} \times \sec x \tan x = \tan x$

Example 24: $y = \ln(3x^2 + 2x)$

$$\Rightarrow \frac{dy}{dx} = \frac{1}{(3x^2+2x)} \times (6x+2) = \frac{2(3x+1)}{x(3x+2)}$$

Logarithmic Algebra

LOG RULES

1. $\log_a M + \log_a N = \log_a(MN)$
2. $\log_a M - \log_a N = \log_a\left(\dfrac{M}{N}\right)$
3. $N\log_a M = \log_a(M^N)$
4. Change of base (COB):
   $\log_a M = \log_b M \times \log_a b$
5. $\log_a 1 = 0$ because $1 = a^0$
6. $\log_a a = 1$ because $a = a^1$
7. $\log_a b = \dfrac{1}{\log_b a}$

Note: $\ln f(x) = \log_e f(x)$

Example 25: If $y = \ln \sec^2 x$ find $\dfrac{dy}{dx}$.

SOLUTION

$y = \ln \sec^2 x = 2\ln \sec x$

$\Rightarrow \dfrac{dy}{dx} = 2\left(\dfrac{1}{\sec x}\right)\sec x \tan x = 2\tan x$

TRICK
Always use log properties before differentiating if you can.

Example 26: Differentiate (i) $\sqrt{\dfrac{1-x}{1+x}}$ and (ii) $\ln\sqrt{\dfrac{1-x}{1+x}}$.

SOLUTION

(i) $y = \left(\dfrac{1-x}{1+x}\right)^{\frac{1}{2}}$

$\Rightarrow \dfrac{dy}{dx} = \dfrac{1}{2}\left(\dfrac{1-x}{1+x}\right)^{-\frac{1}{2}} \dfrac{(1+x)(-1)-(1-x)(1)}{(1+x)^2} = \dfrac{1}{2}\dfrac{(1+x)^{\frac{1}{2}}}{(1-x)^{\frac{1}{2}}}\dfrac{-2}{(1+x)^2}$

$= -\dfrac{1}{(1+x)^{\frac{3}{2}}(1-x)^{\frac{1}{2}}}$

TRICK
It is easier to diff the log of a difficult function using log properties rather than the original difficult function.

(ii) $y = \ln\left(\dfrac{1-x}{1+x}\right)^{\frac{1}{2}} = \dfrac{1}{2}\{\ln(1-x) - \ln(1+x)\}$

$\Rightarrow \dfrac{dy}{dx} = \dfrac{1}{2}\left\{\dfrac{1}{1-x}(-1) - \dfrac{1}{1+x}\right\} = \dfrac{1}{2}\left\{\dfrac{-2}{1-x^2}\right\} = -\dfrac{1}{1-x^2}$

Example 27: Find the derivative of $\dfrac{x}{\ln \sin x}$.

SOLUTION

$$y = \frac{x}{\ln \sin x}$$

$$\frac{dy}{dx} = \frac{\ln \sin x.1 - x\frac{1}{\sin x}\cos x}{(\ln \sin x)^2} = \frac{\ln \sin x - x\cot x}{(\ln \sin x)^2}$$

***e*-ln Trick**: When e and ln come together, they cancel each other out. So $e^{\ln f(x)} = f(x)$ and $\ln e^{f(x)} = f(x)$.

Example 28: If $y = e^{\frac{1}{2}\ln x}$ find $\dfrac{dy}{dx}$.

SOLUTION

$$y = e^{\frac{1}{2}\ln x} = e^{\ln x^{\frac{1}{2}}} = x^{\frac{1}{2}}$$

$$\therefore \frac{dy}{dx} = \frac{1}{2}x^{-\frac{1}{2}} = \frac{1}{2\sqrt{x}}$$

Trick: $\ln e^1 = 1$, $\ln e^2 = 2$, $\ln 1 = \ln e^0 = 0$, $e^{\ln 1} = 1$, $e^{\ln 2} = 2$

Example 29: If $y = \ln e^{\sin x}$ find $\dfrac{dy}{dx}$.

SOLUTION

$$y = \ln e^{\sin x} = \sin x$$

$$\therefore \frac{dy}{dx} = \cos x$$

Exercise 4 (Answers: page **306**)

Log Differentiation

(Answers: page 306)

Differentiate with respect to x:

1. $\ln(2x+3)$
2. $\ln(ax+b)$
3. $\ln\tan x$
4. $\ln 2x$
5. $\ln 5$
6. $\ln e^x$
7. $\ln x^2$
8. $\ln\sin x$
9. $\ln(x^2+2x)$
10. $\ln\operatorname{cosec} x$
11. $\ln\tan(\frac{x}{2})$
12. $\sin\ln x$
13. $\ln(\sec x+\tan x)$
14. $x^3\ln x$
15. $x^n(1-n\ln x)$
16. $(\ln x)^3$
17. $\ln(\frac{1}{x})$
18. $\sin x.\ln x$
19. $\dfrac{\ln x}{\tan x}$
20. $\ln\left(\dfrac{1+x}{1-x}\right)$
21. $\ln\left(\dfrac{a+x}{a-x}\right)$
22. $\ln\left(\dfrac{1+x}{1-x}\right)^{\frac{1}{3}}$
23. $\ln\left[\dfrac{(x-a)^2}{(x-b)^2}\right]$
24. $\ln\left(\dfrac{1+x+x^2}{1-x+x^2}\right)$
25. $\ln\sqrt{\sin x\cos x}$
26. $x(\ln x)^3$
27. $\ln\left(\dfrac{x}{2+3x}\right)$
28. $\ln\left(\dfrac{e^x}{1+e^x}\right)$
29. $\ln(x\sqrt{1+x^2})$
30. $\ln\left\{\dfrac{(2x-3)^{\frac{1}{3}}}{x^2(4-x)}\right\}$
31. $\ln(\ln x)$
32. $\ln\left(\dfrac{1}{\sqrt{1+x^3}}\right)$
33. $\ln(2+\tan^2 x)$
34. $\ln\sec^4 x$
35. $x\ln ax$
36. $\ln\sin^3 4x$
37. $\dfrac{1}{\ln x}$
38. $\dfrac{1}{x\ln x}$
39. $e^x\ln x$
40. $\dfrac{\ln x}{e^x}$
41. $\ln(x\sin x)$
42. $\frac{1}{\sqrt{x}}\ln x$
43. $\ln(e^{\frac{x}{\tan x}})$

[E] Differentiating Inverse Trigonometric (IT) Functions

INVERSE SIN

$$y=\sin^{-1}x \Rightarrow \frac{dy}{dx}=\frac{1}{\sqrt{1-x^2}}, \quad y=\sin^{-1}f(x)\Rightarrow \frac{dy}{dx}=\frac{1}{\sqrt{1-f(x)^2}}\times f'(x)$$

INVERSE TAN

$$y=\tan^{-1}x \Rightarrow \frac{dy}{dx}=\frac{1}{1+x^2}, \quad y=\tan^{-1}f(x)\Rightarrow \frac{dy}{dx}=\frac{1}{1+f(x)^2}\times f'(x)$$

Use the results for $\sin^{-1}f(x)$ and $\tan^{-1}f(x)$ to differentiate IT's. The results on page 41 of the tables are confusing.

Example 30: $y=\sin^{-1}3x \Rightarrow \dfrac{dy}{dx}=\dfrac{3}{\sqrt{1-9x^2}}$

Example 31: $y=\tan^{-1}(3x+1)\Rightarrow \dfrac{dy}{dx}=\dfrac{1}{1+(3x+1)^2}\times 3=\dfrac{3}{9x^2+6x+2}$

Trick: When x is replaced by $f(x)$ you simply multiply by $f'(x)$. This is the chain rule.

Inverse Trigonometric Algebra

There is no significant algebra for the 2 IT's on the LC course: $\sin^{-1}x$ and $\tan^{-1}x$.

Trick: When you write an IT always get out of trig and draw a right-angled triangle (RAT) even if you don't use it. So

$y=\sin^{-1}x \Leftrightarrow \sin y=x$

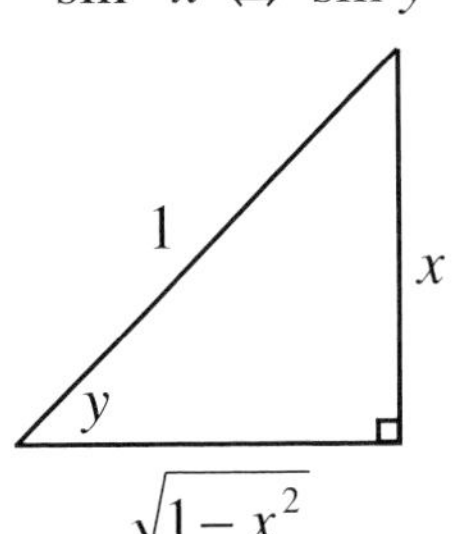

$y=\tan^{-1}x \Leftrightarrow \tan y=x$

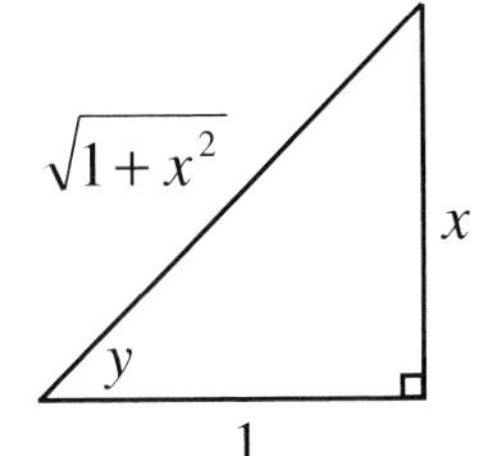

Example 32: Evaluate $\frac{dy}{dx}$ if $y = \sin^{-1}\sqrt{x}$.

SOLUTION

$$y = \sin^{-1}\sqrt{x} \Rightarrow \frac{dy}{dx} = \frac{1}{\sqrt{1-x}}\left(\frac{1}{2}x^{-\frac{1}{2}}\right) = \frac{1}{2\sqrt{x}\sqrt{1-x}}$$

Example 33: If $y = \sin^{-1}\left(\frac{1-x}{1+x}\right)$ find $\frac{dy}{dx}$.

SOLUTION

$$y = \sin^{-1}\left(\frac{1-x}{1+x}\right)$$

$$\Rightarrow \frac{dy}{dx} = \frac{1}{\sqrt{1-\left(\frac{1-x}{1+x}\right)^2}} \times \frac{(1+x)(-1)-(1-x)1}{(1+x)^2}$$

$$= \frac{1}{\sqrt{\frac{(1+x)^2-(1-x)^2}{(1+x)^2}}} \times \frac{-2}{(1+x)^2} = \frac{-2}{\sqrt{4x}}.\frac{1}{(1+x)} = -\frac{1}{(1+x)\sqrt{x}}$$

Example 34: Find the equation to the tangent to the curve $y = 2\tan^{-1}\sqrt{x}$ at $x = 1$.

SOLUTION

$$y = 2\tan^{-1}\sqrt{x}$$

$$\frac{dy}{dx} = 2.\frac{1}{1+x}.\frac{1}{2}x^{-\frac{1}{2}} = \frac{1}{\sqrt{x}(1+x)}$$

$$\Rightarrow \left(\frac{dy}{dx}\right)_{x=1} = \frac{1}{2}$$

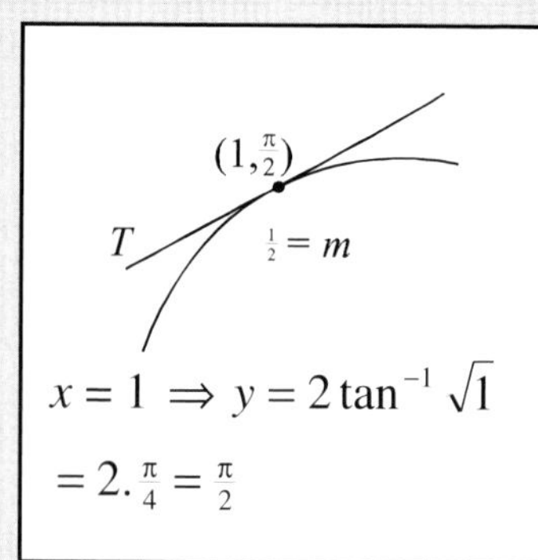

T: $y - \frac{\pi}{2} = \frac{1}{2}(x-1) \Rightarrow x - 2y + (\pi - 1) = 0$

Example 35: Find $\frac{dy}{dx}$ at $x=\frac{1}{2}$ if $y=x\sin^{-1}\sqrt{x}$.

SOLUTION

$y=x\sin^{-1}\sqrt{x}$ (Product rule)

$$\Rightarrow \frac{dy}{dx}=x\left(\frac{1}{\sqrt{1-x}}\right)\frac{1}{2}x^{-\frac{1}{2}}+\sin^{-1}\sqrt{x}(1)=\frac{\sqrt{x}}{2\sqrt{1-x}}+\sin^{-1}\sqrt{x}$$

$$\therefore \left(\frac{dy}{dx}\right)_{\frac{1}{2}}=\frac{\frac{1}{\sqrt{2}}}{2\sqrt{\frac{1}{2}}}+\sin^{-1}\frac{1}{\sqrt{2}}=\frac{1}{2}+\frac{\pi}{4}$$

TRICK

Whenever a trig function and its IT come together they cancel each other out.

$$\sin\sin^{-1}\tfrac{1}{2}=\tfrac{1}{2}$$

$$\sin^{-1}\sin 30^{\circ}=30^{\circ}$$

Exercise 5 (Answers: page **306**)

IT Differentiation

Differentiate with respect to x:

1. $\sin^{-1}2x$
2. $\tan^{-1}ax$, a constant
3. $\sin^{-1}(\frac{5}{x})$
4. $\tan^{-1}(\frac{a-x}{a})$, a constant
5. $\sin^{-1}\sqrt{x}$
6. $\sin^{-1}(\frac{x}{4})$
7. $\sin^{-1}(\cos x)$
8. $\tan^{-1}\sqrt{1-x^2}$
9. $\tan^{-1}(x\sqrt{x})$
10. $x\sin^{-1}x$
11. $(\sin^{-1}x)^2$
12. $(\tan^{-1}x)^2$
13. $\sin^{-1}(\frac{2x-3}{5})$
14. $\frac{\sin^{-1}x}{x}$
15. $\tan^{-1}(\frac{2x}{1-x^2})$

SUMMARY OF DIFFING BY RULE

1. Look at the whole expression and note the types of function involved.
2. Try to simplify it using the appropriate algebra.
3. Starting with a rule begin to diffo. Other rules may be necessary as you go along.
4. Tidy up after diffo.
5. Plonk in numbers if required.

Ways of asking you to Diffo

1. Differentiate with respect to ....,
2. Find $\frac{dy}{dx}$,
3. Find the derivative of ....,
4. Find the slope of the tangent to ....,
5. Find the equation of the tangent to ....,
6. Find $f'(x)$.

3. DIFFERENTIATION TECHNIQUES

3.1 INTRODUCTION

Diffo is the process of finding the slope of the tangent to the curve at a point on the curve. However, the curves can be given in 3 different ways:

1. **Explicit (ordinary) diffo**: y is given as a function of x

Example: $y = \frac{2\sin x}{\ln x}$

i.e. the diffo that we have been doing so far.

2. **Implicit diffo**: y is not given explicitly as a function of x

Example: $x^2y - y^2 = 5\sin x$

3. **Parametric Diffo**: x and y are given separately as a function of another variable (the parameter).
Example: $x = \sin t - \cos t$ and $y = t\cos t - \sin 2t$

3.2 IMPLICIT DIFFERENTIATION

[A] **The Idea**: This is just the chain rule all over again.

Remember if $y = f(x)$ then $\frac{d}{dx}[f(x)]^p = p[f(x)]^{p-1}.f'(x)$

or $\frac{d}{dx}[y]^p = py^{p-1}.\frac{dy}{dx}$

Trick: The chain rule simply states that to diff a function of a function, $g(f(x))$, you diff the outside function g by its rule on page 41 of the tables multiplied by the diff of the inside function f.

Example 1: $\frac{d}{dx}[\sin z] = \cos z \times \frac{dz}{dx}$

Example 2: $\frac{d}{dy}[\cos(x^2)] = -\sin x^2 \times \frac{d(x^2)}{dy} = -\sin x^2 \times 2x\frac{dx}{dy}$

Example 3: $\frac{d}{dx}[x]^{\frac{1}{2}} = \frac{1}{2}x^{-\frac{1}{2}} \times \frac{dx}{dx} = \frac{1}{2}x^{-\frac{1}{2}} \times 1$

Example 4: $\frac{d}{dx}[y]^p = py^{p-1} \times \frac{dy}{dx}$

Example 5: $\frac{d}{dy}[z]^3 = 3z^2 \times \frac{dz}{dy}$

Example 6: $\frac{d}{dy}(x^2+4)^{\frac{1}{2}} = \frac{1}{2}(x^2+4)^{-\frac{1}{2}}\frac{d}{dy}(x^2+4)$

$= \frac{1}{2}(x^2+4)^{-\frac{1}{2}}2x\frac{dx}{dy} = x(x^2+4)^{-\frac{1}{2}}\frac{dx}{dy}$

Example 7: If $x^2 + 3y^2 = 7$ find $\frac{dy}{dx}$.

SOLUTION

$$x^2 + 3y^2 = 7 \Rightarrow \frac{d}{dx}(x)^2 + 3\frac{d}{dx}(y)^2 = \frac{d}{dx}(7)$$

$$\Rightarrow 2x + 3.2y\frac{dy}{dx} = 0 \Rightarrow 6y\frac{dy}{dx} = -2x \Rightarrow \frac{dy}{dx} = -\frac{x}{3y}$$

Example 8: If $xy^2 - 2y = 3x^2$ find $\frac{dy}{dx}$.

SOLUTION

Look out for a product

$$xy^2 - 2y = 3x^2$$

$$\Rightarrow \left\{x(2y)\frac{dy}{dx} + y^2(1)\right\} - 2\frac{dy}{dx} = 6x \Rightarrow 2xy\frac{dy}{dx} - 2\frac{dy}{dx} = 6x - y^2$$

$$\Rightarrow \frac{dy}{dx}(2xy - 2) = 6x - y^2 \Rightarrow \frac{dy}{dx} = \frac{6x - y^2}{2(xy - 1)}$$

[B] **The slope of the tangent to the curve by implicit diffo**

Trick: Diffo every term in the equation of the curve with respect to a variable (x or y).

Example 9: Find the equation of the tangent to the curve $x^2 + e^x = y^2 - 4x$ at the point where $x = 0$, $y > 0$.

SOLUTION

Diffo

$$x^2 + e^x = y^2 - 4x$$

$$\Rightarrow \frac{d}{dx}(x)^2 + \frac{d}{dx}(e^x) = \frac{d}{dx}(y)^2 - 4\frac{d}{dx}(x)$$

$$\Rightarrow 2x + e^x = 2y\frac{dy}{dx} - 4$$

Cont...

$$\Rightarrow \frac{dy}{dx} = \frac{e^x + 2x + 4}{2y}$$

$$\Rightarrow \left(\frac{dy}{dx}\right)_{(0,1)} = \frac{1+4}{2} = \frac{5}{2} = m$$

$$T:\ y - 1 = \tfrac{5}{2}(x - 0) \Rightarrow 0 = 5x - 2y + 2$$

Point

$x = 0 \Rightarrow 0 + e^0 = y^2 - 0$

$\Rightarrow 1 = y^2 \Rightarrow \pm 1 = y$

$\therefore y = 1 \quad (0, 1)$

The hardest curve on the LC involve products of functions of x and y (both variables).

Example 10: Find the equation of the tangent to the curve $3xy^2 - y = 4x - 3$ at the point where $y = 1$.

SOLUTION

Diffo

$3xy^2 - y = 4x - 3$

Product of x and y^2

$$3\left\{x\frac{d}{dx}(y)^2 + y^2\frac{d}{dx}(x)\right\} - \frac{d}{dx}(y) = 4\frac{d}{dx}(x) - \frac{d}{dx}(3)$$

$$\Rightarrow 3x.2y\frac{dy}{dx} + 3y^2.1 - \frac{dy}{dx} = 4.1 \Rightarrow \frac{dy}{dx}(6xy - 1) = 4 - 3y^2$$

$$\Rightarrow \frac{dy}{dx} = \frac{4 - 3y^2}{6xy - 1}$$

$$\text{So } \left(\frac{dy}{dx}\right)_{(2,1)} = \frac{4-3}{12-1} = \frac{1}{11} = m$$

$$T:\ y - 1 = \tfrac{1}{11}(x - 2) \Rightarrow 0 = x - 11y + 9$$

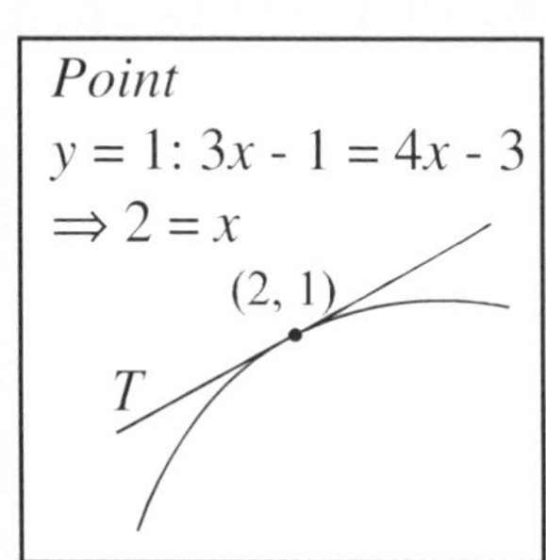

[C] **3 important implicit derivations**

1. If $y = \ln x$ show that $\dfrac{dy}{dx} = \dfrac{1}{x}$.

SOLUTION

$y = \ln x = \log_e x \Rightarrow e^y = x$

$\therefore \dfrac{d}{dx}(e^y) = \dfrac{d}{dx}(x) \Rightarrow e^y.\dfrac{dy}{dx} = 1$

$\therefore \dfrac{dy}{dx} = \dfrac{1}{e^y} = \dfrac{1}{x}$

2. If $y = \sin^{-1} x$ show that $\dfrac{dy}{dx} = \dfrac{1}{\sqrt{1-x^2}}$.

SOLUTION

$y = \sin^{-1} x \Rightarrow \sin y = x$

$\therefore \dfrac{d}{dx}(\sin y) = \dfrac{d}{dx}(x) \Rightarrow \cos y \dfrac{dy}{dx} = 1$

$\Rightarrow \dfrac{dy}{dx} = \dfrac{1}{\cos y} = \dfrac{1}{\sqrt{1-x^2}}$

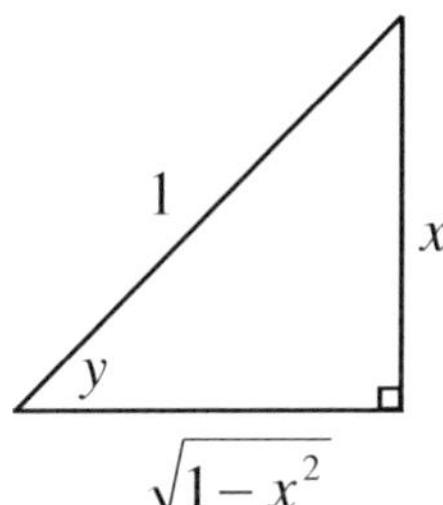

3. If $y = \tan^{-1} x$ show that $\dfrac{dy}{dx} = \dfrac{1}{1+x^2}$.

SOLUTION

$y = \tan^{-1} x \Rightarrow \tan y = x$

$\therefore \dfrac{d}{dx}(\tan y) = \dfrac{d}{dx}(x) \Rightarrow \sec^2 y \dfrac{dy}{dx} = 1$

$\therefore \dfrac{dy}{dx} = \dfrac{1}{\sec^2 y} = \cos^2 y = \dfrac{1}{1+x^2}$

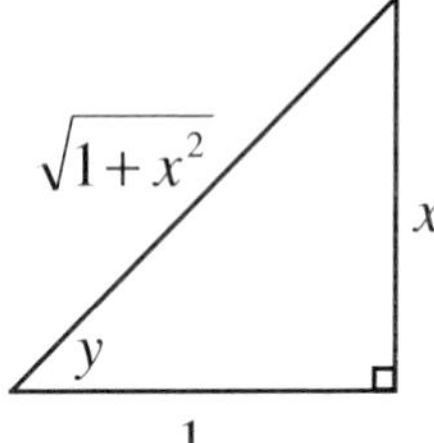

Exercise 6 (Answers: page **307**)
Implicit Differentiation

1. Find $\frac{dy}{dx}$ of the following:

(a) $x^2 + y^2 = 25$

(b) $3x^2 + 4y^2 = 10$

(c) $\sqrt{x} + \sqrt{y} = 25$

(d) $x^2 - 3xy + y^3 = 0$

(e) $x + 2xy^2 - y = 12$

(f) $x^4 + 4x^2 y - y^2 = 20$

(g) $x - \sin y = 10$

(h) $2(xy)^2 - 10 = x^2$

(i) $\tan y - x^2 = 0$

(j) $e^x - x^2 = y^2$

(k) $\ln x - y^2 = x^2$

(l) $\sin^2 y - \cos x = x$

---

2. Find the slope of each of the following curves at the given point:

(a) $x^2 + y^2 = 25$ at (3, 4)

(b) $x^2 + 2xy - 3y^2 + 11 = 0$ at (2, 3)

(c) $x^3 - xy + 3y^2 = 0$ at (1, 1)

(d) $x^3 + 3x^2 y + y^3 = 3$ at (-1, 1)

(e) $\sqrt{2x} + \sqrt{3y} = 5$ at (2, 3)

(f) $xy^3 - 2x^2 y^2 + x^4 - 1 = 0$ at (1, 2)

(g) $x^3 + 2y^3 = 3$ at (1, 1)

(h) $xy^3 = x^2 y^2 + 4$ at (1, 2)

(i) $x = y^2 + 1$ at (2, 1)

(j) $y = x^2 + xy$ at (0, 0)

3.3 PARAMETRIC DIFFERENTIATION

[A] **The Idea**: When the x and y co-ordinates of a curve are given separately as a function of another variable (the parameter) then the slope of the tangent $\frac{dy}{dx}$ is found by the technique called parametric differentiation.

[B] **The Technique**

Trick: Do $\frac{dy}{dt}$ first then do $\frac{dx}{dt}$ and then divide $\frac{\left(\frac{dy}{dt}\right)}{\left(\frac{dx}{dt}\right)} = \frac{dy}{dx}$

The parameter used in LC is usually t or θ.

Example 11: If $x = t - \frac{1}{t}$ and $y = t + \frac{1}{t}$ find $\frac{dy}{dx}$ at $t = 2$.

SOLUTION

$$y = t + \tfrac{1}{t} \Rightarrow \frac{dy}{dt} = 1 - \tfrac{1}{t^2}$$

$$x = t - \tfrac{1}{t} \Rightarrow \frac{dx}{dt} = 1 + \tfrac{1}{t^2}$$

$$\Rightarrow \frac{dy}{dx} = \frac{1 - \frac{1}{t^2}}{1 + \frac{1}{t^2}} = \frac{t^2 - 1}{t^2 + 1} \Rightarrow \left(\frac{dy}{dx}\right)_{t=2} = \frac{3}{5}$$

Example 12: If $x = t - 2\cos t$ and $y = 2\sin t - \cos 2t$ show $\frac{dy}{dx} = 2\cos t$.

SOLUTION

$$y = 2\sin t - \cos 2t \Rightarrow \frac{dy}{dt} = 2\cos t + 2\sin 2t$$

$$x = t - 2\cos t \Rightarrow \frac{dx}{dt} = 1 + 2\sin t$$

Cont...

$$\Rightarrow \frac{dy}{dx} = \frac{2\cos t + 4\sin t\cos t}{1+2\sin t} = \frac{2\cos t(1+2\sin t)}{(1+2\sin t)} = 2\cos t$$

Example 13: If $x = a(\cos t + t\sin t)$ and $y = a(\sin t - t\cos t)$, a constant, show that $\frac{dy}{dx} = \tan t$.

SOLUTION

Look out for a product

$$y = a(\sin t - t\cos t) \Rightarrow \frac{dy}{dt} = a\{\cos t - (-t\sin t + \cos t)\} = at\sin t$$

$$x = a(\cos t + t\sin t) \Rightarrow \frac{dx}{dt} = a\{-\sin t + (t\cos t + \sin t)\} = at\cos t$$

$$\Rightarrow \frac{dy}{dx} = \frac{at\sin t}{at\cos t} = \tan t$$

Example 14: Find the equation of the tangent to the curve $x = 2t - t^3$, $y = t^2 + 3t + 2$ at the point where $t = -2$.

SOLUTION

Diffo

$$y = t^2 + 3t + 2 \quad \Rightarrow \frac{dy}{dt} = 2t + 3$$

$$x = 2t - t^3 \quad \Rightarrow \frac{dx}{dt} = 2 - 3t^2$$

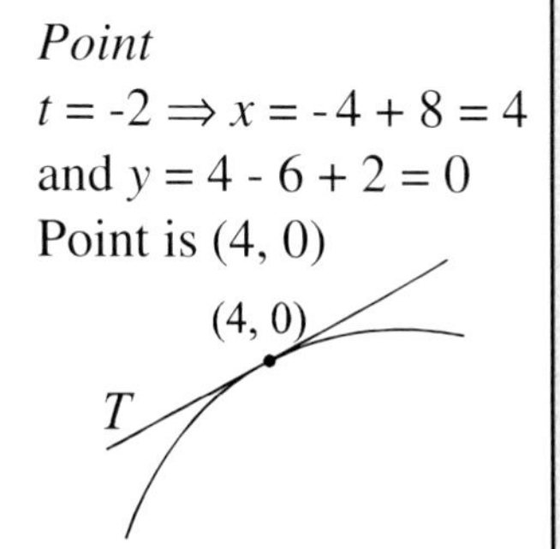

$$\therefore \frac{dy}{dx} = \frac{2t+3}{2-3t^2}$$

$$\Rightarrow \left(\frac{dy}{dx}\right)_{t=-2} = \frac{-1}{-10} = \frac{1}{10} = m$$

T: $y - 0 = \frac{1}{10}(x-4) \Rightarrow 0 = x - 10y - 4$

Exercise 7 (Answers: page **307**)
Parametric Equations

1. Find $\frac{dy}{dx}$ in terms of t or θ:

(a) $x = t^2$, $y = 2t + 1$

(b) $x = t^3$, $y = 3t$

(c) $x = 3t$, $y = \frac{2}{t}$

(d) $x = e^t$, $y = 3e^{-t}$

(e) $x = \cos 2\theta$, $y = \sin\theta$

(f) $x = \ln(t-2)$, $y = t$

(g) $x = e^\theta \cos\theta$, $y = e^\theta \sin\theta$

(h) $x = \sqrt{1-t^2}$, $y = \frac{2t}{t+1}$

(i) $x = \frac{2t}{t^2-1}$, $y = t + 1$

2. Find the slopes and equations of the tangents to the curves at the given point:

(a) $x = t^2$, $y = 2 - t$ at $t = 1$

(b) $x = \frac{t^3}{3}$, $y = \frac{t^2}{2}$ at $t = 2$

(c) $x = -3e^{-t}$, $y = 2e^t$ at $t = 0$

(d) $x = \sin 2\theta$, $y = \cos\theta$ at $x = \frac{\pi}{3}$

---

3. If $x = e^t \cos t$ and $y = e^t \sin t$ show that

$$\left(\frac{dx}{dt}\right)^2 + \left(\frac{dy}{dt}\right)^2 = 2e^{2t} \text{ and } \frac{dy}{dx} = \tan(t + \tfrac{\pi}{4}).$$

4. Find the equation of the tangent to the curve $x = 2(1 - \cos\theta)$, $y = 2(\theta - \sin\theta)$ at $\theta = \frac{\pi}{2}$.

5. If $x = a(\theta - \sin\theta)$ and $y = a(1 - \cos\theta)$ show that

$$\left(\frac{dy}{dx}\right)^2 + 1 = \operatorname{cosec}^2(\tfrac{\theta}{2}).$$

4. OTHER DIFFERENTIATION TOPICS

4.1 HIGHER ORDER DIFFERENTIALS

A function may be differentiated successively many times.

Notation

$y = f(x)$.........The function

$\frac{dy}{dx} = f'(x)$ ....First derivative

$\frac{d^2y}{dx^2} = f''(x)$ ....Second derivative

$\frac{d^3y}{dx^3} = f'''(x)$ ....Third derivative

Example 1: For the function $f(x) = \tan^{-1} x$ find

(i) $f'(x)$ (ii) $f''(x)$ (iii) $f'''(2)$.

SOLUTION

$f(x) = \tan^{-1} x$

$$f'(x) = \frac{1}{1+x^2} = (1+x^2)^{-1}$$

$$f''(x) = -(1+x^2)^{-2}(2x) = \frac{-2x}{(1+x^2)^2}$$

$$f'''(x) = \frac{(1+x^2)^2(-2) - (-2x)2(1+x^2)(2x)}{(1+x^2)^4}$$

$$= \frac{-2\{(1+x^2) - 4x^2\}}{(1+x^2)^3} = \frac{-2(1-3x^2)}{(1+x^2)^3}$$

$$\therefore f'''(2) = \frac{-2(1-12)}{(5)^3} = \frac{22}{125}$$

4.2 DIFFERENTIAL EQUATIONS

These are equations which involve various derivatives.

Example: $5x\dfrac{d^2y}{dx^2} - \left(\dfrac{dy}{dx}\right)^2 = 6y$

You will not be asked to solve differential equations (only if you do Applied Maths). You will be only asked to test solutions, i.e. plonk in.

Trick: Make sure you know the difference between

$\dfrac{d^2y}{dx^2}$ and $\left(\dfrac{dy}{dx}\right)^2$

Example 2: If $y = A\cos(\ln x) + B\sin(\ln x)$ show that

$x^2\dfrac{d^2y}{dx^2} + x\dfrac{dy}{dx} + y = 0$ if A, B constants.

Trick: Set it out as a vertical sum.

SOLUTION

$y = A\cos(\ln x) + B\sin(\ln x)$

$$\frac{dy}{dx} = \frac{-A\sin(\ln x)}{x} + \frac{B\cos(\ln x)}{x} = -Ax^{-1}\sin(\ln x) + Bx^{-1}\cos(\ln x)$$

$$\frac{d^2y}{dx^2} = \frac{-A\cos(\ln x)}{x^2} + \left(\frac{1}{x^2}\right)A\sin(\ln x) - \frac{B\sin(\ln x)}{x^2} - \frac{B\cos(\ln x)}{x^2}$$

$$\therefore x^2\frac{d^2y}{dx^2} = -A\cos(\ln x) + A\sin(\ln x) - B\sin(\ln x) - B\cos(\ln x)$$

$$\therefore x\frac{dy}{dx} = -A\sin(\ln x) + B\cos(\ln x)$$

$$y = A\cos(\ln x) + B\sin(\ln x)$$

$$\therefore x^2\frac{d^2y}{dx^2} + x\frac{dy}{dx} + y = 0$$

Trick: The variables used don't have to be x and y.

Example 3: If $s = e^{kt}$ is a solution of the differential equation

$\frac{d^2s}{dt^2} - 4\frac{ds}{dt} + 3s = 0$ find $k \in R$, k a constant.

SOLUTION

$s = e^{kt}$

$\Rightarrow \frac{ds}{dt} = ke^{kt}$

$\Rightarrow \frac{d^2s}{dt^2} = k^2e^{kt}$

$\therefore \frac{d^2s}{dt^2} \quad = k^2e^{kt}$

$\therefore -4\frac{ds}{dt} \quad = -4ke^{kt}$

$\therefore 3s \quad = 3e^{kt}$

$\therefore \frac{d^2s}{dt^2} - 4\frac{ds}{dt} + 3s = k^2e^{kt} - 4ke^{kt} + 3e^{kt} = 0$

$\Rightarrow e^{kt}(k^2 - 4k + 3) = 0 \Rightarrow (k - 3)(k - 1) = 0$

$\therefore k = 3, 1$

Exercise 8 (Answers: page **308**)

Differential Equations

1. For each of the following find $\frac{dy}{dx}$ and $\frac{d^2y}{dx^2}$:

(a) $y = \sin^2 x$

(b) $y = \frac{e^x - e^{-x}}{e^x + e^{-x}}$

(c) $y = \sin^{-1}(\cos x)$

(d) $y = \tan^{-1}\left(\frac{1-x}{1+x}\right)$

(e) $y = \ln \cot^4 x$

(f) $y = \frac{x}{\sqrt{1-x^2}}$

2. If $y = \tan^2 x$ prove that $\dfrac{d^2y}{dx^2} = 2(1+y)(1+3y)$.

3. If $y = \tan x + \frac{1}{3}\tan^3 x$ show that $\dfrac{dy}{dx} = \sec^4 x$.

4. If $y = \dfrac{\sin x}{x^2}$ prove that $x^2\dfrac{d^2y}{dx^2} + 4x\dfrac{dy}{dx} + (x^2+2)y = 0$.

5. If $y = \dfrac{\cos x}{x}$ prove that $\dfrac{d^2y}{dx^2} + \dfrac{2}{x}\dfrac{dy}{dx} + y = 0$.

6. If $y = x\sin(\frac{1}{x})$ show that $x^4\dfrac{d^2y}{dx^2} + y = 0$.

7. If $y = \dfrac{\sin x}{1+\cos x}$ prove that $\dfrac{d^2y}{dx^2} - y\dfrac{dy}{dx} = 0$.

8. If $y = x^n e^{ax}$ show that $\dfrac{dy}{dx} - ay = \dfrac{ny}{x}$.

9. If $y = e^{kx}$ is a solution of $\dfrac{d^2y}{dx^2} - 4\dfrac{dy}{dx} + 3y = 0$, find k.

10. If $y = \ln(1+x)^{\frac{1}{2}}$ show that $(1+x)\dfrac{dy}{dx} = \dfrac{1}{2}$.

11. If $y = \ln\sin^3 2x$ show that $3\dfrac{d^2y}{dx^2} + \left(\dfrac{dy}{dx}\right)^2 + 36 = 0$.

12. If $y = \cos(\ln x)$ show that $x^2\dfrac{d^2y}{dx^2} + x\dfrac{dy}{dx} + y = 0$.

13. If $y = e^{-2x}\cos 4x$ show that $\dfrac{d^2y}{dx^2} + 4\dfrac{dy}{dx} + 20y = 0$.

14. If $y = (a+bx)e^{-2x}$ show that $\dfrac{d^2y}{dx^2} + 4\dfrac{dy}{dx} + 4y = 0$.

15. If $y = xe^x$ show that $\frac{d^2y}{dx^2} - \frac{dy}{dx} - \frac{y}{x} = 0$.

16. If $y = x\ln x$ show that $x^2\frac{d^2y}{dx^2} - x\frac{dy}{dx} + y = 0$.

17. If $y = \frac{e^x + e^{-x}}{2}$ show that $\left(\frac{dy}{dx}\right)^2 = y^2 - 1$.

18. Find $k \in R$ if e^{-kx} is a solution of $\frac{d^2y}{dx^2} - 8\frac{dy}{dx} - 9y = 0$.

19. If $y = \frac{\sin^{-1}x}{\sqrt{1-x^2}}$ show that $(1-x^2)\frac{dy}{dx} - xy = 1$.

20. If $y = \sin^{-1}(\cos x)$ show that $\frac{dy}{dx} = 1$.

21. If $y = (\tan^{-1}x)^2$ prove that $\frac{d}{dx}\left\{(1+x^2)\frac{dy}{dx}\right\} = \frac{2}{1+x^2}$.

22. If $y = \frac{\sin x - \cos x}{\sin x + \cos x}$ show that $\frac{dy}{dx} = 1 + y^2$.

23. If $y = (x^2 + a^2)^n$, a constant, show that

$$(x^2 + a^2)\frac{d^2y}{dx^2} - 2(n-1)x\frac{dy}{dx} = 2ny.$$

ANSWERS

Exercise 1 [*Algebraic Differentiation* (page **268**)]

1. (a) $4x^3$ (b) -1 (c) x^2

   (d) $\frac{3}{\sqrt{x}}$ (e) $4x$ (f) $-\frac{5}{x^2}$

   (g) $1-\frac{1}{x^2}$ (h) $-\frac{2}{x^2}-\frac{1}{2\sqrt{x}}$ (i) $-\frac{1}{5x^2}$

   (j) $2x+\frac{3}{x^2}$ (k) $3x^2-2x-2$ (l) $8x(2x^2+5)$

   (m) $\frac{5}{2}x^{\frac{3}{2}}+3\sqrt{x}-\frac{3}{2\sqrt{x}}$ (n) $\frac{3}{2}x^{\frac{1}{2}}+\frac{5}{2x^{\frac{3}{2}}}$ (o) $(n-1)x^{n-2}-\frac{1}{x^2}$

   (p) $\frac{11}{3}x^{\frac{8}{3}}+\frac{4}{x^{\frac{1}{3}}}+\frac{1}{x^{\frac{4}{3}}}$ (q) $2x(2ax^2-c)$ (r) $x^2(7ax^4-12b)$

   (s) $\frac{8}{3}x^{\frac{1}{3}}-\frac{2}{x^{\frac{1}{3}}}$ (t) $\frac{1}{4\sqrt{x}}-\frac{3}{2x^{\frac{3}{2}}}$ (u) $\frac{18}{x^3}(4-\frac{3}{x^2})^2$

2. (a) $2x(3x-1)$ (b) $2(3x-1)$ (c) $2(8x+1)$

   (d) $6x(x^2-3)^2$ (e) $3x^2-10x-29$

   (f) $x(5x^3-8x^2+21x-12)$

   (g) $2x - 1$ (h) $20+\frac{15}{2x^{\frac{3}{2}}}-\frac{9}{x^{\frac{5}{2}}}$

3. (a) $-\frac{10}{(x-2)^2}$ (b) $\frac{2}{(x+1)^2}$ (c) $-\frac{4x(7x^3+10)}{(7x^3-5)^2}$

   (d) $\frac{-(11x^2-14x+5)}{(2x^2-3x+1)^2}$ (e) $\frac{2(x-1)(x+4)}{(2x+3)^2}$ (f) $\frac{-(a+c)}{(a+x)^2}$

   (g) $\frac{adx^2+2agx+bg-dc}{(dx+g)^2}$ (h) $\frac{-16x}{(4+x^2)^2}$

(i) $\dfrac{1}{\sqrt{x}(\sqrt{x}+1)^2}$ (j) $\dfrac{x^{\frac{2}{3}}+2x^{\frac{1}{3}}+6}{3x^{\frac{2}{3}}(1+x^{\frac{1}{3}})^2}$

4. (a) $18x(3x^2-5)^2$ (b) $576x(6x^2+5)^{47}$

(c) $\frac{3}{x^2}(1-\frac{1}{x})^2$ (d) $6(\frac{3}{\sqrt{x}}-4)(3\sqrt{x}-2x)^{11}$

(e) $\dfrac{x^2+1}{2x^{\frac{3}{2}}(x^2-1)^{\frac{1}{2}}}$ (f) $\dfrac{1}{\sqrt{x}(\sqrt{x}+2)^2}$

(g) $\dfrac{-6x}{(3x^2+2)^2}$ (h) $\dfrac{-1}{2\sqrt{x}(1+\sqrt{x})^2}$

(i) $\dfrac{14x}{3(7x^2-4)^{\frac{2}{3}}}$ (j) $\dfrac{-1}{6\sqrt{x}(1-\sqrt{x})^{\frac{2}{3}}}$

5. (a) $2x(2x-1)^3(6x-1)$ (b) $2(6x-1)(3x-2)^2$

(c) $5(6x-1)(3x+1)^2(2x-1)$ (d) $\dfrac{3(1-2x)}{2\sqrt{x}}$

(e) $\dfrac{3x+2}{2\sqrt{x+1}}$ (f) $\dfrac{-5x^2+6x-2}{\sqrt{3-2x}}$

(g) $\dfrac{x(2a^2-3x^2)}{\sqrt{a^2-x^2}}$ (h) $\dfrac{x(5x-4)}{2\sqrt{x-1}}$

(i) $\dfrac{4x^2+3x+8}{\sqrt{x^2+4}}$ (j) $3(x^4-\frac{1}{x^2})^2(4x^2+\frac{2}{x^3})$

(k) $-\dfrac{1}{2(1+x)^{\frac{3}{2}}}$ (l) $\dfrac{30x^2}{(2-5x^3)^3}$

(m) $nx^{n-1}(1+2x^n)$

6. (a) $\dfrac{1+2x}{(1-x)^4}$ (b) $\dfrac{-9(1+x)}{(3x-1)^3}$

(c) $\dfrac{(x+1)(x-3)}{(x-1)^2}$ (d) $\dfrac{3-x-3x^2-2x^3}{(x^2-x+1)^3}$

(e) $\dfrac{-a^2}{x^2\sqrt{a^2-x^2}}$ (f) $\dfrac{\sqrt{a}}{\sqrt{x}(\sqrt{a}-\sqrt{x})^2}$

(g) $\dfrac{39(2x-3)^2}{(3x+2)^4}$ (h) $\dfrac{2}{\sqrt{1+2x}(1-2x)^{\frac{3}{2}}}$

(i) $\dfrac{(ad-bc)n(ax+b)^{n-1}}{(cx+d)^{n+1}}$ (j) $\dfrac{x(2-x^2)}{(1+x^2)^{\frac{5}{2}}}$

(k) $-\frac{3}{x^3}(1+\frac{1}{x^2})^{\frac{1}{2}}$ (l) $\dfrac{\sqrt{x}(3+2x)}{2(1+x)^{\frac{3}{2}}}$

(m) $\dfrac{-5(1-x)^{\frac{3}{2}}}{(1+x)^{\frac{7}{2}}}$ (n) $\dfrac{3}{(2-3x)^4}$

(o) $\dfrac{x-a}{(2ax-x^2)^{\frac{3}{2}}}$ (p) $\dfrac{(x-1)(x+1)}{x^2}$

(q) $\dfrac{-c}{(1-cx)^{\frac{1}{2}}(1+cx)^{\frac{3}{2}}}$ (r) $\dfrac{-20}{3(2-5x)^{\frac{2}{3}}(2+5x)^{\frac{4}{3}}}$

(s) $\dfrac{-13-6x}{6(1-3x)^{\frac{1}{2}}(1+2x)^{\frac{4}{3}}}$ (t) $\dfrac{-2(1+\sqrt{x})}{x^{\frac{3}{2}}(2+\sqrt{x})^2}$

7. (a) $\dfrac{2}{3x^{\frac{1}{3}}}$ (b) $c-\dfrac{a}{x^2}$

(c) $\dfrac{x+4}{4x^{\frac{3}{2}}}$

(d) $\dfrac{-a+bx+3cx^2}{2x^{\frac{3}{2}}}$

(e) $-\dfrac{1}{\sqrt{1-2x}}$

(f) $\frac{2b}{x^2}(a-\frac{b}{x})$

(g) $\dfrac{2a+3bx}{2\sqrt{a+bx}}$

(h) $\dfrac{9+2x^2}{\sqrt{9+x^2}}$

(i) $\dfrac{36x}{(9-x^2)^2}$

(j) $\dfrac{x^2(3a^2-2x^2)}{(a^2-x^2)^{\frac{3}{2}}}$

(k) $\dfrac{-3}{(1-3x)^{\frac{1}{2}}(1+3x)^{\frac{3}{2}}}$

(l) $\dfrac{2(1+2x)}{(2+3x)^{\frac{2}{3}}}$

(m) $\dfrac{3}{(2-3x)^{\frac{5}{4}}(2+3x)^{\frac{3}{4}}}$

(n) $\dfrac{-(3a+2bx)}{3x^2(a+bx)^{\frac{2}{3}}}$

(o) 0

(p) $\dfrac{-5x}{\sqrt{a^2-x^2}}$

(q) $\dfrac{-(a^{\frac{3}{5}}-x^{\frac{3}{5}})^{\frac{2}{3}}}{x^{\frac{2}{5}}}$

(r) $\dfrac{(x+2)(3x^2+2x+4)}{\sqrt{x^2+2}}$

(s) $\dfrac{-10x(x^2+2)^4}{(x^2+1)^6}$

(t) $100x^4(1-2x^5)(x^5-x^{10})^{19}$

Exercise 2 [*Trigonometric Differentiation* (page **275**)]

I. 1. $\sec^2 x$

2. $\sec x \tan x$

3. $-\operatorname{cosec} x \cot x$

4. $-\operatorname{cosec}^2 x$

5. $5\cos 5x$

6. $-\frac{1}{3}\sin(\frac{x}{3})$

7. $14x\sec^2 7x^2$

8. $2(3x-1)\sec(3x^2-2x+1)\tan(3x^2-2x+1)$

9. $3\sin 4x \sin 2x$

10. $\tan^3(\frac{x}{4})\sec^2(\frac{x}{4})$

11. $-2x\mathrm{cosec}^3(\frac{x^2}{3})\cot(\frac{x^2}{3})$

12. $-\dfrac{x\,\mathrm{cosec}^2\sqrt{x^2-1}}{\sqrt{x^2-1}}$

13. $\dfrac{-\cos x}{(1-\sin x)^{\frac{1}{2}}(1+\sin x)^{\frac{3}{2}}}$

14. $-2(\sin 2x+2\sin 4x)$

15. $\frac{3}{2}(3\cos 3x-\cos x)$

16. $\frac{1}{2}(5\cos 5x+\cos x)$

17. $2\sec^2 x$

18. $2\cos 2x$

19. $\sin 2x$

20. $2x\cos x^2$

21. $x(2\cos x^3-3x^3\sin x^3)$

22. $2x\cot x-x^2\mathrm{cosec}^2 x+x\mathrm{cosec}\, x\cot x-\mathrm{cosec}\, x$

23. $-\sin x$

24. $\dfrac{\cos 2}{\cos^2(x+2)}$

25. $\dfrac{x+\sin x}{1+\cos x}$

26. $-\sin x\cos(\cos x)$

27. $\cos^{n-1}x\sin^{m-1}x(m\cos^2 x-n\sin^2 x)$

28. $\dfrac{\cos\sqrt{x}}{2\sqrt{x}}$

29. $-3\cos 3x\mathrm{cosec}^2(\sin 3x)$

30. $\frac{2}{x^2}\sin(\frac{2}{x})$

31. $\dfrac{-3\sin x\sqrt{\cos x}}{2}$

32. $\dfrac{-2}{(\sin x-\cos x)^2}$

II. 1. 0 2. -1 3. 0 4. $-\frac{3\sqrt{6}}{4}$

Exercise 3 [*Exponential Differentiation* (page **278**)]

1. $-\frac{1}{e^x}$
2. $3e^{3x}$
3. $2xe^{x^2}$
4. $(5x^4-3)e^{x^5-3x}$
5. $\dfrac{e^{\sqrt{x-1}}}{2\sqrt{x-1}}$
6. $3x^2e^{x^3}$
7. $-\dfrac{e^{\frac{1}{x}}}{x^2}$
8. e^x-e^{-x}
9. $\sec^2 x\, e^{\tan x}$
10. 0
11. ae^{ax+b}
12. $5(x-2)^4e^{(x-2)^5}$
13. $\dfrac{-xe^{\sqrt{1-x^2}}}{\sqrt{1-x^2}}$
14. $\frac{2x}{3}e^{\frac{x^2}{3}+4}$
15. $\dfrac{(x-1)}{8}e^{(\frac{x-1}{4})^2}$
16. $\dfrac{e^{x^{\frac{1}{3}}}}{3x^{\frac{2}{3}}}$
17. $\frac{5}{2}x^{\frac{3}{2}}e^{x^{\frac{5}{2}}-1}$
18. $e^{\sin^2 x}\sin 2x$
19. $2x(1+x)e^{2x}$
20. xe^x
21. $x^{n-1}e^{ax}(n+ax)$
22. $15e^{3x}$
23. $e^x(\sin x+\cos x)$
24. e^{e^x+x}
25. $3(\sin x+x\cos x)e^{3x\sin x}$
26. $\dfrac{2-x^2}{e^x}$
27. $\dfrac{4}{(e^x+e^{-x})^2}$
28. $\dfrac{(\sec^2 x-\tan x)}{e^x}$
29. $\dfrac{e^x(\sin x-\cos x)}{\sin^2 x}$
30. $-\dfrac{2}{e^{2x}}+\dfrac{6}{e^{3x}}$
31. $\dfrac{(2x-1)e^{2x+1}}{x^2}$
32. $e^{x^2}(2x^2+1)$
33. $\dfrac{-2e^x}{3(1+e^x)^{\frac{4}{3}}(1-e^x)^{\frac{2}{3}}}$
34. $\dfrac{-(\sin x+\cos x)}{e^x}$
35. $\dfrac{(\cos x-\sin x)}{e^x}$
36. $\dfrac{e^x(x\sin x-x\cos x-\sin x)}{x^2\sin^2 x}$
37. $e^{\sin x}(\sin x+\sec^2 x)$

38. $\frac{2(a-b)e^{(a+b)x}}{(e^{ax}+e^{bx})^2}$ 39. $\frac{e^{\sqrt{x}+1}}{2\sqrt{x}}$ 40. 0

Exercise 4 [*Log Differentiation* (page **282**)]

1. $\frac{2}{2x+3}$ 2. $\frac{a}{ax+b}$ 3. $\frac{1}{\sin x\cos x}$
4. $\frac{1}{x}$ 5. 0 6. 1
7. $\frac{2}{x}$ 8. $\cot x$ 9. $\frac{2(x+1)}{x(x+2)}$
10. $-\cot x$ 11. $\operatorname{cosec} x$ 12. $\frac{\cos(\ln x)}{x}$
13. $\sec x$ 14. $x^2(1+3\ln x)$ 15. $-n^2x^{n-1}\ln x$
16. $\frac{3(\ln x)^2}{x}$ 17. $-\frac{1}{x}$ 18. $\frac{\sin x}{x}+\cos x\ln x$
19. $\frac{\tan x - x\sec^2 x\ln x}{x\tan^2 x}$ 20. $\frac{2}{1-x^2}$ 21. $\frac{2a}{a^2-x^2}$
22. $\frac{2}{3(1-x^2)}$ 23. $\frac{2(a-b)}{(x-a)(x-b)}$ 24. $\frac{2-2x^2}{1+x^2+x^4}$
25. $\cot 2x$ 26. $(\ln x)^2(3+\ln x)$ 27. $\frac{2}{x(2+3x)}$
28. $\frac{1}{1+e^x}$ 29. $\frac{2x^2+1}{x(1+x^2)}$ 30. $\frac{2}{3(2x-3)}-\frac{2}{x}+\frac{1}{4-x}$
31. $\frac{1}{x\ln x}$ 32. $\frac{-3x^2}{2(1+x^3)}$ 33. $\frac{2\tan x\sec^2 x}{1+\sec^2 x}$
34. $4\tan x$ 35. $1+\ln(ax)$ 36. $12\cot 4x$
37. $-\frac{1}{x(\ln x)^2}$ 38. $-\frac{(1+\ln x)}{(x\ln x)^2}$ 39. $\frac{e^x}{x}(1+x\ln x)$
40. $\frac{1-x\ln x}{xe^x}$ 41. $\frac{1}{x}+\cot x$ 42. $\frac{(2-\ln x)}{2x^{\frac{3}{2}}}$
43. $\frac{(\tan x - x\sec^2 x)}{\tan^2 x}$

Exercise 5 [*IT Differentiation* (page **285**)]

1. $\frac{2}{\sqrt{1-4x^2}}$ 2. $\frac{a}{1+a^2x^2}$ 3. $\frac{-5}{x\sqrt{x^2-25}}$

4. $-\dfrac{a}{2a^2-2ax+x^2}$ 5. $\dfrac{1}{2\sqrt{x(1-x)}}$ 6. $\dfrac{1}{\sqrt{16-x^2}}$

7. -1 8. $\dfrac{-x}{\sqrt{1-x^2}\,(2-x^2)}$ 9. $\dfrac{3\sqrt{x}}{2(1+x^3)}$

10. $\dfrac{x}{\sqrt{1-x^2}}+\sin^{-1}x$ 11. $\dfrac{2\sin^{-1}x}{\sqrt{1-x^2}}$ 12. $\dfrac{2\tan^{-1}x}{1+x^2}$

13. $\dfrac{1}{\sqrt{(4-x)(1+x)}}$ 14. $\dfrac{x-\sqrt{1-x^2}\sin^{-1}x}{x^2\sqrt{1-x^2}}$

15. $\dfrac{2}{1+x^2}$

Exercise 6 [*Implicit Differentiation* (page **291**)]

1. (a) $-\frac{x}{y}$ (b) $-\frac{3x}{4y}$ (c) $-\sqrt{\frac{y}{x}}$

(d) $\frac{2x-3y}{3x-3y^2}$ (e) $\frac{1+2y^2}{1-4xy}$ (f) $\frac{2x^3+4xy}{y-2x^2}$

(g) $\frac{1}{\cos y}$ (h) $\frac{1-2y^2}{2xy}$ (i) $2x\cos^2 y$

(j) $\frac{e^x-2x}{2y}$ (k) $\frac{1-2x^2}{2xy}$ (l) $\frac{1-\sin x}{\sin 2y}$

2. (a) $-\frac{3}{4}$ (b) $\frac{5}{7}$ (c) $-\frac{2}{5}$

(d) $\frac{1}{2}$ (e) -1 (f) 1

(g) $-\frac{1}{2}$ (h) 0 (i) $\frac{1}{2}$

(j) 0

Exercise 7 [*Parametric Equations* (page **294**)]

1. (a) $\frac{1}{t}$ (b) $\frac{1}{t^2}$ (c) $-\frac{2}{3t^2}$

(d) $-\frac{3}{e^{2t}}$ (e) $-\frac{1}{4}\operatorname{cosec}\theta$ (f) t - 2

(g) $\dfrac{\cos\theta+\sin\theta}{\cos\theta-\sin\theta}$ (h) $\dfrac{-2\sqrt{1-t^2}}{t(t+1)^2}$ (i) $\dfrac{(t^2-1)^2}{-2(1+t^2)}$

2. (a) $-\frac{1}{2}$, $x + 2y - 3 = 0$

   (b) $\frac{1}{2}$, $3x + 6y + 4 = 0$

   (c) $\frac{2}{3}$, $2x - 3y + 12 = 0$

   (d) $\frac{\sqrt{3}}{2}$, $2\sqrt{3}x-4y-1=0$

4. $x-y+\pi-4=0$

Exercise 8 [*Differential Equations* (page **297**)]

1. (a) $\sin 2x$, $2\cos 2x$

   (b) $\dfrac{4}{(e^x+e^{-x})^2}$, $\dfrac{-8(e^x+e^{-x})}{(e^x+e^{-x})^3}$

   (c) -1, 0

   (d) $-\dfrac{1}{1+x^2}$, $\dfrac{2x}{(1+x^2)^2}$

   (e) $-8\operatorname{cosec} 2x$, $16\operatorname{cosec} 2x\cot 2x$

   (f) $\dfrac{1}{(1-x^2)^{\frac{3}{2}}}$, $\dfrac{3x}{(1-x^2)^{\frac{5}{2}}}$

9. $k = 1, 3$

18. $k = 1, -9$

Applications of Differentiation

1. CURVES

1.1 SLOPES AND TANGENTS

All functions are curves.

$\frac{dy}{dx}$ = Slope of a tangent, T, to a curve, C, at a point, p, on the curve = m = $\tan\alpha$. The point p is on the tangent and the curve.

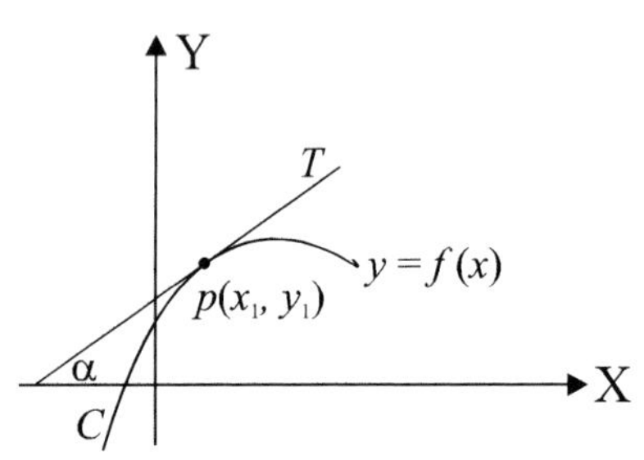

TRICK

To find the equation of a tangent you need 2 things:

1. A point $p(x_1, y_1)$ and

2. A slope $m = \frac{dy}{dx}$

Example 1: Find the points on the curve $y = 3 + \frac{1}{x}$ where the slope is $-\frac{1}{4}$.

SOLUTION

C: $y = 3 + \frac{1}{x} = 3 + x^{-1}$

$\therefore \frac{dy}{dx} = -x^{-2} = -\frac{1}{x^2}$

Slope: $\frac{dy}{dx} = -\frac{1}{x^2} = -\frac{1}{4} \Rightarrow x^2 = 4 \Rightarrow x = \pm 2$

Points: $x = 2 \Rightarrow y = \frac{7}{2}$

$x = -2 \Rightarrow y = \frac{5}{2}$

$\therefore (2, \frac{7}{2}), (-2, \frac{5}{2})$ are the points.

Example 2: Find the equation of the tangent to the curve $y = \sin^2 x$ at $x = \frac{\pi}{4}$.

SOLUTION

1. Draw a squiggle for the curve C and draw a tangent T. Find slope m at point of contact:

$$y = (\sin x)^2 \Rightarrow \frac{dy}{dx} = 2\sin x \cos x = \sin 2x$$

$$\therefore \left(\frac{dy}{dx}\right)_{\frac{\pi}{4}} = \sin\frac{\pi}{2} = 1$$

$\therefore m = 1$

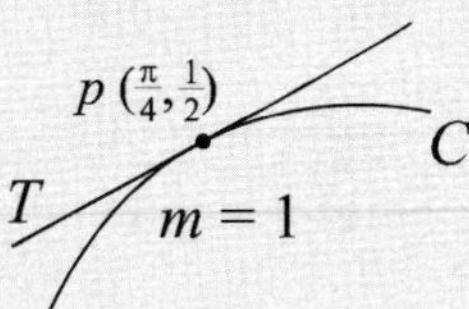

2. Find the point of contact p from the equation of the curve.

$x = \frac{\pi}{4} \Rightarrow y = (\sin\frac{\pi}{4})^2 = \frac{1}{2}$

$\therefore p(x_1, y_1) = (\frac{\pi}{4}, \frac{1}{2})$

> **TRICK**
> You can put p into the equation of curve C and equation of line T.

3. Plonk p into equation of T.

$m = 1,\ p(\frac{\pi}{4}, \frac{1}{2})$

Equation T: $x - y + k = 0$

Plonk in $(\frac{\pi}{4}, \frac{1}{2}) \in T \Rightarrow \frac{\pi}{4} - \frac{1}{2} + k = 0$

$\therefore k = \frac{1}{2} - \frac{\pi}{4}$

T: $x - y + \frac{1}{2} - \frac{\pi}{4} = 0 \Rightarrow 4x - 4y + 2 - \pi = 0$

1.2 FEATURES OF CURVES

[A] Increasing/Decreasing

1. **Increasing** (I):

$$\Rightarrow \text{slope} = \tan\alpha = m = \frac{dy}{dx} > 0$$

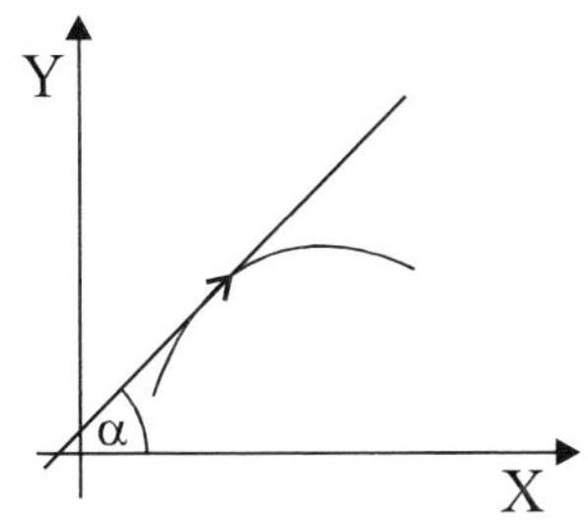

2. **Decreasing** (D):

$\Rightarrow$ slope $= \tan\beta = m = \dfrac{dy}{dx} < 0$

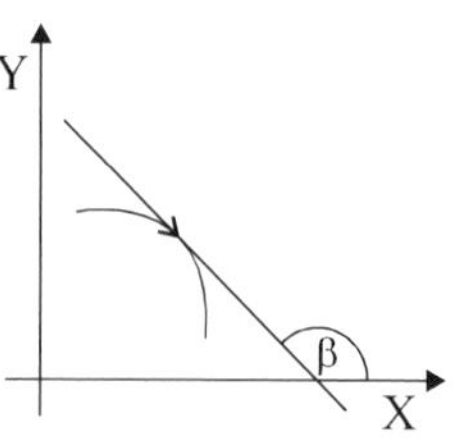

Example 3: Show that the curve $y = \dfrac{x^2 - 1}{x^2 + 1}$ is decreasing at the point where $x = -2$.

SOLUTION

$$y = \frac{x^2 - 1}{x^2 + 1}$$

$$\Rightarrow \frac{dy}{dx} = \frac{(x^2+1)2x - (x^2-1)2x}{(x^2+1)^2} = \frac{2x\{x^2 + 1 - x^2 + 1\}}{(x^2+1)^2}$$

$$= \frac{4x}{(x^2+1)^2} \therefore \left(\frac{dy}{dx}\right)_{x=-2} = \frac{-8}{25} < 0 \therefore \text{D}$$

Example 4: Show that curve $y = \dfrac{e^x}{e^x - 1}$ is always decreasing.

SOLUTION

$$y = \frac{e^x}{e^x - 1}$$

$$\Rightarrow \frac{dy}{dx} = \frac{(e^x - 1)e^x - e^x.e^x}{(e^x - 1)^2} = \frac{e^x\{e^x - 1 - e^x\}}{(e^x - 1)^2}$$

$$= \frac{-e^x}{(e^x - 1)^2} < 0 \text{ for all } x \therefore \text{curve is always D}$$

Trick: $e^{\text{anything}} > 0$ ALWAYS

[B] **Turning Point (TP)**

This just means a point at which the curve flattens out. It is also called a stationary point.

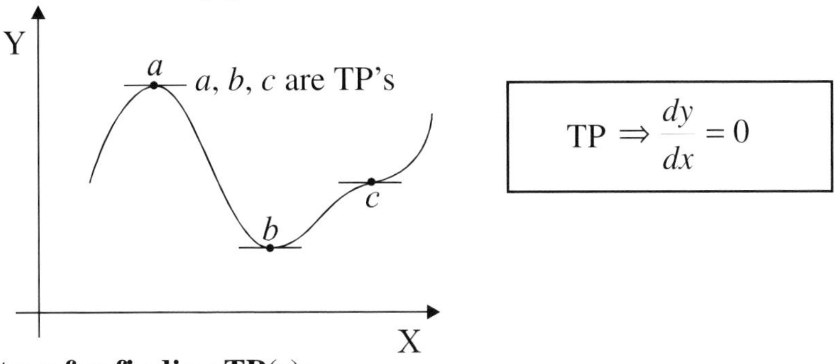

$$\text{TP} \Rightarrow \frac{dy}{dx} = 0$$

Steps for finding TP(s):

STEPS

1. Find $\frac{dy}{dx}$.
2. Set $\frac{dy}{dx} = 0$.
3. Solve for x.

Example 5: Find the TP(s) of $y = \frac{x^2}{x+2}$ if any.

SOLUTION

$$y = \frac{x^2}{x+2}$$

Step 1. $\frac{dy}{dx} = \frac{(x+2)2x - x^2(1)}{(x+2)^2} = \frac{x\{2x+4-x\}}{(x+2)^2} = \frac{x(x+4)}{(x+2)^2}$

Step 2/3. $\frac{dy}{dx} = 0 \Rightarrow x(x+4) = 0 \Rightarrow x = 0, x = -4$

$\therefore$ 2 TP's: $x = 0 \Rightarrow y = 0 \therefore$ TP: (0, 0)

$x = -4 \Rightarrow y = -8 \therefore$ TP: (-4, -8)

Example 6: Show that $y = \dfrac{x-1}{x+2}$ has no TP's.

SOLUTION

$$y = \frac{x-1}{x+2}$$

Step 1. $\dfrac{dy}{dx} = \dfrac{(x+2)(1)-(x-1)(1)}{(x+2)^2} = \dfrac{3}{(x+2)^2}$

Step 2/3. $\dfrac{dy}{dx} = 0 \Rightarrow \dfrac{3}{(x+2)^2} = 0 \Rightarrow 3 = 0$

$\therefore$ No solutions $\therefore$ No TP's

Example 7: The curve $y = \dfrac{p+qx}{x^2+2x}$ has a TP at (1, 2).

Show $p = -2$ and find q.

SOLUTION

TP at (1, 2) $\Rightarrow \left(\dfrac{dy}{dx}\right)_{(1,\,2)} = 0$

(1, 2)

$$y = \frac{p+qx}{x^2+2x} \Rightarrow \frac{dy}{dx} = \frac{(x^2+2x)q-(p+qx)(2x+2)}{(x^2+2x)^2}$$

$\left(\dfrac{dy}{dx}\right)_{(1,\,2)} = \dfrac{3q-(p+q)4}{9} = 0 \Rightarrow 3q - 4p - 4q = 0 \Rightarrow q = -4p$..(**1**)

(1, 2) is on the curve

C: $y = \dfrac{p+qx}{x^2+2x}$ $\therefore$ plonk in $\Rightarrow 2 = \dfrac{p+q}{3} \Rightarrow p+q = 6$..(**2**)

Solving (**1**) and (**2**) simultaneously $\Rightarrow -3p = 6$

$\therefore p = -2, q = 8$

[C] **CUP/CAP/PI**

1. **CUP** = Concave up which means the curve has a general cup shape. ∪

CUP ⇒ slope is increasing ⇒ $\frac{d}{dx}\left(\frac{dy}{dx}\right) > 0$

∴ $\boxed{\text{CUP} \Rightarrow \frac{d^2y}{dx^2} > 0}$

2. **CAP** = Concave down which means the curve has a general cap (on your head) shape. ∩

CAP ⇒ slope is decreasing ⇒ $\frac{d}{dx}\left(\frac{dy}{dx}\right) < 0$

∴ $\boxed{\text{CAP} \Rightarrow \frac{d^2y}{dx^2} < 0}$

3. **PI** = Point of Inflexion which is a point where a curve changes from CUP to CAP or vice versa.

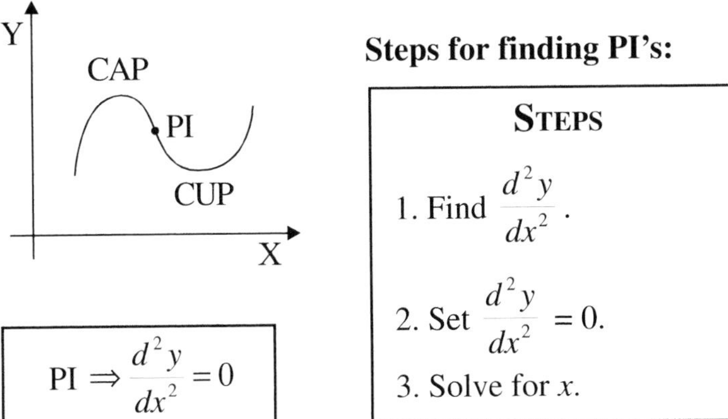

Steps for finding PI's:

STEPS

1. Find $\frac{d^2y}{dx^2}$.
2. Set $\frac{d^2y}{dx^2} = 0$.
3. Solve for x.

$\boxed{\text{PI} \Rightarrow \frac{d^2y}{dx^2} = 0}$

Example 8: Find the PI's if any of the curve $y = \frac{1-x^2}{1+x^2}$.

SOLUTION

$$y = \frac{1-x^2}{1+x^2}$$

Step 1. $\frac{dy}{dx} = \frac{(1+x^2)(-2x)-(1-x^2)(2x)}{(1+x^2)^2} = \frac{2x\{-1-x^2-1+x^2\}}{(1+x^2)^2}$

$$= \frac{-4x}{(1+x^2)^2}$$

$$\frac{d^2y}{dx^2} = \frac{(1+x^2)^2(-4)-(-4x)2(1+x^2)2x}{(1+x^2)^4}$$

$$= \frac{(1+x^2)4\{-1-x^2+4x^2\}}{(1+x^2)^4} = \frac{4\{3x^2-1\}}{(1+x^2)^3}$$

Step 2/3. $\frac{d^2y}{dx^2} = 0 \Rightarrow 3x^2 - 1 = 0 \Rightarrow x^2 = \frac{1}{3} \Rightarrow x = \pm\frac{1}{\sqrt{3}}$

$\therefore$ 2 PI's: $x = \frac{1}{\sqrt{3}} \Rightarrow y = \frac{1-\frac{1}{3}}{1+\frac{1}{3}} = \frac{1}{2}$ and $x = -\frac{1}{\sqrt{3}} \Rightarrow y = \frac{1}{2}$

Solutions: $(\frac{1}{\sqrt{3}}, \frac{1}{2})$, $(-\frac{1}{\sqrt{3}}, \frac{1}{2})$ are the PI's.

Example 9: The curve $y = ax^3 + bx^2 + cx + d$ has a TP at (0, 2) and a PI at (1, -1). Find a, b, c, d.

SOLUTION

TP at (0, 2) $\Rightarrow \left(\frac{dy}{dx}\right)_{(0,2)} = 0$

$\frac{dy}{dx} = 3ax^2 + 2bx + c \Rightarrow \left(\frac{dy}{dx}\right)_{(0,2)} = c = 0 \Rightarrow c = 0$

PI at (1, -1) $\Rightarrow \left(\frac{d^2y}{dx^2}\right)_{(1,-1)} = 0$

$\frac{d^2y}{dx^2} = 6ax + 2b \Rightarrow \left(\frac{d^2y}{dx^2}\right)_{(1,-1)} = 6a + 2b = 0 \Rightarrow b = -3a$

$y = ax^3 - 3ax^2 + d$

(0, 2) is on the curve $\Rightarrow 2 = d \Rightarrow y = ax^3 - 3ax^2 + 2$

(1, -1) is on the curve $\Rightarrow -1 = a - 3a + 2 \Rightarrow a = \frac{3}{2}$

$\therefore b = -\frac{9}{2}$

[D] **Crossing the axes**

1. X: If the curve crosses the X-axis, $y = 0$.

$\therefore$ Put $y = 0$ and solve for x.

Example 10: Find where the curve $y = x - \frac{1}{x}$ crosses the X-axis.

SOLUTION

$y = x - \frac{1}{x} \Rightarrow x^2 - 1 = 0 \therefore x = \pm 1$

$x = 1 \Rightarrow y = 0$

$x = -1 \Rightarrow y = 0$

$\therefore$ crosses X-axis at (1, 0) and (-1, 0)

2. Y: If the curve crosses the Y-axis, $x = 0$.
$\therefore$ Put $x = 0$ and solve for y.

Example 11: Find where the curve $y = x^3 - 3x^2 + 5x - 7$ crosses the Y axis.

SOLUTION

$y = x^3 - 3x^2 + 5x - 7$

$\therefore x = 0 \Rightarrow y = -7$

$\therefore$ crosses Y-axis at (0, -7)

SUMMARY TABLE

	>0	<0	$=0$
$\frac{dy}{dx}$	I	D	TP Flat
$\frac{d^2y}{dx^2}$	CUP	CAP	PI

Exercise 1 (Answers: page **352**)

Curves

1. Find the equation of the tangent to the curve $y = x^3 - 3x$ at (2, 2). Find the points at which the slope of the tangent is zero.

2. Find the equation of the tangent to $y = x^3 - 2x^2 - 3x + 1$ at a(2, -5). Find the points at which the slope of the tangent is 1.

3. Find the co-ordinates of the points of zero slope on the curve $y = x^2(x - 2)$.

4. The curve $y = ax^3 + bx^2 + cx + d$ passes through the origin and $(-\frac{3}{2}, 0)$. The tangent at the origin is the X-axis while the

slope of the tangent at $(-\frac{3}{2}, 0)$ is 9. Find a, b, c and d.

5. Prove that for all points on the curve $xy = c^2$, c constant, that $\frac{y}{x} + \frac{dy}{dx} = 0$.

6. If $f(x) = x^3 - 4x^2 + 4x - 1$ find the equation T of the tangent at $x = \frac{1}{2}$. If this tangent cuts the X-axis at c, find c. Show $f(\frac{1}{2}) = \frac{1}{8}$.

7. Find the points where the tangents $y = \dfrac{a^2 x}{a^2 + x^2}$, a constant, are parallel to the X-axis.

8. If the tangent to $y = x^2 - 3$ at $x = a$ $(a > 0)$ meets the X and Y axes at p and q, find p and q in terms of a. Show that the area Δopq is given by $\dfrac{(3 + a^2)^2}{4a}$ where o is the origin.

9. Show that the slope of the tangent to the curve $y = -1 + 3x - \frac{x^2}{4}$ at $x = 2$ is double that at the point where $x = 4$. At what point is the slope -1.

10. If $y = 6x - 10x^2 + 3x^3$ find the x co-ordinates of the points where the slope of the tangent is 2.

11. Find c if the tangent to $y = x(c - x^2)$ at the origin makes an angle of 45° with the X-axis.

12. For what values of x are the tangents to $y = \frac{2x^3}{3} + \frac{x^2}{2}$ equally inclined to the X and Y axis.

13. Find the points on the curves where the slope has the value given:

(a) $y = 2x^2 - 3x + 4$, slope 5

(b) $y = x^3 + x^2$, slope 1

(c) $y = 3 + \frac{1}{x}$, slope $-\frac{1}{4}$

14. Investigate if the following curves are increasing or decreasing at the given point:

(a) $y = x + \frac{4}{x}$ at $x = 1$

(b) $y = \tan^2(\frac{x}{4})$ at $x = \pi$

(c) $y = \ln\left(\frac{1-x}{1+x}\right)$ at $x = 3$

(d) $y = \sin^{-1}\sqrt{x}$ at $x = \frac{1}{2}$

(e) $y = \frac{e^x}{e^x + 1}$ at $x = 0$

15. Investigate if the following curves are CUP or CAP at the given point:

(a) $y = x^2 - \frac{1}{x}$ at $x = 3$

(b) $y = \sin^2 x$ at $x = \frac{x}{6}$

(c) $y = xe^x$ at $x = 0$

(d) $y = \tan^{-1} x$ at $x = 2$

(e) $y = \frac{x}{\ln x}$ at $x = e^{-1}$

16. Show that:

(a) $y = x^2 - 3x + 4$ is increasing everywhere.

(b) $y = \tan^{-1} x$ is increasing everywhere.

(c) $y = \cot x$ is decreasing everywhere.

(d) $y = \sin^{-1}(\cos x)$ is decreasing everywhere.

17. Find the TP's and PI's of the following:

(a) $y = \ln(1 + x^2)$

(b) $y = \frac{x}{\ln x}$

(c) $y = \frac{1}{2}(e^x - e^{-x})$

2. MAXIMISING AND MINIMISING FUNCTIONS

2.1 THE IDEA

Local Maximum (LMax): The only point of a cap region where the curve flattens out.

Trick: At a LMax $\frac{dy}{dx} = 0$ (flat) and $\frac{d^2y}{dx^2} < 0$ (CAP)

Local Minimum (LMin): The only point of a cup region where the curve flattens out.

Trick: At a LMin $\frac{dy}{dx} = 0$ (flat) and $\frac{d^2y}{dx^2} > 0$ (CUP)

Steps for finding LMax/LMin of functions:

STEPS

1. Give the function a suitable symbol (usually y) if not already specified in the question.
2. Make sure the function is written in terms of a single variable (usually x). If not, use extra information.
3. Do $\frac{dy}{dx}$, set = 0 and solve for x to get the turning point(s). Solving for x is the hard part.
4. Find $\frac{d^2y}{dx^2}$ and plonk in TP(s).

If $\left(\frac{d^2y}{dx^2}\right)_{\text{TP}} < 0$ then TP is LMax.

If $\left(\frac{d^2y}{dx^2}\right)_{\text{TP}} > 0$ then TP is LMin.

5. Plonk TP(s) into original function y to get the max/min value(s) of the function.

2.2 FINDING THE LOCAL MAX/MIN OF 4 FUNCTIONS

There are 4 functions to be treated:

1. Algebraic (Al) 2. Exponential (Exp)
3. Logarithmic (Log) 4. Trigonometric (Trig)

Example 1 (Al): Find the local max and local min if any of

$$y = \frac{4-x^2}{4+x^2}.$$

SOLUTION

Step 1. $y = \dfrac{4-x^2}{4+x^2}$

Step 2. $\dfrac{dy}{dx} = \dfrac{(4+x^2)(-2x)-(4-x^2)(2x)}{(4+x^2)^2}$

$$= \frac{2x\{-4-x^2-4+x^2\}}{(4+x^2)^2} = \frac{-16x}{(4+x^2)^2}$$

$\therefore \dfrac{dy}{dx} = 0 \Rightarrow x = 0.$ This is the only turning point.

Step 3. $\dfrac{d^2y}{dx^2} = \dfrac{(4+x^2)^2(-16)-(-16x)2(4+x^2)2x}{(4+x^2)^4}$

$$= \frac{(4+x^2)16\{-4-x^2+4x^2\}}{(4+x^2)^4} = \frac{16\{3x^2-4\}}{(4+x^2)^3}$$

Step 4. $\left(\dfrac{d^2y}{dx^2}\right)_0 = \dfrac{(-16)(4)}{(4)^3} < 0 \Rightarrow x = 0$ is a local max.

Step 5. $x = 0 \Rightarrow y = \dfrac{4-0}{4+0} = 1$ is the max. value of the function and (0, 1) is the point on the curve at which the function has its max value.

Trick for solving Exp and Log equations

e-ln trick: When *e* and ln come together they cancel each other out. This is very useful when solving expo and log equations. So $e^{\ln f(x)} = f(x)$ and $\ln e^{f(x)} = f(x)$.

Example 2 (Exp): Find the local maxima/local minima if any of $y = 1 + e^x - 2x$.

SOLUTION

Step 1. $y = 1 + e^x - 2x$

Step 2. $\frac{dy}{dx} = e^x - 2$

$\therefore \frac{dy}{dx} = 0 \Rightarrow e^x - 2 \Rightarrow e^x = 2$

Taking the ln of both sides gives: $\ln e^x = \ln 2$

$\therefore x = \ln 2$ is the only turning point.

Step 3. $\frac{d^2y}{dx^2} = e^x$

Step 4. $\left(\frac{d^2y}{dx^2}\right)_{\ln 2} = e^{\ln 2} = 2 > 0 \Rightarrow x = \ln 2$ is a local min.

Step 5. $x = \ln 2 \Rightarrow y = 1 + e^{\ln 2} - 2\ln 2 = 1 + 2 - \ln 4 = 3 - \ln 4$

The local min. is $(\ln 2, 3 - \ln 4)$.

Example 3 (Log): Find the local max/local min if any of

$y = \frac{\ln x}{x}$.

SOLUTION

Step 1. $y = \frac{\ln x}{x}$

Step 2. $\frac{dy}{dx} = \frac{x(\frac{1}{x}) - \ln x}{x^2} = \frac{1 - \ln x}{x^2}$

$\therefore \frac{dy}{dx} = 0 \Rightarrow 1 - \ln x = 0 \Rightarrow \ln x = 1$

Putting both sides to power e gives: $e^{\ln x} = e^1$

$\therefore x = e$ is the only turning point.

Step 3. $\frac{d^2y}{dx^2} = \frac{x^2(-\frac{1}{x}) - (1 - \ln x)(2x)}{x^4}$

$= \frac{-1 - 2 + 2\ln x}{x^3} = \frac{2\ln x - 3}{x^3}$

Step 4. $\left(\frac{d^2y}{dx^2}\right)_e = \frac{2\ln e - 3}{e^3} = -\frac{1}{e^3} < 0 \;\Rightarrow\; x = e$ is a local max.

Step 5. $x = e \;\Rightarrow\; y = \frac{\ln e}{e} = \frac{1}{e}$

The local max. is $(e, \frac{1}{e})$.

Example 4 (Trig): Find the local max/local min of

$y = \sin x - \frac{x}{2},\ 0 \le x \le 2\pi$.

TRICK
When solving trig equations use **ASTC** to get all answers.

SOLUTION

Step 1. $y = \sin x - \frac{x}{2}$

Step 2. $\frac{dy}{dx} = \cos x - \frac{1}{2}$

$\therefore \frac{dy}{dx} = 0 \Rightarrow \cos x = \frac{1}{2}$

$\therefore x = \frac{\pi}{3}$ (first quadrant) and $x = \frac{5\pi}{3}$ (fourth quadrant) are TP's.

Step 3. $\frac{d^2y}{dx^2} = -\sin x$

Step 4. $\left(\frac{d^2y}{dx^2}\right)_{\frac{\pi}{3}} = -\sin\frac{\pi}{3} = -\frac{\sqrt{3}}{2} < 0 \Rightarrow x = \frac{\pi}{3}$ is a local max.

$\left(\frac{d^2y}{dx^2}\right)_{\frac{5\pi}{3}} = -\sin\frac{5\pi}{3} = \frac{\sqrt{3}}{2} > 0 \Rightarrow x = \frac{5\pi}{3}$ is a local min.

Step 5. $x = \frac{\pi}{3} \Rightarrow y = \sin\frac{\pi}{3} - \frac{\pi}{6} = \frac{\sqrt{3}}{2} - \frac{\pi}{6}$

$\therefore (\frac{\pi}{3}, \frac{\sqrt{3}}{2} - \frac{\pi}{6})$ is a local max.

$x = \frac{5\pi}{3} \Rightarrow y = \sin\frac{5\pi}{3} - \frac{5\pi}{6} = -\frac{\sqrt{3}}{2} - \frac{5\pi}{6}$

$\therefore (\frac{5\pi}{3}, -\frac{\sqrt{3}}{2} - \frac{5\pi}{6})$ is a local max.

Exercise 2 (Answers: page **352**)

Max/Min

1. Find the max and min values of:

(a) $y = 12x - x^3$

(b) $y = \frac{1}{4}x^3 + \frac{3}{4}x^2 - 1$

(c) $y = x^3 - 6x^2 - 36x + 5$

(d) $y = \dfrac{2x}{x^2 + 4}$

(e) $y = \dfrac{x^2}{x+2}$

(f) $y = \dfrac{x-1}{x+2}$

(g) $y = x + \frac{4}{x^2}$

(h) $y = x^2 + \frac{2a^3}{x}$

2. Find LMax/LMin of:

(a) $y = 4x - e^{2x}$

(b) $y = x \ln x$

(c) $y = xe^x$

(d) $y = xe^{-4x}$

(e) $y = \frac{x}{\ln x}$

(f) $y = 2x + \frac{1}{x} - \ln x$

3. Find LMax/LMin of the following given that $0 \le x \le 2\pi$:

(a) $y = \frac{x}{2} - \cos x$

(b) $y = x + \ln \cos x$

(c) $y = 2\sin x - x$

(d) $y = \sin x + \cos x$

4. If $y = 1 - x$ find the maximum value of xy.

5. If $\frac{1}{x} + \frac{1}{y} = \frac{1}{2}$ express y in terms of x, $x > 0$. Find the minimum value of $x + y$.

6. If $y = \dfrac{1}{1+x^2}$ find the minimum value of xy.

7. If the minimum value of $\dfrac{k^2+1}{k}$ is 2, find k.

8. If the maximum value of A occurs at $t = 6$, find $c > 0$ if

$$A = \frac{5t}{1 + (\frac{t}{c})^2}, \; c \text{ constant.}$$

9. If $c = x^2 + 4xy + y^2$ and $x + y = 2$, express c in terms of x and hence find the maximum value of c.

3. CURVE SKETCHING

There are 2 types of curve to be sketched on the LC course.

CUBICS: $y = f(x) = ax^3 + bx^2 + cx + d$

RATIONAL: $y = f(x) = \dfrac{ax + b}{cx + d}$

If asked to sketch a curve do it on graph paper.

3.1 CUBICS: $y = f(x) = ax^3 + bx^2 + cx + d$

Sketching a Cubic Equation:
A cubic equation may have LMax/LMin/PI's. There are no **asymptotes** (these will be explained later).

STEPS

1. **Find the LMax/LMin** using the steps on page 321.

2. **Find the PI's** using the steps on page 315.

3. **Find a Free Point**: Put $x = 0$ and find y (where curve crosses X-axis).

Example 1: Find LMax/LMin of $y = f(x) = -2x^3 - 3x^2 + 12x + 10$. Find also the PI and sketch it roughly.

SOLUTION

$y = f(x) = -2x^3 - 3x^2 + 12x + 10$

Step 1. $\frac{dy}{dx} = -6x^2 - 6x + 12$

$\frac{dy}{dx} = 0 \Rightarrow -6x^2 - 6x + 12 = 0$

$\Rightarrow x^2 + x - 2 = 0 \Rightarrow (x - 1)(x + 2) = 0$

$\therefore x = 1, x = -2$ (TP's) TP: (1, 17), (-2, -10)

$\frac{d^2y}{dx^2} = -12x - 6$

$\left(\frac{d^2y}{dx^2}\right)_1 = -12 - 18 < 0$ LMax (1, 17)

$\left(\frac{d^2y}{dx^2}\right)_{-2} = 24 - 6 > 0$ LMin (-2, -10)

Step 2. PI: $\frac{d^2y}{dx^2} = 0 \Rightarrow -12x - 6 = 0 \Rightarrow x = -\frac{1}{2}$ $\therefore$ PI $\left(-\frac{1}{2}, \frac{7}{2}\right)$

Step 3. Free Point: $x = 0 \Rightarrow y = 10$ (0, 10)

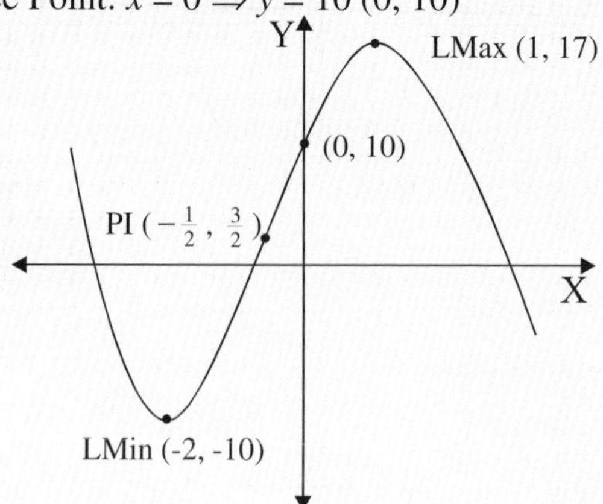

PLOTTING CURVES

1. 3 real different roots has LMax and LMin on opposite sides of the X-axis.

$$y = (x - \alpha)(x - \beta)(x - \gamma)$$

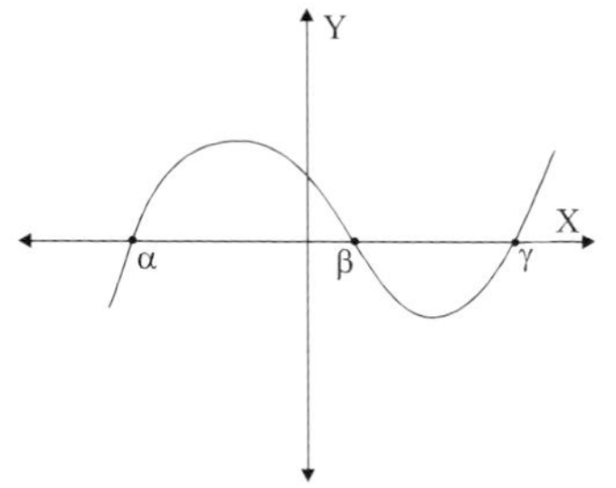

2. 3 real roots with 2 the same has LMax or LMin at the double root on the X axis.

$$y = (x - \alpha)^2(x - \beta)$$

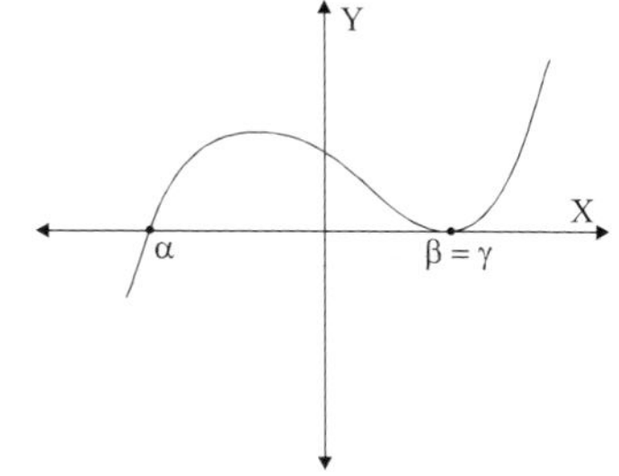

3. 3 real roots all the same has PI at the root on the X-axis.

$$y = (x - \alpha)^3$$

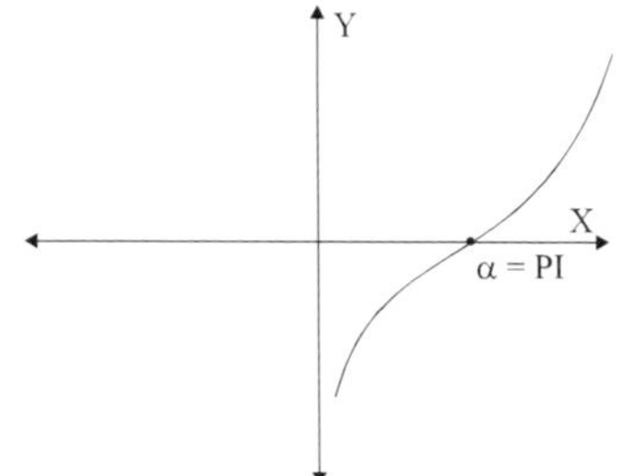

4. One real root (2 complex) has LMax and LMin the same side of the X-axis.

$$y = (x - \alpha)(\text{Quadratic})$$

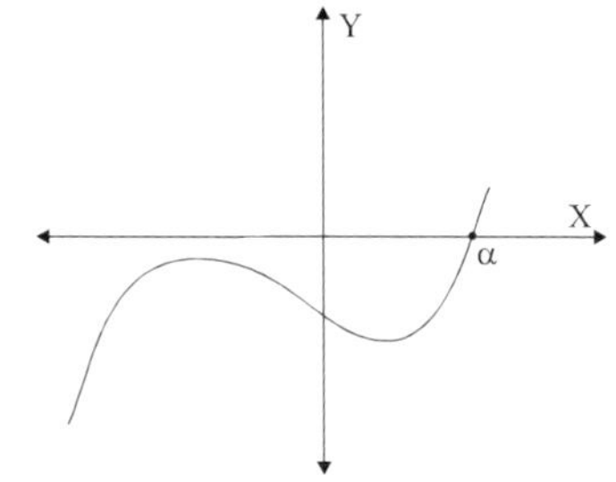

Example 2: Show that $y = f(x) = 2x^3 + 12x^2 + 18x - 3$ has only one real root.

SOLUTION

$y = f(x) = 2x^3 + 12x^2 + 18x - 3$

$$\frac{dy}{dx} = 6x^2 + 24x + 18$$

$$\frac{dy}{dx} = 0 \Rightarrow 6x^2 + 24x + 18 = 0$$

$\Rightarrow x^2 + 4x + 3 = 0 \Rightarrow (x + 3)(x + 1) = 0$

$\therefore x = -3, x = -1$ (TP's)

TP: (-3, -3), (-1, -11)

$$\frac{d^2y}{dx^2} = 12x + 24$$

$$\left(\frac{d^2y}{dx^2}\right)_{-3} = -36 + 24 = -12 < 0 : \text{LMax } (-3, -3)$$

$$\left(\frac{d^2y}{dx^2}\right)_{-1} = -12 + 24 = 12 > 0 : \text{LMin } (-1, -11)$$

The LMax (-3, -3) and LMin (-1, -11) are on the same side of the X-axis. Therefore there is only one real root.

3.2 RATIONALS

They have no LMax, no LMin, no PI's. They have **asymptotes** (skimmers). There are 2 types. Asymptotes are straight lines often known as tangents at infinity.

[A] **X-type (Vertical)**

Steps to find the X-type asymptote (AS):

STEPS

1. Tidy up the algebra.
2. Put denominator = 0.

Example 3: Find X-type asymptote of the curve $y=\frac{x+1}{x-3}$.

SOLUTION

$y=\frac{x+1}{x-3}$; Put x - 3 = 0 $\Rightarrow$ $\boxed{x=3}$ (X-type AS)

[B] **Y-type (Horizontal)**

Steps to find the Y-type asymptote:

STEPS

1. Take out highest power of x from numerator.
2. Take out highest power of x from denominator.
3. Simplify factors.
4. Let $x \to \infty$, find y, i.e. do $\lim\limits_{x\to\infty} y$.

Example 4: Find Y-type asymptote of the curve $y=\frac{2x-3}{x+1}$.

SOLUTION

$$y=\frac{2x-3}{x+1} \Rightarrow y=\frac{\cancel{x}(2-\frac{3}{x})}{\cancel{x}(1+\frac{1}{x})} \Rightarrow \lim_{x\to\infty} y=\lim_{x\to\infty}\frac{(2-\frac{3}{x})}{(1+\frac{1}{x})}=2$$

$\therefore$ $\boxed{y=2}$ is a Y-type AS.

Example 5: Find Y-type asymptote of the curve $y = \dfrac{3}{x-2}$.

SOLUTION

$$y = \frac{3}{x-2} \Rightarrow y = \frac{3}{x(1-\frac{2}{x})} \Rightarrow \lim_{x\to\infty} y = \lim_{x\to\infty} \frac{3}{x(1-\frac{2}{x})} = \frac{3}{\infty(1)} = 0$$

$\therefore \boxed{y = 0}$ is a Y-type AS.

[C] Steps for plotting rational curves:

STEPS

1. Find asymptotes.
2. Build up a table by choosing 2 points to the left and 2 points to the right of the X-type AS.
3. **Free points**: Put $y = 0$, find x.
Put $x = 0$, find y.
4. Plot skimming along the asymptotes.

Example 6: Show that the curve $y = \dfrac{x+1}{x-2}$ has no LMax, LMin or PI's. Find the AS and plot it roughly. If the tangent at x_1 is parallel to the tangent at x_2 show $x_1 + x_2 = 4$ ($x_1 \neq x_2$).

SOLUTION

$$y = f(x) = \frac{x+1}{x-2}$$

$$\frac{dy}{dx} = \frac{(x-2)1-(x+1)1}{(x-2)^2} = \frac{-3}{(x-2)^2} = -3(x-2)^{-2}$$

Cont...

$$\frac{dy}{dx} = 0 \Rightarrow \frac{-3}{(x-2)^2} = 0 \Rightarrow -3 = 0$$

$\therefore$ no solutions, $\therefore$ no LMax or LMin

$$\frac{d^2y}{dx^2} = 6(x-2)^{-3} = \frac{6}{(x-2)^3} = 0 \Rightarrow 6 = 0$$

$\therefore$ no solutions, $\therefore$ no PI's

Step 1. AS (i) X-type: $x = 2$

(ii) Y-type: $y = \dfrac{x+1}{x-2} = \dfrac{\not{x}(1+\frac{1}{x})}{\not{x}(1-\frac{2}{x})}$

$\therefore x \to \infty, \Rightarrow y \to \frac{1}{1} = 1$

$\therefore y = 1$

Step 2. Draw up a table ($x = 2$ is the AS)

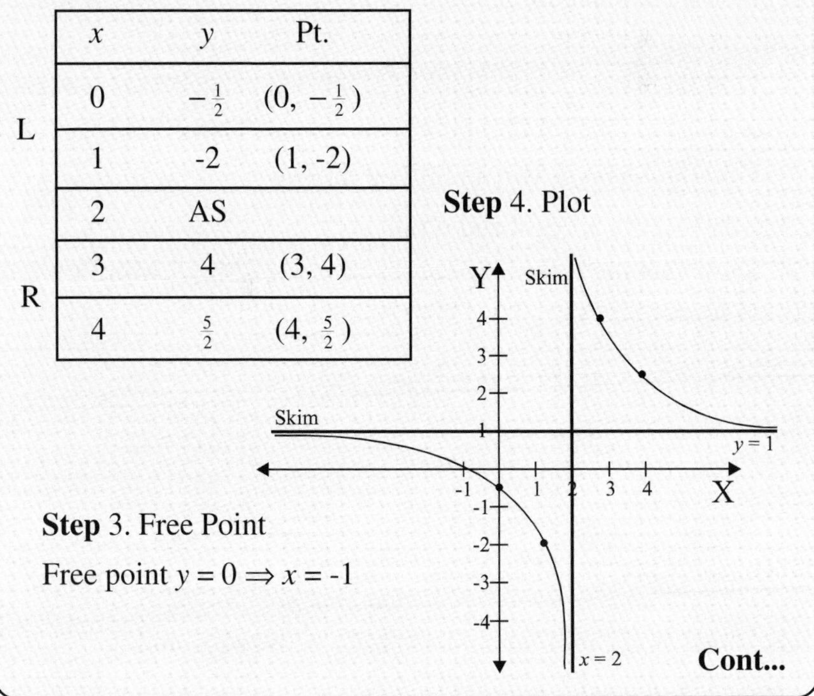

	x	y	Pt.
L	0	$-\frac{1}{2}$	$(0, -\frac{1}{2})$
L	1	-2	(1, -2)
	2	AS	
R	3	4	(3, 4)
R	4	$\frac{5}{2}$	$(4, \frac{5}{2})$

Step 4. Plot

Step 3. Free Point

Free point $y = 0 \Rightarrow x = -1$

Cont...

$$\left(\frac{dy}{dx}\right)_{x_1} = \left(\frac{dy}{dx}\right)_{x_2}$$

Slope at x_1 = slope at x_2

$$\Rightarrow -\frac{3}{(x_1-2)^2} = -\frac{3}{(x_2-2)^2}$$

$$\Rightarrow (x_2-2)^2 = (x_1-2)^2 \Rightarrow x_2 - 2 = \pm(x_1-2)$$

⊕	⊝
$x_2 - 2 = x_1 - 2$	$x_2 - 2 = -x_1 + 2$
$\Rightarrow x_1 = x_2$	$\Rightarrow x_1 + x_2 = 4$

Exercise 3 (Answers: page **353**)

Curve Sketching

1. Find the LMax/LMin and PI's if any of $y = x^3 - 6x^2 + 9x$ and plot it.
2. Find the LMax/LMin and PI's if any of $y = x^3 - 3x^2 - 9x + 2$ and plot it.
3. Find the LMax/LMin and PI's if any of $y = 2x^3 - 3x^2 - 12x + 4$ and plot it.
4. Show that the following curves have no LMax/LMin/PI's. Find the asymptotes and sketch roughly.

(a) $y = \dfrac{x}{x+1}$ (b) $y = \dfrac{4}{x-2}$ (c) $y = \dfrac{x-1}{x+1}$

(d) $y = \dfrac{5x}{2x-1}$ (e) $y = \dfrac{2x-3}{x+4}$ (f) $y = \dfrac{1}{x-3}$

5. If the slope of the tangent to $y = \dfrac{x-1}{x+2}$ at (x_1, y_1) is equal to the slope at (x_2, y_2) find a relationship between x_1 and x_2.

6. Show $y = \frac{x-1}{x-2}$ has no LMax/LMin/PI's. Find the asymptotes and sketch it roughly. If the tangent at $x_1 = 3$ is parallel to the tangent at (x_2, y_2), find (x_2, y_2).

7. Find LMax/LMin/PI of the curve $y = x^3 + 5x^2 + 3x - 9$. Show it has 2 real roots. What are they?

8. Find the LMax/LMin of the curve $y = 2x^3 - 9x^2 + 12x + 20$. Without sketching it show it has only one root.

4. RATE OF CHANGE (ROC)

Rate of change problems all involve differentiating with respect to **time** t. So the rate of change of volume $= \frac{dV}{dt}$.

TRICK

Increasing $\Rightarrow$ ROC > 0

Decreasing $\Rightarrow$ ROC < 0

Max/Min $\Rightarrow$ ROC $= 0$

4.1 ROC PROBLEMS

Steps for ROC problems:

STEPS

1. Write down ROC(s) given.
2. Write down ROC to be found.
3. Write down a formula involving the non-time variables.
4. Differentiate this formula implicitly with respect to time (t).
5. Plonk in the numbers.

Trick: To write down a formula connecting the non-time variables, 3 situations arise:
1. You are given the formula (thank you).
2. You know the formula (cop on).
3. You are led to the formula (Help).

Example 1: A monkey throws a banana along a path given by $y = x^2 - \frac{3}{x}$. If the x co-ordinate is increasing at 2 cm/s find the rate of change of the y co-ordinate when $x = 7$ cm.

SOLUTION

Step 1. $\frac{dx}{dt} = +2$ (ROC given)

Step 2. $\frac{dy}{dt} = ?$ (ROC to be found)

Step 3. $y = x^2 - \frac{3}{x} \Rightarrow y = x^2 - 3(x)^{-1}$ (Formula involving non-time variables given)

Step 4. $\frac{dy}{dt} = 2x\frac{dx}{dt} + 3x^{-2}\frac{dx}{dt}$ (Differentiate implicitly wrt t)

Step 5. $\frac{dy}{dt} = 2.7.2 + \frac{3}{49}.2 = 28\frac{6}{49}$ cm/s (Plonk in $x = 7$)

Example 2: If the radius of a circle is increasing at 5 m/s, find the rate of change of the area when the radius is 22 m.

SOLUTION

Step 1. $\frac{dr}{dt} = 5$

Step 2. $\frac{dA}{dt} = ?$

Step 3. $A = \pi r^2$

Step 4. $\frac{dA}{dt} = \pi(2r)\frac{dr}{dt}$

Step 5. $\frac{dA}{dt} = \pi \times 2 \times 22 \times 5 = 220\pi\ \text{m}^2/\text{s}$

Example 3: If the perimeter is 15 cm, express θ in terms of r. Express the area A in terms of r. If the area increases at 40 cm²/s find the rate of change of radius when the radius is 20 cm.

Solution

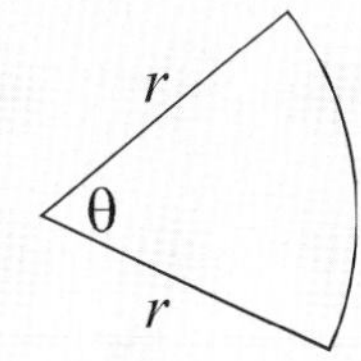

$$15 = 2r + r\theta \Rightarrow \theta = \frac{15-2r}{r}$$

$$A = \tfrac{1}{2}r^2\theta = \tfrac{1}{2}r^2\left(\frac{15-2r}{r}\right) \Rightarrow A = \tfrac{15}{2}r - r^2$$

Step 1. $\frac{dA}{dt} = 40$

Step 2. $\frac{dr}{dt} = ?$

Step 3. $A = \tfrac{15}{2}r - r^2$

Step 4. $\frac{dA}{dt} = \frac{15}{2}\frac{dr}{dt} - 2r\frac{dr}{dt}$

Step 5. $40 = \frac{15}{2}\frac{dr}{dt} - 2.20\frac{dr}{dt} \Rightarrow 40 = \frac{dr}{dt}(\tfrac{15}{2} - 40)$

$$\therefore -\frac{(2)(40)}{65} = \frac{dr}{dt} \Rightarrow \frac{dr}{dt} = -\frac{16}{13}\text{ cm/s}$$

Example 4: o is the centre of a circle of radius 1 cm. Express l^2 in terms of θ using the cosine rule. If θ is increasing at 2 rad/s find the rate of change of l when $\theta = \frac{\pi}{3}$.

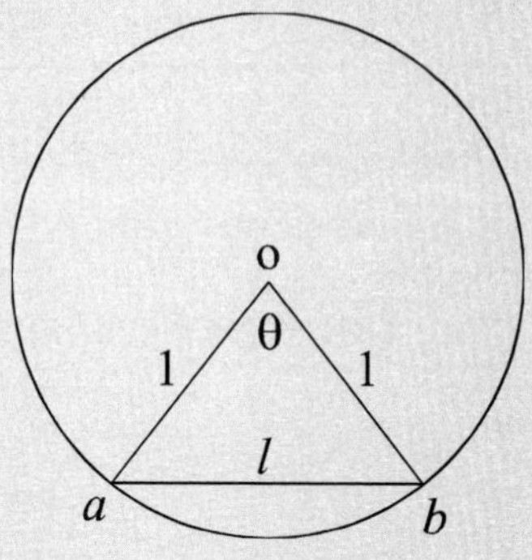

SOLUTION

$l^2 = 1^2 + 1^2 - 2.1.1\cos\theta$

$\Rightarrow l^2 = 2 - 2\cos\theta$

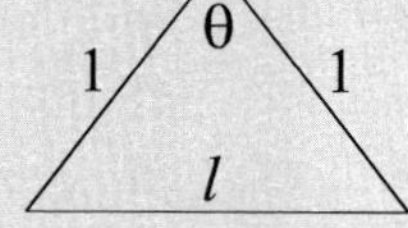

Step 1. $\frac{d\theta}{dt} = 2$

Step 2. $\frac{dl}{dt} = ?$

Step 3. $l^2 = 2 - 2\cos\theta$

Step 4. $2l\frac{dl}{dt} = 2\sin\theta\frac{d\theta}{dt}$

Step 5. $2.1.\frac{dl}{dt} = 2\sin\frac{\pi}{3}.2$

$\theta = \frac{\pi}{3} \Rightarrow l^2 = 2 - 2\cos\frac{\pi}{3}$
$= 2 - 1$
$\therefore l = 1$

$\therefore \frac{dl}{dt} = \frac{2\sqrt{3}}{2} = \sqrt{3}$ cm/s

4.2 DISPLACEMENT/VELOCITY/ACCELERATION

1. s = **Displacement** (Position, distance, height) (**Unit**: m)
2. $v = \dfrac{ds}{dt}$ = **Velocity** (Speed) (**Unit**: m/s)
3. $\therefore a = \dfrac{dv}{dt} = v\dfrac{dv}{ds}$ = **Acceleration** (**Unit**: m/s^2)

Example 5: The displacement s for a body travelling in a straight line in metres is given by: $s = t^3 - 6t^2 + 9t$, after t seconds. Find
(i) initial velocity
(ii) when the body is at rest
(iii) displacement after 4 seconds
(iv) initial acceleration
(v) when the acceleration is zero.

SOLUTION

Trick: Draw up a s, v, a box

$$s = t^3 - 6t^2 + 9t$$

$$v = \frac{ds}{dt} = 3t^2 - 12t + 9$$

$$a = \frac{dv}{dt} = 6t - 12$$

Step 1. $v = ?, t = 0$

$v = 3t^2 - 12t + 9$
$\therefore t = 0 \Rightarrow v = 9$ m/s

Step 2. $t = ?, v = 0$

$v = 3t^2 - 12t + 9 = 0$
$\Rightarrow t^2 - 4t + 3 = 0$
$\Rightarrow (t - 1)(t - 3) = 0$
$\therefore t = 1$ s, 3 s

Step 3. $s = ?, t = 4$

$s = t^3 - 6t^2 + 9t$
$t = 4 \Rightarrow s = 64 - 96 + 36 = 4$ m

Step 4. $a = ?, t = 0$

$a = 6t - 12$
$t = 0 \Rightarrow a = -12$ m/s^2

Step 5. $t = ?, a = 0$ $\Rightarrow a = 6t - 12 = 0 \Rightarrow t = 2$ s

Exercise 4 (Answers: page **353**)

Rate of Change (ROC)

1. The side of a square is increasing at 2 cm/s. At what rate is the area increasing when the length of a side is 10 cm?

2. If $y = \frac{1000}{x}$ and $\frac{dx}{dt} = 50$ find $\frac{dy}{dt}$ when $x = 200$.

3. Find an expression for the area of the rectangle. If $\frac{dx}{dt} = 2$ cm/s find $\frac{dA}{dt}$ when $x = 10$ cm.

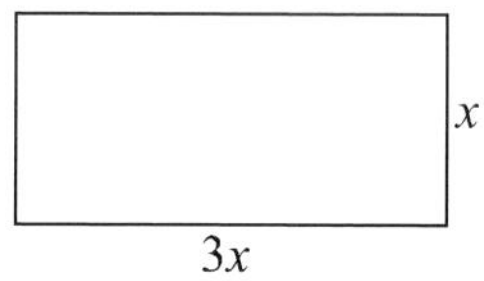

4. The area of a circle is increasing at a rate of 4 cm²/min. Find the rate at which the radius is increasing when the circumference is 20 cm.

5. Express (i) volume V, (ii) surface area, A, in terms of x. If $\frac{dx}{dt} = 1$ find (a) $\frac{dV}{dt}$, (b) $\frac{dA}{dt}$ when the volume is 40 cm³.

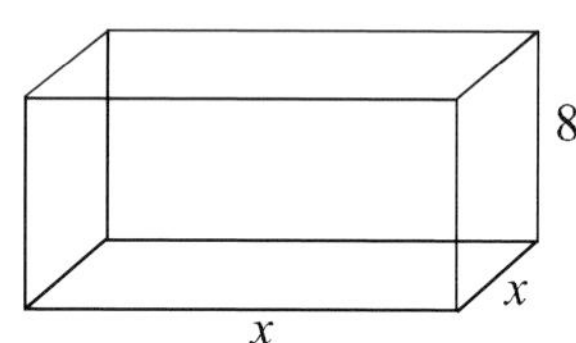

6. The side x of an equilateral triangle is increasing at p m/hr. How fast is the area increasing when $x = \frac{2p}{\sqrt{3}}$?

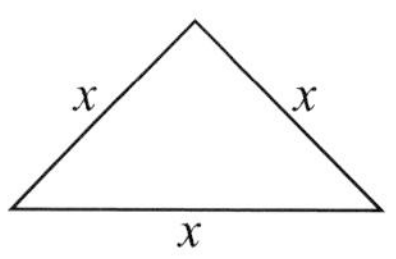

7. A point moves along the curve $y^2 = 6x$. At what point do the x and y co-ordinates increase at the same rate?

8. A point moves on the curve $3x^2 - y^2 = 12$ so that the y co-ordinate increases at 12 m/s. At what rate is the x co-ordinate changing when $x = 4$? ($y > 0$)

9. If $\frac{1}{u} + \frac{1}{v} = \frac{1}{10}$ find $\frac{dv}{dt}$ if $\frac{du}{dt} = 5$ cm/s when $u = 25$ cm.

10. The volume of a sphere is increasing at a constant rate. Find the rate of change of the surface area in terms of the radius.

11. If $y = x^2 - \frac{2}{x}$ find $\frac{dy}{dx}$ if $\frac{dx}{dt} = 4$ when $x = 2$.

12. The area of a circle is increasing at 6 m²/s. How fast is the radius increasing when the radius is 2 m?

13. In the right circular cone, h is a constant. Express l^2 in terms of h and r. If $\frac{dr}{dt} = \sqrt{2}$ find $\frac{dl}{dt}$ when $r = h$. Find

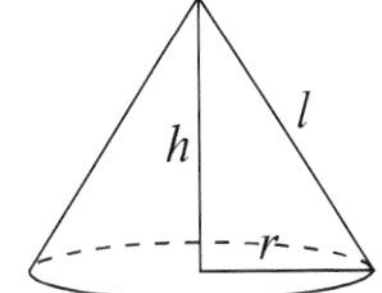

(a) $\frac{dV}{dt}$ when $r = h$, (b) $\frac{dA}{dt}$ when $r = h$.

(A is the total surface area.)

14. If $\cos\theta + \sin\theta = x$ and $\frac{d\theta}{dt} = 5$ find $\frac{dx}{dt}$ when $\theta = \frac{\pi}{6}$.

15. o is the centre of a circle of radius 1. Use the Cosine rule to express l^2 in terms of θ. If $\frac{d\theta}{dt} = 3$ rad/s find $\frac{dl}{dt}$ when

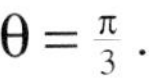
$\theta = \frac{\pi}{3}$.

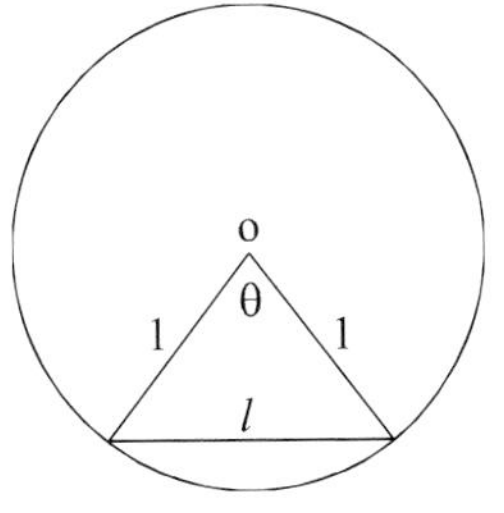

16. In the right angled triangle $\frac{d\theta}{dt} = 2$ rad/s.

Find $\frac{dh}{dt}$ when $\theta = \frac{\pi}{3}$.

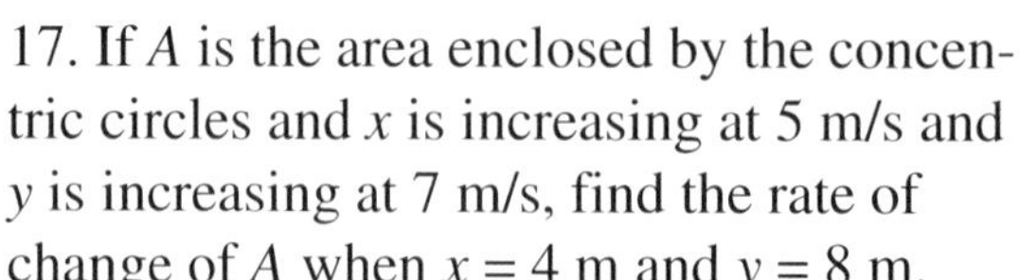

17. If A is the area enclosed by the concentric circles and x is increasing at 5 m/s and y is increasing at 7 m/s, find the rate of change of A when $x = 4$ m and $y = 8$ m.

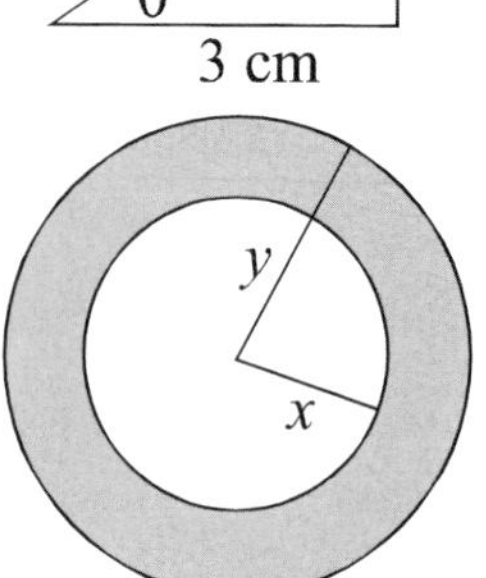

18. If the perimeter is 16 cm, express θ in terms of r. Also express the area A in terms of r. If r increases at 0.2 cm/s, find the rate of change of A when $r = 5$ cm.

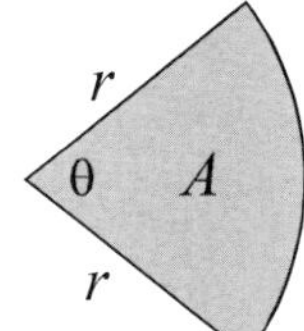

19. An astronaut p at x km above the earth's surface moves away at a rate of $\frac{dx}{dt} = \frac{r}{5}$ km/hr where r is the radius of the earth. Express x in terms of r and θ. Find $\frac{d\theta}{dt}$ when $x = r$.

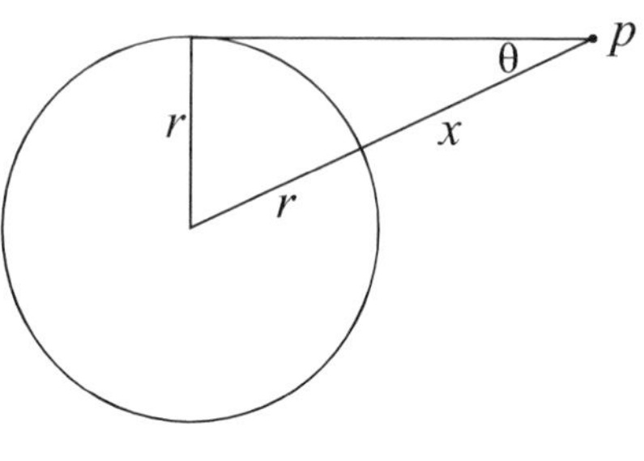

20. The displacement s for a body travelling in a straight line is given by $s = 2t^3 - 15t^2 + 36t$ after time t secs. Find
(a) the initial velocity,
(b) when the body is at rest,
(c) the displacement when $t = 4$,
(d) the initial acceleration,
(e) when the acceleration is zero.

21. A ball is thrown vertically upwards. After t seconds its height is s metres where $s = 12 + 14t - 4.9t^2$. Find
(a) the height when $t = 2$,
(b) the velocity when $t = 1$,
(c) the acceleration at $t = 2$.

22. If $s = 4 + 10t + 5t^2$ show that the acceleration is constant and find its value.

23. The velocity of a particle is related to its displacement by $v^2 = 10s - s^2$. Find
(a) its velocity when $s = 1$,
(b) its acceleration when $s = 1$.

24. If the velocity time formula is $v = 4t^2 - 4t - 3$, find the acceleration when the velocity is 5 m/s. Find the velocity when the acceleration is 0 m/s^2.

5. NEWTON-RAPHSON APPROXIMATION (NRA)

The NRA is a formula to find the approximate roots of equations. On the LC course this means approximate roots of quadratic and cubic equations.

5.1 THE NRA FORMULA

If x_n is the $n^{th.}$ approximation to a root of an equation $f(x) = 0$ then

$$x_{n+1} = x_n - \frac{f(x_n)}{f'(x_n)} \qquad n = \{0, 1, 2, ...\}$$

is a better approximation, etc..

Notes: 1. This is an iterative formula, i.e. it can be applied again and again to get a better and better approx.

For $n = 1$: $x_2 = x_1 - \dfrac{f(x_1)}{f'(x_1)}$. For $n = 2$: $x_3 = x_2 - \dfrac{f(x_2)}{f'(x_2)}$.

2. Roots are places where the curve crosses the X-axis.

TRICK

If a function crosses the X-axis between 2 whole numbers, a and b, the value of the function at these numbers changes sign.

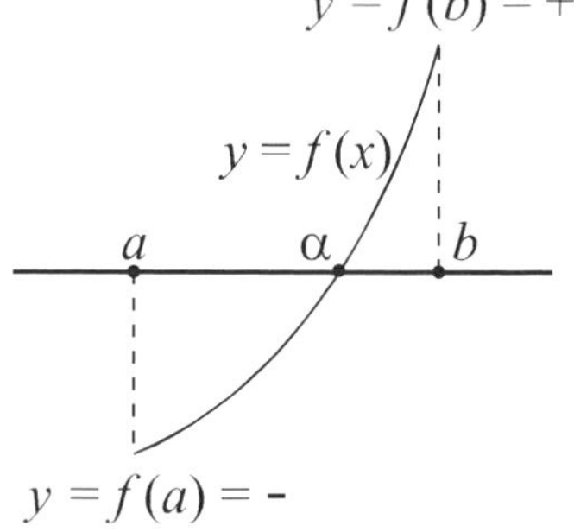

Example 1: Show $f(x) = x^3 + x^2 - 4x - 10 = 0$ has a root between 2 and 3.

SOLUTION

$f(x) = x^3 + x^2 - 4x - 10$

$f(2) = 8 + 4 - 8 - 10 = -6 < 0$ The value of the function

$f(3) = 27 + 9 - 12 - 10 = 14 > 0$ changes sign.

$\therefore$ root between 2 and 3.

5.2 USING NRA

STEPS

1. Write down $f(x)$.
2. Do $f'(x)$.
3. Plonk starting value x_n into $x_{n+1} = x_n - \dfrac{f(x_n)}{f'(x_n)}$.
4. Repeat if asked.

Example 2: Using $x_1 = 1$ find x_2 and x_3 from NRA for the function $f(x) = x^3 + 3x^2 + x - 2$.

SOLUTION

Step 1. $f(x) = x^3 + 3x^2 + x - 2$

Step 2. $f'(x) = 3x^2 + 6x + 1$

Step 3. $x_1 = 1 \Rightarrow x_2 = 1 - \dfrac{(1+3+1-2)}{(3+6+1)} = 1 - \dfrac{3}{10} = \dfrac{7}{10} = 0.7$

Step 4. $x_2 = 0.7 \Rightarrow x_3 = 0.7 - \dfrac{(0.7^3 + 3\times0.7^2 + 0.7 - 2)}{(3\times0.7^2 + 6\times0.7 + 1)}$

$= 0.7 - \dfrac{0.513}{6.67} = 0.7 - 0.0769 = 0.62$

Example 3: For $f(x) = x^3 - x^2 - x + 7$ use NRA to show that

$x_{n+1} = \dfrac{2x_n^3 - x_n^2 - 7}{(3x_n + 1)(x_n - 1)}$. If $x_2 = k$ when $x_1 = -2$, find k.

SOLUTION

Step 1. $f(x) = x^3 - x^2 - x + 7$

Step 2. $f'(x) = 3x^2 - 2x - 1$

Step 3. $x_{n+1} = x_n - \dfrac{(x_n^3 - x_n^2 - x_n + 7)}{(3x_n^2 - 2x_n - 1)}$

$$= \frac{3x_n^3 - 2x_n^2 - x_n - x_n^3 + x_n^2 + x_n - 7}{(3x_n + 1)(x_n - 1)}$$

$$\Rightarrow x_{n+1} = \frac{2x_n^3 - x_n^2 - 7}{(3x_n + 1)(x_n - 1)}$$

Step 4. $n = 1$: $x_2 = \dfrac{2(-2)^3 - (-2)^2 - 7}{(3(-2)+1)(-2-1)} = \dfrac{-16-4-7}{(-5)(-3)} = -\dfrac{27}{15} = k$

Exercise 5 (Answers: page **354**)

Newton Raphson

1. Show that $x^3 + 2x^2 - 5x - 7 = 0$ has a root between 2 and 3. Find x_2 using $x_1 = 2$ correct to one decimal place.

2. Using NR for $f(x) = x^3 - 3x + 1$ to show $x_{n+1} = \dfrac{2x_n^3 - 1}{3x_n^2 - 3}$.

3. Use NR for $f(x) = 3x^3 - x - 1$ to show $x_{n+1} = \dfrac{6x_n^3 + 1}{9x_n^2 - 1}$. Show that $3x^3 - x - 1 = 0$ has a root between 0 and 1. Use $x_1 = 1$ to find x_3 correct to 2 decimal places.

4. For $f(x) = x^3 - 12x + 1$ show that $x_{n+1} = \dfrac{2x_n^3 - 1}{3(x_n - 2)(x_n + 2)}$.

If $x_2 = k$ when $x_1 = 1$, find k.

5. Show $f(x) = x^3 - 4x^2 + 2 = 0$ has
(a) root α between -1 and 0,
(b) root β between 0 and 1,
(c) root γ between 1 and 4.
Use NR to find x_2 for α using $x_1 = -1$.

6. Find LMax/LMin of $y = f(x) = x^3 - 2x^2 + x + 2$. Show that $f(x) = x^3 - 2x^2 + x + 2 = 0$ has only one real root. Show that this root is between -1 and 0. Using $x_1 = -1$ in NR as a first approximation find x_2.

APPLICATIONS OF DIFFERENTIATION REVISION QUESTIONS

These 3 part questions are similar to the questions on the LC paper. The answers to these questions and hints to help you solve them are available on our website:

www.studentxpress.ie

1. (a) Find the derivatives of (i) $2x - \frac{3}{x^2+1}$, (ii) $\frac{1}{x^2+1}$.

(b) If $y = x^3 + \frac{1}{x^3}$ prove that $3y + x\frac{dy}{dx} = 6x^3$.

(c) Find the local max./local min. of $y = \sin x - \cos x$, $0 \le x \le 2\pi$.

2. (a) Differentiate $y = \sin x$ from first principles.
(b) Find the equation of the tangent to the curve
$3x^3 + 2xy^2 = 2y + 3$ at the point (1, 0).

(c) Show that the maximum value of $y = 1 + 2x - e^x$ is $\ln\left(\frac{4}{e}\right)$.

3. (a) Differentiate $y = \sqrt{x}$ from first principles.

(b) If $y = \tan^{-1} x$ show that $\frac{d^2y}{dx^2} + 2x\left(\frac{dy}{dx}\right)^2 = 0$.

(c) If $f(x) = \frac{1}{2}(e^x - e^{-x})$ show that $\frac{f''(2x)}{f(x)} = 2f'(x)$.

4. (a) Differentiate with respect to x: (i) $\ln\left(\frac{1-x}{1+x}\right)$, (ii) $(\sin x)^2$.

(b) If $y = \tan^2 x$ show $\frac{d^2y}{dx^2} = 2(1+y)(1+3y)$.

(c) If $x = \theta - \sin\theta$, $y = 1 - \cos\theta$ show $\frac{dy}{dx} = \cot\left(\frac{\theta}{2}\right)$.

5. (a) Find where the tangents to $y = x^3 - 12x + 4$ are parallel to the X-axis.

(b) Differentiate wrt x: (i) $\frac{1-\cos x}{\sin x}$, (ii) $\ln\cos^2 x$, (iii) $\sqrt{\frac{1-e^x}{1+e^x}}$.

(c) If $y = e^{kx}$ and $\frac{d^2y}{dx^2} - 3\frac{dy}{dx} + 2y = 0$, find $k \in R$.

6. (a) Differentiate $y = \cos x$ from first principles.

(b) Differentiate wrt x: (i) $\frac{1+\cos x}{1-\cos x}$, (ii) $\frac{1+\ln x}{x}$.

(c) Find the equation of the tangent to the curve $x = \frac{1}{2}(1-e^{-t})$, $y = 2t + e^t$ at the point where $x = 0$.

7. (a) Find the equation of the tangent to the curve $y = \sin(\frac{1}{x})$ at $x = \frac{1}{\pi}$.

(b) If $f(x) = \frac{1}{2}(e^x + e^{-x})$ show

$[f'(x)]^2 = [f(x)]^2 - 1$.

(c) S is a circle of radius 2, centre o. Use the cosine rule to express l in terms of θ. If θ increases at 5 rad/s, find the rate of change of l when $\theta = \frac{\pi}{6}$.

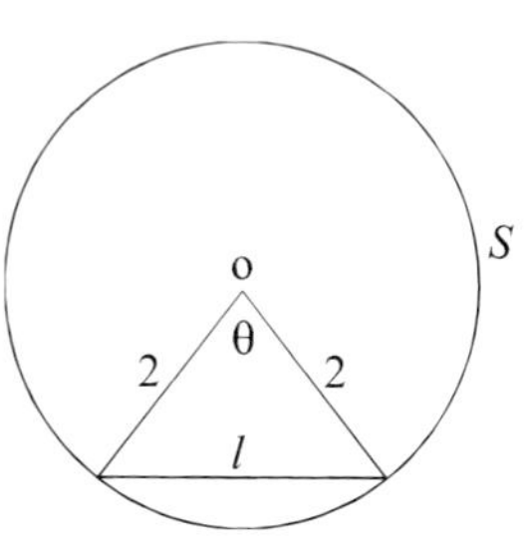

8. (a) Show $x^3 + 2x^2 - 5x - 7 = 0$ has a root between 2 and 3. If $x_1 = 2$, find x_2 correct to one decimal point using the Newton-Raphson formula.

(b) $y = ax^2 + bx + c$ passes through (2, 4) and $y = x + 1$ is a tangent at (0, 1). Find a, b, c.

(c) If $f(x) = xe^{-x}$ show $f''(x) + 2f'(x) + f(x) = 0$.

9. (a) If $y = \sin^{-1}\sqrt{x}$ show $\dfrac{dy}{dx} = \dfrac{1}{\sin 2y}$.

(b) (i) If $y = \tan x + \frac{1}{3}\tan^3 x$ show $\dfrac{dy}{dx} = \sec^4 x$.

(ii) If $y = (k + x)\cos x$, k const., show $\dfrac{d^2y}{dx^2} + y$ is independent of k.

(c) If the perimeter of oab is 30 cm express θ in terms of r. Hence, express the area of oab in terms of r. If the radius is increasing at 2 cm/s find the rate of change of the area when the radius is 3 cm.

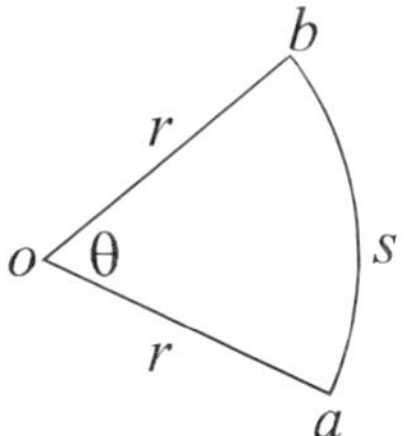

10. (a) Differentiate $y = \frac{1}{x}$ from first principles.

(b) If $y = \ln \sin^3 2x$ show $3\dfrac{d^2y}{dx^2} + \left(\dfrac{dy}{dx}\right)^2 + 36 = 0$.

(c) Show $f(x) = \dfrac{1-x}{1+x}$ has no local max./local min. or PI's. Find the asymptotes and sketch it roughly.

11. (a) If $y = (\tan x + \sec x)^m$ show $\dfrac{dy}{dx} = my\sec x$.

(b) Find the local max. and local min. of the curve $y = 2x^3 - 9x^2 + 12x + 20$. Show it has only one real root.

(c) If $x = e^{kt}\cos t$, $y = e^{kt}\sin t$ show $\dfrac{dy}{dx} = \tan(\alpha + t)$ where

$\tan\alpha = \frac{1}{k}$.

12. (a) Differentiate with respect to x: $y = \tan^{-1}\left(\dfrac{2x}{1-x^2}\right)$.

(b) Find the equation of the tangent to the curve $\sqrt{x} + \sqrt{y} = 5$ at $x = 4$.

(c) The curve $y = \dfrac{px+q}{x^3+1}$ has a slope of zero at (1, 3). Show that

$p = 9$ and find q if p and q are constants.

13. (a) Differentiate with respect to x: (i) $2\sin x\cos x$ at $x = \frac{\pi}{8}$,

(ii) $x^2 \ln x$ at $x = e$.

(b) If $y = \dfrac{2x-1}{4}e^{2x}$ find the value of $\dfrac{dy}{dx}$ when $x = \ln 3$.

(c) Find the equation of the tangent to the curve $y = \tan^{-1}(x\sqrt{x})$ at the point where $x = 1$.

14. (a) If $f(x) = \frac{1}{2}(e^x - e^{-x})$ show $f(x).f'(x) = \frac{1}{2}f(2x)$.

(b) If (i) $y = \ln(2x^2 - 3)$ find $\dfrac{dy}{dx}$ at $x = 2$.

(ii) $y = \ln\left(\dfrac{1+x}{1-x}\right)$ find $\dfrac{dy}{dx}$ in the form $\dfrac{p}{q - x^n}$.

(c) Find the $\frac{1}{x} + \frac{1}{y} = 2$ express y in terms of x and hence find the minimum value of xy, $x, y \neq 0$.

Answers and hints to Applications of Differentiation Revision Questions available on: **www.studentxpress.ie**

ANSWERS

Exercise 1 [*Curves* (page **318**)]

1. $9x - y - 16 = 0$, (1, -2), (-1, 2)
2. $x - y - 7 = 0$, (2, -5), $(-\frac{2}{3}, \frac{49}{27})$
3. (0, 0), $(\frac{4}{3}, -\frac{32}{27})$
4. $a = 4, b = 6, c = 0, d = 0$
6. $3x - 4y - 1 = 0$, $c = \frac{1}{3}$
7. $(-a, -\frac{a}{2}), (a, \frac{a}{2})$
9. (8, 7)
10. $x = 2$, $x = \frac{2}{9}$
11. $c = 1$
12. -1, $\frac{1}{2}$
13. (a) (2, 6), (b) $(\frac{1}{3}, \frac{4}{27})$, (-1, 0), (c) $(2, \frac{7}{2})$, $(-2, \frac{5}{2})$
14. (a) D, (b) I, (c) I, (d) I, (e) I
15. (a) CUP, (b) CUP, (c) CUP, (d) CUP, (e) CAP
17. (a) TP (0, 0); PI (-1, ln 2), (1, ln 2)

(b) TP (e, e); PI $(e^2, \frac{e}{2})$

(c) no TP's; PI (0, 0)

Exercise 2 [*Max/Min* (page **326**)]

1. (a) (2, 16), (-2, -16) (b) (-2, 0), (0, -1) (c) (-2, 45), (6, -211)
   (d) $(-2, -\frac{1}{2}), (2, \frac{1}{2})$ (e) (0, 0), (-4, -8) (f) None
   (g) LMin: (2, 3) (h) LMin: $(a, 3a^2)$
2. (a) LMax: $(\frac{1}{2}\ln 2, 2\ln 2 - 2)$ (b) LMin: $(\frac{1}{e}, -\frac{1}{e})$
   (c) LMin: $(-1, -\frac{1}{e})$ (d) LMax: $(\frac{1}{4}, \frac{1}{4e})$(e) LMin: (e, e)
   (f) LMin: (1, 3)
3. (a) LMax: $(\frac{7\pi}{6}, \frac{7\pi}{12} + \frac{\sqrt{3}}{2})$, LMin: $(\frac{11\pi}{6}, \frac{11\pi}{12} - \frac{\sqrt{3}}{2})$

(b) LMax: ($\frac{\pi}{4}$, $\frac{\pi}{4} - \ln\sqrt{2}$), LMax: ($\frac{5\pi}{4}$, $\frac{5\pi}{4} + \ln\sqrt{2}$)

(c) LMax: ($\frac{\pi}{3}$, $\sqrt{3} - \frac{\pi}{3}$), LMin: ($\frac{5\pi}{3}$, $-\sqrt{3} - \frac{5\pi}{3}$)

(d) LMax: ($\frac{\pi}{4}$, $\sqrt{2}$), LMin: ($\frac{5\pi}{4}$, $-\sqrt{2}$)

4. $\frac{1}{4}$ 5. 8 6. $-\frac{1}{2}$

7. 1 8. 6 9. 6

Exercise 3 [*Curve Sketching* (page **334**)]

1. LMax: (1, 4); LMin: (3, 0); PI: (2, 2)
2. LMax: (-1, 7); LMin: (3, -25); PI: (1, 9)
3. LMax: (-1, 11); LMin: (2, -16); PI: ($\frac{1}{2}$, $-\frac{5}{2}$)
4. (a) $x = -1$, $y = 1$ (b) $x = 2$, $y = 0$ (c) $x = -1$, $y = 1$
   (d) $x = \frac{1}{2}$, $y = \frac{5}{2}$ (e) $x = -4$, $y = 2$ (f) $x = 3$, $y = 0$
5. $x_1 + x_2 = -4$
6. Asymptotes: $x = 2$, $y = 1$; $(x_2, y_2) = (1, 0)$
7. LMax: (-3, 0); LMin: ($-\frac{1}{3}$, $-\frac{256}{27}$); PI: ($-\frac{5}{3}$, $-\frac{128}{27}$)
8. LMax: (1, 25); LMin: (2, 24); PI: ($\frac{3}{2}$, $24\frac{1}{2}$)

Exercise 4 [*Rate of Change ROC* (page **340**)]

1. 40 cm^2 s^{-1} 2. $-1\frac{1}{4}$ 3. 120 cm^2/s

4. $\frac{1}{5}$ cm/min. 5. (a) $16\sqrt{5}$ cm^3/s, (b) $4(\sqrt{5}+8)$ cm^2/s

6. p^2 m^2/hr 7. ($\frac{3}{2}$, 3) 8. 6 m/s

9. $-\frac{20}{9}$ cm/s 10. $\frac{2c}{r}$ 11. 18

12. $\frac{3}{2\pi}$ m/s 13. 1, $\frac{2\sqrt{2}\pi h^2}{3}$, $\pi h(3+2\sqrt{2})$

14. $\frac{5}{2}(\sqrt{3}-1)$ 15. $\frac{3\sqrt{3}}{2}$ cm/s 16. 24 cm/s

17. 72π m^2/s 18. $\frac{16-2r}{r}$, $8r - r^2$, -0.4 cm^2/s

19. $-\frac{1}{10\sqrt{3}}$ rad/s

20. (a) 36 m/s, (b) 3 s, 2 s, (c) 32 m, (d) -30 m/s^2, (e) 2.5 s
21. (a) 20.4 m, (b) 4.2 m/s, (c) -9.8 m/s^2
22. 10 m/s^2
23. (a) $v = \pm 3$ m/s, (b) $a = 4$ m/s^2
24. 12 m/s^2, -4 m/s

Exercise 5 [*Newton Raphson Approximation NRA* (page **347**)]

1. $\frac{31}{15}$
3. 0.85
4. $-\frac{1}{9}$
5. $-\frac{8}{11}$
6. $-\frac{3}{4}$

Integration

1. THE IDEA

Integration is the opposite to **differentiation**. It could be called anti-differentiation.

Notation: $\int f(x)dx$ = Think of a function which when you differentiate with respect to x you get $f(x)$.

Note: $f(x)$ is called the **integrand**.

Example 1: Evaluate $\int x^2 dx$.

SOLUTION

$\int x^2 dx$ = Can you think of a function which when you differentiate with respect to x you get x^2.

$\int x^2 dx = \frac{x^3}{3} + 4$ *OR* $\int x^2 dx = \frac{x^3}{3} + \frac{1}{2}$ *OR*

$\int x^2 dx = \frac{x^3}{3} +$ any constant c

This is known as indefinite integration as the constant c is indeterminable.

TRICK

Don't forget the c!

Example 2: $\int x^7 dx = \frac{x^8}{8} + c$

Example 3: $\int x^{\frac{1}{2}} dx = \frac{x^{\frac{3}{2}}}{\frac{3}{2}} + c = \frac{2x^{\frac{3}{2}}}{3} + c$

Example 4: $\int \frac{1}{x^3} dx = \int x^{-3} dx = \frac{x^{-2}}{-2} + c = -\frac{1}{2x^2} + c$

2. STARTING INTEGRATION

2.1 THE RULES

[A] **POWER RULE**: $\int x^p dx = \frac{x^{p+1}}{p+1} + c$ for all $p \in R$

except p = -1 (Odd Man Out OMO)

NOTE: This is a nifty trick for integrating Algebraic functions, i.e. functions of the form $\int x^p dx$.

TRICK

$\int x^p dx$ = Add 1 to the power of x and divide by the new power + c

Example 1: $\int x^{\frac{1}{3}} dx = \frac{x^{\frac{4}{3}}}{\frac{4}{3}} + c = \frac{3}{4} x^{\frac{4}{3}} + c$

Example 2: $\int \frac{1}{x^2} dx = \int x^{-2} dx = \frac{x^{-1}}{-1} + c = -\frac{1}{x} + c$

Example 3: $\int \frac{1}{t^{\frac{1}{2}}} dt = \int t^{-\frac{1}{2}} dt = \frac{t^{\frac{1}{2}}}{\frac{1}{2}} + c = 2t^{\frac{1}{2}} + c$

[B] **SUM RULE**

$$\int (f(x) + g(x))\, dx = \int f(x)\, dx + \int g(x)\, dx$$

Trick: You can integrate each function in a sum of functions separately.

Example 4: $\int (x^2 + x^3)\, dx = \int x^2\, dx + \int x^3\, dx = \frac{x^3}{3} + \frac{x^4}{4} + c$

You can do it all in one go by integrating each function as you go along.

Example 5: $\int \left(\frac{1}{x^2} + \sqrt{x} \right) dx = \int (x^{-2} + x^{\frac{1}{2}})\, dx = \frac{x^{-1}}{-1} + \frac{x^{\frac{3}{2}}}{\frac{3}{2}} + c$

$= -\frac{1}{x} + \frac{2}{3} x^{\frac{3}{2}} + c$

[C] **MULTIPLICATION BY A CONSTANT RULE**

$$\int kf(x)\,dx = k\int f(x)\,dx$$

Trick: You can take constants out of integrals.

Example 6: $\int 3x^7 dx = 3\int x^7 dx = \frac{3}{8}x^8 + c$

You can do it all in one go by writing down the constant and multiplying it by the integral of the function.

Example 7: $\int\left(\frac{2}{\sqrt{x}} + \frac{3}{x^2}\right)dx = \int (2x^{-\frac{1}{2}} + 3x^{-2})\,dx$

$= \frac{2x^{\frac{1}{2}}}{\frac{1}{2}} + \frac{3x^{-1}}{-1} + c = 4\sqrt{x} - \frac{3}{x} + c$

[D] **THE ONE RULE**

$$\int dx = \int 1dx = \int x^0 dx = \frac{x^1}{1} + c$$

$$\therefore \int dx = x + c$$

Example: $\int dt = t + c$

Example: $\int dl = l + c$

2.2 DEFINITE INTEGRATION

Sometimes at the end of doing an integral you are required to fill in values (limits of integration).

$$\int_a^b f(x)dx = [g(x)]_a^b = g(b) - g(a)$$

Steps for doing a definite integral $\int_a^b f(x)dx$:

STEPS
1. Do the integral as normal.
2. Don't write a constant c.
3. Put the values in a box with the limits as shown: $\left[\quad\right]_a^b$
4. Plonk in b for the variable first and then subtract off the value when a is plonked in.

Trick 1: $\displaystyle\int_a^a f(x)\,dx = 0$

Trick 2: $\displaystyle -\int_a^b f(x)\,dx = \int_b^a f(x)\,dx$

Try to prove both tricks.

Example 8: $\displaystyle\int_1^3 x^2 dx = \left[\frac{x^3}{3}\right]_1^3 = \left(\frac{27}{3} - \frac{1}{3}\right) = \frac{26}{3}$

Trick: You can take out constants as factors from the boxes.

Example 9: $\displaystyle\int_1^4 x^{\frac{1}{2}} dx = \left[\frac{x^{\frac{3}{2}}}{\frac{3}{2}}\right]_1^4 = \tfrac{2}{3}[x^{\frac{3}{2}}]_1^4 = \tfrac{2}{3}(4^{\frac{3}{2}} - 1^{\frac{3}{2}}) = \tfrac{2}{3}(8-1) = \tfrac{14}{3}$

Trick: Never plonk into negative powers

Example 10: $\displaystyle\int_1^2 (3x^2 + \tfrac{2}{x^2})\,dx = \int_1^2 (3x^2 + 2x^{-2})\,dx = \left[x^3 + \frac{2x^{-1}}{-1}\right]_1^2$

$\displaystyle = \left[x^3 - \frac{2}{x}\right]_1^2 = (8 - \tfrac{2}{2}) - (1 - \tfrac{2}{1}) = 7 + 1 = 8$

3. TECHNIQUES OF INTEGRATION

The most important technique on the course is substitution. It is used for products, quotients of functions and composite functions (lousy brackets) which cannot be simplified into a sum of simple functions.

> Let u = that part of the integrand such that when you differentiate it you get a multiple of another part of the integrand.

Types of integrals on the LC course

3.1 **ALINT**: Integrals with pure algebraic functions
3.2 **EXPINT**: Integrals with any hint of the exponential function
3.3 **LOGINT**: The inverse linear function and e-ln
3.4 **TRIGINT**: Integrals with pure trig functions
3.5 **SPECIALS**: 3 algebraic functions that require unusual substitutions

Always call your integral, I.

3.1 ALGEBGRAIC INTEGRATION (ALINT)

This is the integration of pure algebraic functions. The basis of ALINT is:

$$\int x^p dx = \frac{x^{p+1}}{p+1} + c \text{ for all } p \in R \text{ except } p = -1 \text{ when}$$

$$\int x^{-1} dx = \int \frac{1}{x} dx = \int \frac{dx}{x} = \ln x + c$$ (**Odd Man Out** (OMO))

In words: Add 1 to the power of x and divide by the new power for all powers except -1 when the answer is ln x.

NOTES: 1. $\int \frac{dx}{x} = \ln x + c$ could be regarded as the **Odd Man Out** (**OMO**). Keep an eye out for it.

2. $\int dx = \int 1\, dx = x + c$

Types of ALINT

[A] **Straights**: Sum of multiples of x^p.

STEPS

1. Tidy up the algebra (multiply out brackets etc..).
2. Integrate out term by term.

Example 1: Evaluate $\int\left(x+\frac{1}{\sqrt{x}}\right)^2 dx$.

SOLUTION

$$I=\int\left(x+\frac{1}{\sqrt{x}}\right)^2 dx=\int(x^2+2x^{\frac{1}{2}}+\tfrac{1}{x})\,dx=\frac{x^3}{3}+\frac{4x^{\frac{3}{2}}}{3}+\ln x+c$$

Example 2: $\int\left(\frac{3x^2-x}{2x}\right)dx$.

SOLUTION

$$I=\int\left(\frac{3x^2-x}{2x}\right)dx=\int\left(\frac{3x}{2}-\frac{1}{2}\right)dx=\frac{3x^2}{4}-\frac{x}{2}+c$$

Example 3: Evaluate $\int_1^2(2x-\tfrac{1}{x})\,dx$.

TRICK

ln 1 = 0 always.
Do you know why?

SOLUTION

$$I=\int_1^2(2x-\tfrac{1}{x})\,dx=\left[x^2-\ln x\right]_1^2=(4-\ln 2)-(1-\ln 1)$$

$$=4-\ln 2-1=3-\ln 2$$

[B] **Products and Quotients of Algebraic Functions** which cannot be simplified into sums of multiples of x^p.

STEPS

1. Tidy up the algebra (factors in particular).
2. Let u = the function inside the complicated bracket.

Example 4: Evaluate $\int x^2\sqrt{x^3+1}\,dx$.

SOLUTION

$$I = \int x^2\sqrt{x^3+1}\,dx = \int \sqrt{x^3+1}.x^2dx$$

Let $u = x^3 + 1 \Rightarrow du = 3x^2dx \Rightarrow \frac{1}{3}du = x^2dx$

Rewriting: $I = \frac{1}{3}\int u^{\frac{1}{2}}\,du$ (Put $\frac{1}{3}$ out in front, du at the back)

$$\therefore I = \tfrac{1}{3}\left(\frac{2}{3}u^{\frac{3}{2}}\right) + c = \tfrac{2}{9}(x^3+1)^{\frac{3}{2}} + c$$

Example 5: Evaluate $\int \frac{3x\,dx}{x^4-4x^2+4}$.

SOLUTION

$$I = 3\int \frac{x\,dx}{(x^2-2)^2}$$ (Take out 3 and factorise the denominator)

Let $u = x^2 - 2 \Rightarrow du = 2xdx \Rightarrow \frac{1}{2}du = xdx$

Rewriting: $I = \frac{3}{2}\int u^{-2}du = \frac{3}{2}\left(\frac{u^{-1}}{-1}\right) + c = -\frac{3}{2u} + c$

$$\therefore I = -\frac{3}{2(x^2-2)} + c$$

Trick: If you make a substitution don't forget to change the limits

Example 6: Evaluate $\int_1^4 \frac{dx}{\sqrt{x}(2+\sqrt{x})}$.

SOLUTION

$$I = \int_1^4 \frac{dx}{\sqrt{x}(2+\sqrt{x})}$$

Let $u = 2+\sqrt{x} \Rightarrow du = \frac{1}{2\sqrt{x}}dx$

$$\Rightarrow 2du = \frac{1}{\sqrt{x}}dx$$

Changing the limits

$u = 2+\sqrt{x}$

$x = 1 \Rightarrow u = 2+\sqrt{1} = 3$

$x = 4 \Rightarrow u = 2+\sqrt{4} = 4$

Rewriting: $I = 2\int_3^4 \frac{du}{u} = 2[\ln u]_3^4 = 2(\ln 4 - \ln 3) = 2\ln(\frac{4}{3})$

Example 7: Evaluate $\int_0^1 \frac{(x+2)\,dx}{(x+1)^2}$.

SOLUTION

$$I = \int_0^1 \frac{(x+2)\,dx}{(x+1)^2}$$

Let $u = x+1 \Rightarrow du = dx$

Changing the limits

$u = x+1$

$x = 0 \Rightarrow u = 0+1 = 1$

$x = 1 \Rightarrow u = 1+1 = 2$

Rewriting: $I = \int_1^2 \frac{(u+1)\,du}{u^2}$ because $u = x+1 \Rightarrow u+1 = x+2$

$$\therefore I = \int_1^2 (u^{-1}+u^{-2})\,du = \left[\ln u - \frac{1}{u}\right]_1^2 = (\ln 2 - \tfrac{1}{2}) - (\ln 1 - \tfrac{1}{1})$$

$$= \ln 2 - \tfrac{1}{2} + 1 = \ln 2 + \tfrac{1}{2}$$

Exercise 1 (Answers: page **414**)

Algebraic Integration

I. **Straights**

1. $\int_{-1}^{2}(5x^4+3x^2-4)\,dx$

2. $\int_{1}^{2}\frac{x^3+1}{x^2}\,dx$

3. $\int_{1}^{3}\frac{(l-1)^2}{l^4}\,dl$

4. $\int_{0}^{4}s(s-1)(s-2)\,ds$

5. $\int(1-p^2)\sqrt{p}\,dp$

6. $\int(\frac{1}{\theta^3}+\frac{1}{\theta^2}-2)\,d\theta$

7. $\int_{1}^{4}\frac{ax^2+bx+c}{\sqrt{x}}\,dx$

8. $\int\frac{ax^{-2}+bx^{-1}+c}{x^{-3}}\,dx$

9. $\int\left(\phi-\frac{1}{\sqrt{\phi}}\right)^2\,d\phi$

10. $\int(\sqrt{x}+3)(x+2)\,dx$

11. $\int_{-4}^{-2}(x+\frac{2}{x})^2\,dx$

12. $\int_{1}^{4}\frac{x+1}{\sqrt{x}}\,dx$

13. $\int\frac{x^2+2x+1}{x^3}\,dx$

14. $\int(2x+\frac{3}{x})(2x-\frac{3}{x})\,dx$

15. $\int_{0}^{1}(m-\sqrt{m})(m+\sqrt{m})\,dm$

16. $\int_{-\frac{1}{3}}^{\frac{4}{5}}k\,dt$

17. $\int_{1}^{3}1\,dt$

18. $\int_{-1}^{-1}f(x)\,dx$

19. $\int\frac{x^3-5}{x^2}\,dx$

20. $\int(\frac{1}{x^2}+\frac{1}{x^3}-\frac{1}{x})\,dx$

II. Algebraic Substitution

1. $\int_1^2 \frac{5x}{(3x^2-2)^2}\,dx$

2. $\int_0^3 x\sqrt{x^2+16}\,dx$

3. $\int_4^8 \frac{x}{\sqrt{x^2-15}}\,dx$

4. $\int_0^3 (8x+4)(x^2+x+4)^{\frac{3}{2}}\,dx$

5. $\int_4^5 \frac{x}{(x-3)^3}\,dx$

6. $\int \frac{x^2-1}{x^2}\left(x+\frac{1}{x}\right)^{\frac{5}{4}}\,dx$

7. $\int (4x+3)(2x-5)^7\,dx$

8. $\int_0^1 (1-p)^{99}\,dp$

9. $\int_0^1 \frac{(1+t^{\frac{2}{3}})^{\frac{5}{3}}}{t^{\frac{1}{3}}}\,dt$

10. $\int_0^1 \frac{(1+\sqrt{x})^7}{3\sqrt{x}}\,dx$

11. $\int_1^2 \frac{x+2}{x^2+4x}\,dx$

12. $\int_0^4 \frac{l+4}{(l^2+8l+1)}\,dl$

13. $\int_0^4 \frac{dx}{(6x+1)^{\frac{1}{2}}}$

14. $\int_2^3 \frac{x^2}{x-1}\,dx$

15. $\int_0^1 \frac{dx}{(2-\sqrt{x})^2\sqrt{x}}$

16. $\int_1^2 3\sqrt{t-1}\,dt$

17. $\int_2^3 \frac{x+1}{x+2}\,dx$

18. $\int_1^0 x(1-x)^{12}\,dx$

19. $\int_0^1 \frac{(x+1)^2-1}{x+1}\,dx$

20. $\int_2^4 \frac{k^2}{k^3-5}\,dk$

3.2 Exponential Integration (ExpInt)

This is the integration of any function containing the Expofn.

The basis of ExpInt is $\int e^x dx = e^x + c$. This is the easiest function on the course to integrate because when you integrate it you get the same function back again. It can be extended:

$$\int e^{ax+b} dx = \tfrac{1}{a} e^{ax+b} + c$$

Types of ExpInt

[A] **Straights**: Expofunctions which can be simplified into sums of expofunctions of the form e^{ax+b}

Steps

1. Tidy up expoalgebra.
2. Integrate out term by term using $\int e^{ax+b} dx = \tfrac{1}{a} e^{ax+b} + c$.

Example 8: Evaluate $\int \sqrt{\dfrac{e^{2x-1}}{e^{-4x-5}}}\, dx$.

Solution

$$I = \int \left(\frac{e^{2x-1}}{e^{-4x-5}}\right)^{\frac{1}{2}} dx = \int (e^{6x+4})^{\frac{1}{2}} dx = \int e^{3x+2} dx = \tfrac{1}{3} e^{3x+2} + c$$

Example 9: Evaluate $\int (e^x + e^{-x})^2\, dx$.

Solution

$$I = \int (e^x + e^{-x})^2 dx = \int (e^{2x} + 2 + e^{-2x})\, dx$$

$$= \tfrac{1}{2} e^{2x} + 2x - \tfrac{1}{2} e^{-2x} + c = \tfrac{e^{2x}}{2} + 2x - \tfrac{1}{2e^{2x}} + c$$

TRICK
When e and ln come together they cancel each other out (e-ln trick)
$$e^{\ln f(x)} = f(x)$$
$$\ln e^{f(x)} = f(x)$$

Example 10: Evaluate $\int_0^{\ln 2} \sqrt{e^x}\,dx$.

SOLUTION

$$I = \int_0^{\ln 2} \sqrt{e^x}\,dx = \int_0^{\ln 2} e^{\frac{1}{2}x}\,dx = 2[e^{\frac{1}{2}x}]_0^{\ln 2}$$

$$= 2(e^{\frac{1}{2}\ln 2} - e^0) = 2(e^{\ln\sqrt{2}} - 1) = 2(\sqrt{2} - 1)$$

[B] **Products and Quotients of Expo and non-expo functions**

STEPS
1. Tidy up the algebra.
2. Let u = the power of the expofunction.

Example 11: Evaluate $\int_1^4 \frac{\sqrt{x}e^{\sqrt{x}}dx}{x}$.

SOLUTION

$$I = \int_1^4 \frac{\sqrt{x}e^{\sqrt{x}}dx}{x} = \int_1^4 x^{-\frac{1}{2}}e^{\sqrt{x}}dx$$

Let $u = \sqrt{x} = x^{\frac{1}{2}} \Rightarrow du = \frac{1}{2}x^{-\frac{1}{2}}dx$

$\Rightarrow 2du = x^{-\frac{1}{2}}dx$

Changing the limits
$$u = \sqrt{x}$$
$$x = 1 \Rightarrow u = \sqrt{1} = 1$$
$$x = 4 \Rightarrow u = \sqrt{4} = 2$$

Rewriting: $I = 2\int_1^2 e^u\,du = 2[e^u]_1^2 = 2(e^2 - e) = 2e(e-1)$

Example 12: Evaluate $\int \frac{e^{\cos^2 x} \sin 2x dx}{e^{\sin^2 x}}$.

SOLUTION

$$I = \int \frac{e^{\cos^2 x} \sin 2x dx}{e^{\sin^2 x}} = \int e^{\cos 2x} \sin 2x dx$$

Let $u = \cos 2x \Rightarrow du = -2\sin 2x\, dx \Rightarrow -\frac{1}{2} du = \sin 2x dx$

Rewriting: $I = -\frac{1}{2} \int e^u du = -\frac{1}{2} e^u + c$

$\therefore I = -\frac{1}{2} e^{\cos 2x} + c$

Example 13: Evaluate $\int_1^9 \frac{e^{(x-1)^{\frac{2}{3}}}}{(x-1)^{\frac{1}{3}}} dx$.

SOLUTION

$$I = \int_1^9 \frac{e^{(x-1)^{\frac{2}{3}}}}{(x-1)^{\frac{1}{3}}} dx$$

Let $u = (x-1)^{\frac{2}{3}}$

$\Rightarrow du = \frac{2}{3}(x-1)^{-\frac{1}{3}} dx$

$\Rightarrow \frac{3}{2} du = \frac{dx}{(x-1)^{\frac{1}{3}}}$

Changing the limits

$u = (x-1)^{\frac{2}{3}}$

$x = 1 \Rightarrow u = (1-1)^{\frac{2}{3}} = 0$

$x = 9 \Rightarrow u = (9-1)^{\frac{2}{3}} = 8^{\frac{2}{3}} = 4$

$\therefore I = \frac{3}{2} \int_0^4 e^u du = \frac{3}{2} [e^u]_0^4 = \frac{3}{2}(e^4 - 1)$

[C] **Products and Quotients** of pure expofns which cannot be simplified into a sum of expofns of the form e^{ax+b}.

STEPS

1. Tidy up the algebra.
2. Let u = the expofn inside the complicated bracket.

Example 14: Evaluate $\displaystyle\int \frac{e^x dx}{(e^x+7)^2}$.

SOLUTION

$$I = \int \frac{e^x dx}{(e^x+7)^2}$$

Let $u = e^x + 7 \Rightarrow du = e^x dx$

Rewriting: $\displaystyle I = \int u^{-2} du = -\frac{1}{u} + c$

$$\therefore I = -\frac{1}{(e^x+7)} + c$$

Example 15: Evaluate $\displaystyle\int_0^{\ln 2} \frac{e^x(e^x-1)\,dx}{e^{2x}-2e^x+5}$.

SOLUTION

$$I = \int_0^{\ln 2} \frac{e^x(e^x-1)\,dx}{e^{2x}-2e^x+5}$$

Let $u = e^{2x} - 2e^x + 5$

$\Rightarrow du = (2e^{2x} - 2e^x)\,dx$

$\Rightarrow \frac{1}{2}du = e^x(e^x-1)\,dx$

Changing the limits

$u = e^{2x} - 2e^x + 5$

$x = 0 \quad \Rightarrow u = e^0 - 2e^0 + 5 = 4$

$x = \ln 2 \quad \Rightarrow u = e^{2\ln 2} - 2e^{\ln 2} + 5$

$= e^{\ln 4} - 2e^{\ln 2} + 5$

$= 4 - 2(2) + 5 = 5$

Rewriting: $\displaystyle I = \tfrac{1}{2}\int_4^5 \frac{du}{u} = \tfrac{1}{2}[\ln u]_4^5 = \tfrac{1}{2}(\ln 5 - \ln 4) = \tfrac{1}{2}\ln(\tfrac{5}{4})$

Example 16: Evaluate $\int \frac{e^{x}-e^{-x}}{e^{x}+e^{-x}}\,dx$.

SOLUTION

$$I=\int \frac{e^{x}-e^{-x}}{(e^{x}+e^{-x})}\,dx$$

Let $u=e^{x}+e^{-x} \Rightarrow du=(e^{x}-e^{-x})\,dx$

$$\therefore I=\int \frac{du}{u}=\ln u+c$$

Rewriting: $I=\ln(e^{x}+e^{-x})+c$

Exercise 2 (Answers: page **414**)

Exponential Integration

I. **Straights**

1. $\int_{0}^{1} e^{-x}\,dx$

2. $\int_{0}^{1} e^{3x}\,dx$

3. $\int_{-1}^{0} e^{4x+5}\,dx$

4. $\int_{-1}^{0} \frac{1}{e^{2x-3}}\,dx$

5. $\int_{0}^{2} \frac{e^{x}}{e^{2x-5}}\,dx$

6. $\int_{0}^{1} (e^{x+2})^{2}\,dx$

7. $\int_{0}^{\ln 2} (e^{x})^{\frac{1}{3}}\,dx$

8. $\int_{0}^{1} 5e^{3x-6}\,dx$

9. $\int_{0}^{1} (e^{x}+e^{-x})^{2}\,dx$

10. $\int_{0}^{\ln 2} (e^{x}-2)(e^{3x}+4)\,dx$

11. $\int_{\frac{7}{4}}^{2} \frac{3e^{3x}}{e^{-x+7}}\,dx$

12. $\int_{0}^{1} (3e^{5x+6}+7)\,dx$

II. **Products and Quotients of Expos and non-expos**:

1. $\displaystyle\int_{-1}^{0} x^3 e^{-x^4}\, dx$

2. $\displaystyle\int_{1}^{2} (2x-1)e^{x^2-x}\, dx$

3. $\displaystyle\int_{4}^{9} \frac{\sqrt{x}e^{\sqrt{x}}}{x}\, dx$

4. $\displaystyle\int_{-2}^{-1} \frac{xe^{-\frac{1}{x}}}{x^3}\, dx$

5. $\displaystyle\int_{1}^{9} \frac{e^{(t-1)^{\frac{2}{3}}}}{(t-1)^{\frac{1}{3}}}\, dt$

6. $\displaystyle\int_{1}^{4} \frac{\sqrt{x}e^{\frac{1}{\sqrt{x}}}}{x^2}\, dx$

7. $\displaystyle\int_{0}^{1} (2x+1)e^{x}.e^{x^2}\, dx$

8. $\displaystyle\int_{0}^{\frac{\pi}{3}} \frac{\sin x\, e^{\sec x}}{\cos^2 x}\, dx$

9. $\displaystyle\int_{0}^{2} 2x\, e^{\frac{1}{4}x^2+8}\, dx$

10. $\displaystyle\int_{0}^{\frac{\pi}{4}} \frac{e^{\tan x}}{\cos^2 x}\, dx$

III. **Products and Quotients of exponential functions which cannot be simplified into a single function**.

1. $\displaystyle\int_{0}^{\ln 2} \frac{e^x}{(e^x+7)^3}\, dx$

2. $\displaystyle\int_{0}^{\ln 2} \frac{e^x}{e^x+3}\, dx$

3. $\displaystyle\int_{0}^{\ln 2} \frac{e^x(4e^x-1)}{\sqrt{6e^{2x}-3e^x+1}}\, dx$

4. $\displaystyle\int_{0}^{\ln 2} \frac{e^x-e^{-x}}{e^x+e^{-x}}\, dx$

5. $\displaystyle\int_{\ln 2}^{\ln 3} \frac{e^x}{(e^x+1)^2}\, dx$

3.3 LOGARITHMIC INTEGRATION (LOGINT)

This is integration of the inverse linear function (**OMO**) and *e*-ln.

[A] The Inverse Linear Function

It is based on $\int \frac{dx}{x} = \ln x + c$. However, this can be extended to

$$\int \frac{dx}{ax+b} = \frac{1}{a}\ln(ax+b)+c.$$

Example 17: Evaluate $\int \frac{dx}{3x-4}$.

SOLUTION

$$\mathrm{I} = \int \frac{dx}{3x-4} = \tfrac{1}{3}\ln(3x-4)+c$$

Example 18: Evaluate $\int_0^1 \frac{dx}{x+1}$.

SOLUTION

$$\mathrm{I} = \int_0^1 \frac{dx}{x+1} = [\ln(x+1)]_0^1 = \ln 2 - \ln 1 = \ln 2$$

Example 19: Evaluate $\int_2^3 \frac{dx}{3x}$.

SOLUTION

$$\mathrm{I} = \int_2^3 \frac{dx}{3x} = \tfrac{1}{3}\int_2^3 \frac{dx}{x} = \tfrac{1}{3}[\ln x]_2^3 = \tfrac{1}{3}(\ln 3 - \ln 2) = \tfrac{1}{3}\ln(\tfrac{3}{2})$$

[B] e-ln: Remember the e-ln trick.

Example 20: Evaluate $\int_1^2 \ln e^{3x}\, dx$.

SOLUTION

$$I = \int_1^2 \ln e^{3x}\, dx = \int_1^2 3x\, dx = \tfrac{3}{2}[x^2]_1^2 = \tfrac{3}{2}(4-1) = \tfrac{9}{2}$$

Example 21: Evaluate $\int_0^1 e^{\frac{1}{2}\ln x}\, dx$.

SOLUTION

$$\int_0^1 e^{\frac{1}{2}\ln x}\, dx = \int_0^1 e^{\ln x^{\frac{1}{2}}}\, dx = \int_0^1 x^{\frac{1}{2}}\, dx = \tfrac{2}{3}[x^{\frac{3}{2}}]_0^1 = \tfrac{2}{3}(1-0) = \tfrac{2}{3}$$

Exercise 3 (Answers: page **415**)

Log Integration

1. $\int_2^3 \frac{dx}{x-1}$
2. $\int_1^4 \frac{dx}{3x+1}$
3. $\int_2^4 \frac{dx}{-x+5}$
4. $\int_8^{12} \frac{dx}{\frac{x}{2}-3}$
5. $\int_0^1 \frac{dx}{1+2x}$
6. $\int_0^1 \frac{4dx}{-2x-1}$
7. $\int_5^7 \ln e^x\, dx$
8. $\int_1^2 \ln e^{2x}\, dx$
9. $\int_2^3 \ln e^{x^2}\, dx$
10. $\int \ln 7e^{x^p}\, dx$
11. $\int_1^2 e^{\ln x}\, dx$
12. $\int_1^3 e^{\ln x^2}\, dx$
13. $\int_1^4 e^{\frac{1}{2}\ln x}\, dx$
14. $\int_1^4 e^{2-\ln x}\, dx$

3.4 TRIGONOMETRIC INTEGRATION (TRIGINT)

This is the integration of pure trig functions. The basis of TRIGINT is 3 results:

(a) $\int \sin(ax+b)\,dx = -\frac{1}{a}\cos(ax+b)+c$

(b) $\int \cos(ax+b)\,dx = \frac{1}{a}\sin(ax+b)+c$

(c) $\int \sec^2(ax+b)\,dx = \frac{1}{a}\tan(ax+b)+c$

Types of TRIGINT

[A] **Straights**: Simple trig functions

STEPS
Integrate according to (a), (b), (c) above.

Example 22: Evaluate $\int \sin 3x\,dx$.

SOLUTION

$$I = \int \sin 3x\,dx = -\tfrac{1}{3}\cos 3x + c$$

Example 23: Evaluate $\int_0^{\frac{\pi}{3}} \cos 4x\,dx$.

SOLUTION

$$I = \int_0^{\frac{\pi}{3}} \cos 4x\,dx = \tfrac{1}{4}[\sin 4x]_0^{\frac{\pi}{3}} = \tfrac{1}{4}(\sin\tfrac{4\pi}{3} - \sin 0) \;= \tfrac{1}{4}(-\tfrac{\sqrt{3}}{2} - 0) = -\tfrac{\sqrt{3}}{8}$$

Example 24: Evaluate $\int \sec^2(3x-2)\,dx$.

SOLUTION

$$I = \int \sec^2(3x-2)\,dx = \tfrac{1}{3}\tan(3x-2)+c$$

[B] **Prodsums**: These are products of sin nx, cos nx.

STEPS

1. Change these products into sums using the prodsum formulae on page 9 of the tables.
2. Integrate each part using the standard integrals in (a), (b), (c).

Example 25: Evaluate $\int \sin 2x \cos 3x \, dx$.

TRICK

You must supply a **2** for the Prodsum formulae to work.

SOLUTION

$$I = \int \sin 2x \cos 3x \, dx = \tfrac{1}{2} \int 2 \sin 2x \cos 3x \, dx$$

$$= \tfrac{1}{2} \int (\sin 5x + \sin(-x)) \, dx = \tfrac{1}{2} \int (\sin 5x - \sin x) \, dx$$

$$= \tfrac{1}{2}(-\tfrac{1}{5}\cos 5x + \cos x) + c$$

Example 26: Evaluate $\int_0^{\frac{\pi}{4}} \cos 2x \cos 4x \, dx$.

SOLUTION

$$I = \int_0^{\frac{\pi}{4}} \cos 2x \cos 4x \, dx = \tfrac{1}{2} \int_0^{\frac{\pi}{4}} 2\cos 2x \cos 4x \, dx$$

$$= \tfrac{1}{2} \int_0^{\frac{\pi}{4}} (\cos 6x + \cos(-2x)) \, dx$$

NOTE: Always deal with negative signs inside trig functions immediately.
sin $(-x)$ = - sin x (Minus filters out)
tan $(-x)$ = - tan x (Minus filters out)
cos $(-x)$ = cos x (Minus rubs out)

$$= \tfrac{1}{2} \int_0^{\frac{\pi}{4}} (\cos 6x + \cos 2x) \, dx$$

$$= \tfrac{1}{2}\left[\tfrac{1}{6}\sin 6x + \tfrac{1}{2}\sin 2x\right]_0^{\frac{\pi}{4}}$$

$$= \tfrac{1}{2}\left\{(\tfrac{1}{6}\sin(\tfrac{3\pi}{2}) + \tfrac{1}{2}\sin(\tfrac{\pi}{2})) - (\tfrac{1}{6}\sin 0 + \tfrac{1}{2}\sin 0\right\} = \tfrac{1}{2}(-\tfrac{1}{6} + \tfrac{1}{2}) = \tfrac{1}{6}$$

[C] **Quotients**: These are quotients of trig functions.

STEPS

1. Make sure the angles are the same. These trig identities may be useful:
   $\cos 2x = \cos^2 x - \sin^2 x$ and $\sin 2x = 2\sin x \cos x$
2. Let u = trig function in the bracket on the bottom.
3. These trig identities may be useful:
   $\sin^2 x + \cos^2 x = 1$ and $\sec^2 x = 1 + \tan^2 x$

Example 27: Evaluate $\int_0^{\frac{\pi}{3}} \frac{\sin x}{\sqrt{\cos x}}\, dx$.

SOLUTION

$$I = \int_0^{\frac{\pi}{3}} \frac{\sin x}{(\cos x)^{\frac{1}{2}}}\, dx$$

Let $u = \cos x \Rightarrow du = -\sin x dx$

Changing the limits

$u = \cos x$

$x = 0 \Rightarrow u = \cos 0 = 1$

$x = \frac{\pi}{3} \Rightarrow u = \cos\frac{\pi}{3} = \frac{1}{2}$

$$\therefore I = -\int_1^{\frac{1}{2}} \frac{1}{u^{\frac{1}{2}}}\, du = -\int_1^{\frac{1}{2}} u^{-\frac{1}{2}}\, du = -2[u^{\frac{1}{2}}]_1^{\frac{1}{2}} = -2(\tfrac{1}{\sqrt{2}} - 1) = 2(1 - \tfrac{1}{\sqrt{2}})$$

Example 28: Evaluate $\int \frac{\cos^3 x\, dx}{\sin^2 x}$.

SOLUTION

$$I = \int \frac{\cos^3 x\, dx}{(\sin x)^2}$$

Let $u = \sin x \Rightarrow du = \cos x dx$

Use $\cos^2 x = 1 - \sin^2 x = 1 - u^2$

TRICK

Grab one of the $\cos x$'s and stick it to the dx.

$$\Rightarrow I = \int \frac{\cos^2 x(\cos x\, dx)}{(\sin x)^2} = \int \frac{(1-u^2)\, du}{u^2} = \int (u^{-2} - 1)\, du$$

$$= \tfrac{u^{-1}}{-1} - u + c = -\tfrac{1}{u} - u + c$$

$$\therefore I = -\tfrac{1}{\sin x} - \sin x + c$$

Example 29: Evaluate $\int_0^{\frac{\pi}{3}} \frac{\sin x}{1+\cos 2x}\,dx$.

SOLUTION

$$I = \int_0^{\frac{\pi}{3}} \frac{\sin x}{1+\cos 2x}\,dx$$

The angles are different.
Use $\cos 2x = \cos^2 x - \sin^2 x$ to make the angles the same.

$$\therefore I = \int_0^{\frac{\pi}{3}} \frac{\sin x}{1+\cos^2 x - \sin^2 x}\,dx$$

$$= \tfrac{1}{2}\int_0^{\frac{\pi}{3}} \frac{\sin x}{(\cos x)^2}\,dx$$

Changing the limits

$u = \cos x$

$x = 0 \Rightarrow u = \cos 0 = 1$

$x = \frac{\pi}{3} \Rightarrow u = \cos\frac{\pi}{3} = \frac{1}{2}$

Let $u = \cos x \Rightarrow du = -\sin x\,dx$
Rewriting:

$$\therefore I = -\tfrac{1}{2}\int_1^{\frac{1}{2}} u^{-2}\,du = -\tfrac{1}{2}\left[\frac{u^{-1}}{-1}\right]_1^{\frac{1}{2}} = \tfrac{1}{2}\left[\frac{1}{u}\right]_1^{\frac{1}{2}} = \tfrac{1}{2}(2-1) = \tfrac{1}{2}$$

[D] **Powers of sin and cos**

(a) **Squares**: These are the integrals of $\sin^2 nx$ and $\cos^2 nx$.

Trick: Get rid of the squares immediately using:

$$\sin^2 A = \tfrac{1}{2}(1-\cos 2A)$$
$$\cos^2 A = \tfrac{1}{2}(1+\cos 2A)$$

from page 9 of the tables.

Example 30: Evaluate $\int_0^{\frac{\pi}{16}} \sin^2 4x\, dx$.

SOLUTION

$$I = \int_0^{\frac{\pi}{16}} \sin^2 4x dx = \tfrac{1}{2}\int_0^{\frac{\pi}{16}} (1 - \cos 8x)\, dx = \tfrac{1}{2}\left[x - \frac{\sin 8x}{8}\right]_0^{\frac{\pi}{16}}$$

$$= \tfrac{1}{2}\{\tfrac{\pi}{16} - \tfrac{1}{8}\sin\tfrac{\pi}{2}\} = \tfrac{1}{2}\{\tfrac{\pi}{16} - \tfrac{1}{8}\} = \tfrac{1}{32}(\pi - 2)$$

Example 31: Evaluate $\int \sin^2 3x \cos^2 3x\, dx$.

SOLUTION

$$I = \int \sin^2 3x \cos^2 3x\, dx = \tfrac{1}{2}.\tfrac{1}{2}\int (1 - \cos 6x)(1 + \cos 6x)\, dx$$

$$= \tfrac{1}{4}\int (1 - \cos^2 6x)\, dx = \tfrac{1}{4}\int \sin^2 6x\, dx = \tfrac{1}{8}\int (1 - \cos 12x)\, dx$$

$$= \tfrac{1}{8}(x - \tfrac{1}{12}\sin 12x) + c$$

(b) **Powers**: These are products of $\sin^n ax$, $\cos^m ax$, n, m not both even, $n \in N_0$.

(i) **EO**: One even power and one odd power.

STEPS

1. Bracket the even power trig function.
2. Break off one of the odd power trig functions and bracket it with dx.
3. Let u = trig function with even power.
4. Remember $\sin^2 x + \cos^2 x = 1$

Example 32: Evaluate $\int \sin x \cos^{18} x\,dx$.

SOLUTION

$$I = \int (\cos x)^{18} (\sin x\,dx)$$

Let $u = \cos x \Rightarrow du = -(\sin x)\,dx$

$$\therefore I = -\int u^{18}\,du = -\tfrac{1}{19}u^{19} + c$$

Rewriting: $I = -\tfrac{1}{19}(\cos x)^{19} + c$

Example 33: Evaluate $\int \sin^3 x \cos^4 x\,dx$.

SOLUTION

$$I = \int (\cos x)^4 \sin^2 x (\sin x)\,dx$$

Let $u = \cos x \Rightarrow du = -(\sin x)\,dx$

$$\therefore I = -\int u^4(1-u^2)\,du = -\int (u^4 - u^6)\,du = -\tfrac{u^5}{5} + \tfrac{u^7}{7} + c$$

$$\therefore I = -\tfrac{1}{5}\cos^5 x + \tfrac{1}{7}\cos^7 x + c$$

(ii) **OO**: 2 odd powers

STEPS

1. Bracket the higher powered trig function.
2. Break off one of the other trig functions and bracket with dx.
3. Let $u =$ trig function with the higher power.
4. Remember $\sin^2 x + \cos^2 x = 1$

Example 34: Evaluate $\int_0^{\frac{\pi}{6}} \sin^3 x \cos x \, dx$.

SOLUTION

$$I = \int_0^{\frac{\pi}{6}} (\sin x)^3 (\cos x \, dx)$$

Let $u = \sin x \Rightarrow du = \cos x \, dx$

$$\therefore I = \int_0^{\frac{1}{2}} u^3 du = \tfrac{1}{4}[u^4]_0^{\frac{1}{2}} = \tfrac{1}{4}(\tfrac{1}{16} - 0) = \tfrac{1}{64}$$

Exercise 4 (Answers: page **415**)

Trigonometric Integration

1. **Straights**

(a) $\int_0^{\frac{\pi}{4}} \cos 2x \, dx$

(b) $\int_0^{\pi} \sin \tfrac{1}{2} x \, dx$

(c) $\int_0^{\frac{\pi}{2}} \cos 7x \, dx$

(d) $\int_{\frac{3}{2}}^{3} \sin(2x-3) \, dx$

(e) $\int \cos(5x-7) \, dx$

(f) $\int_0^{1} \sin(\tfrac{x}{2}+5) \, dx$

(g) $\int \cos(3x-1) \, dx$

(h) $\int \cos(\tfrac{x}{2}+5) \, dx$

2. **Prodsums**

(a) $\int_0^{\frac{\pi}{2}} 7 \sin 2x \sin 3x \, dx$

(b) $\int_0^{\frac{\pi}{2}} \cos 5x \sin 3x \, dx$

(c) $\int \cos mx \sin nx \, dx$

(d) $\int_0^{\frac{\pi}{2}} -\tfrac{1}{2} \sin 4x \sin 3x \, dx$

(e) $\int_0^{\frac{\pi}{2}} -5\cos x\cos 2x\,dx$

(f) $\int \sin nx\cos nx\,dx$

3. **Quotients**

(a) $\int_0^{\frac{\pi}{3}} \frac{\sin x}{\cos^2 x}\,dx$

(b) $\int_0^{\frac{\pi}{2}} \frac{\cos^3 x}{\sin^4 x}\,dx$

(c) $\int_0^{\frac{\pi}{4}} \frac{\sec^2 x}{\tan x+7}\,dx$

(d) $\int_0^{\frac{\pi}{4}} \frac{\cos^2 x\sin x}{\cos^5 x}\,dx$

(e) $\int_0^{\frac{\pi}{2}} \frac{\cos 2x}{\cos x-\sin x}\,dx$

4. **Powers**

(a) $\int_0^{\frac{\pi}{2}} \sin^2 x\cos x\,dx$

(b) $\int_0^{\frac{\pi}{2}} \cos^6 x\sin x\,dx$

(c) $\int_0^{\frac{\pi}{2}} \sin x\cos^2 x\,dx$

(d) $\int_0^{\frac{\pi}{2}} \sin^3 x\cos^2 x\,dx$

(e) $\int_0^{\frac{\pi}{2}} \sin^2 4x\cos^2 4x\,dx$

(f) $\int_0^{\frac{\pi}{4}} \sin^2 2x\cos 2x\,dx$

(g) $\int_0^{\frac{\pi}{4}} \cos^2 3x\,dx$

3.5 SPECIALS

These are 3 integrals that require special substitutions. Two are on page 41. The other one must be practiced.

[A] **The inverse quadratic function**

$$\int \frac{dx}{(a)^2+(x)^2} = \frac{1}{a}\tan^{-1}\left(\frac{x}{a}\right)+c$$

It can be extended to

$$\int \frac{dx}{(a)^2+(x\pm b)^2} = \frac{1}{a}\tan^{-1}\left(\frac{x\pm b}{a}\right)+c$$

TRICK
It only works if the coefficient of $x^2 = 1$. You must have a 1 in front of x^2, i.e. $1x^2$.

3 levels of difficulty arise: T1 (Easy), T2 (Medium) and T3 (Hard)

T1 (Easy)

Example 35: Evaluate $\int_0^3 \frac{dx}{9+x^2}$.

Solution

$$I = \int_0^3 \frac{dx}{(3)^2+(1x)^2} = \tfrac{1}{3}[\tan^{-1}\tfrac{x}{3}]_0^3 = \tfrac{1}{3}(\tan^{-1}1 - \tan^{-1}0)$$

$$= \tfrac{1}{3}(\tfrac{\pi}{4} - 0) = \tfrac{\pi}{12}$$

T2 (Medium)

Example 36: Evaluate $\int_0^{\frac{3}{2}} \frac{dx}{4+9x^2}$

Solution

You must get a 1 in front of the x^2. So take out 9 on the bottom as a factor.

$$I = \int_0^{\frac{3}{2}} \frac{dx}{4+9x^2}$$

$$\therefore I = \tfrac{1}{9}\int_0^{\frac{3}{2}} \frac{dx}{\frac{4}{9}+x^2} = \tfrac{1}{9}\int_0^{\frac{3}{2}} \frac{dx}{(\frac{2}{3})^2+(x)^2} = \tfrac{1}{9}(\tfrac{3}{2})[\tan^{-1}(\tfrac{3x}{2})]_0^{\frac{3}{2}}$$

$$= \tfrac{1}{6}(\tan^{-1}1 - \tan^{-1}0) = \tfrac{1}{6}(\tfrac{\pi}{4} - 0) = \tfrac{\pi}{24}$$

T3 (HARD)

Example 37: Evaluate $\int_{-3}^{-2} \frac{dx}{x^2+6x+10}$.

SOLUTION

We have to put $x^2 + 6x + 10$ into the form $a^2 + (1x \pm b)^2$ by completing the square (CS).

$$I = \int_{-3}^{-2} \frac{dx}{x^2+6x+10} = \int_{-3}^{-2} \frac{dx}{(1)^2+(1x+3)^2}$$

CS: $(x^2 + 6x) + 10$
$= (x + 3)^2 - 9 + 10$
$= 1 + (x + 3)^2$
$= (1)^2 + (1x + 3)^2$

$$= \tfrac{1}{1}\left[\tan^{-1}\left(\frac{x+3}{1}\right)\right]_{-3}^{-2} = \tan^{-1}1 - \tan^{-1}0 = \tfrac{\pi}{4}$$

[B] **The square root of the inverse quadratic function**

$$\int \frac{dx}{\sqrt{(a)^2-(x)^2}} = \sin^{-1}\left(\frac{x}{a}\right) + c \text{ (page 41)}$$

It can be extended to $\int \frac{dx}{\sqrt{(a)^2-(x\pm b)^2}} = \sin^{-1}\left(\frac{x\pm b}{a}\right) + c$

Trick: It only works if the number in front of the x^2 is 1.

3 levels of difficulty arise: T1 (Easy), T2 (Medium) and T3 (Hard)

T1 (EASY)

Example 38: Evaluate $\int_0^2 \frac{dx}{\sqrt{4-x^2}}$.

SOLUTION

$$I = \int_0^2 \frac{dx}{\sqrt{(2)^2-(1x)^2}} = [\sin^{-1}(\tfrac{x}{2})]_0^2 = \sin^{-1}1 - \sin^{-1}0 = \tfrac{\pi}{2}$$

T2 (MEDIUM)

Example 39: Evaluate $\int_0^2 \frac{dx}{\sqrt{16-4x^2}}$.

SOLUTION

You must get a 1 in front of x^2. So take out 4 on the bottom as a factor. When it comes through the square root sign it becomes 2.

$$I = \int_0^2 \frac{dx}{\sqrt{16-4x^2}} = \tfrac{1}{2}\int_0^2 \frac{dx}{\sqrt{4-x^2}} = \tfrac{1}{2}\int_0^2 \frac{dx}{\sqrt{(2)^2-(1x)^2}}$$

$$= \tfrac{1}{2}[\sin^{-1} \tfrac{x}{2}]_0^2 = \tfrac{1}{2}(\sin^{-1} 1 - \sin^{-1} 0) = \tfrac{1}{2}(\tfrac{\pi}{2} - 0) = \tfrac{\pi}{4}$$

T3 (HARD)

Example 40: Evaluate $\int_4^7 \frac{dx}{\sqrt{8x-x^2-7}}$.

SOLUTION

We have to put $8x - x^2 - 7$ into the form $a^2 - (1x \pm b)^2$ by completing the square (CS). This is difficult because of the $-x^2$. **Trick**: Take out a factor of -1 before completing the square.

$$I = \int_4^7 \frac{dx}{\sqrt{8x-x^2-7}}$$

$$= \int_4^7 \frac{dx}{\sqrt{(3)^2-(1x-4)^2}}$$

$$= \left[\sin^{-1}\left(\frac{x-4}{3}\right)\right]_4^7 = \sin^{-1} 1 - \sin^{-1} 0 = \tfrac{\pi}{2}$$

CS: $8x - x^2 - 7$
$= -\{(x^2 - 8x) + 7\}$
$= -\{(x - 4)^2 - 16 + 7\}$
$= -\{(x - 4)^2 - 9\}$
$= 9 - (x - 4)^2$

[C] The Louser: The square root of the quadratic function

$$\int \sqrt{a^2 - 1x^2}\, dx$$

TRICK
You must make a special substitution. Let $x = a\sin u$

Example 41: Evaluate $\int_0^{\frac{3}{2}} \sqrt{9-x^2}\, dx$.

SOLUTION

$$\mathrm{I} = \int_0^{\frac{3}{2}} \sqrt{9-x^2}\, dx = \int_0^{\frac{3}{2}} \sqrt{(3)^2-(x)^2}\, dx$$

Let $x = 3\sin u \Rightarrow dx = 3\cos u\, du$

Changing the limits
$x = 3\sin u$
$x = 0 \Rightarrow u = 0$
$x = \frac{3}{2} \Rightarrow u = \frac{\pi}{6}$

$$\therefore \mathrm{I} = 3\int_0^{\frac{\pi}{6}} \sqrt{9-9\sin^2 u}\cos u\, du$$

$$= 9\int_0^{\frac{\pi}{6}} \sqrt{1-\sin^2 u}\cos u\, du$$

$\cos^2 A = \frac{1}{2}(1+\cos 2A)$

$$= 9\int_0^{\frac{\pi}{6}} \cos^2 u\, du = \frac{9}{2}\int_0^{\frac{\pi}{6}} (1+\cos 2u)\, du = \frac{9}{2}[u + \tfrac{1}{2}\sin 2u]_0^{\frac{\pi}{6}}$$

$$= \frac{9}{2}\{(\tfrac{\pi}{6} + \tfrac{1}{2}\sin(\tfrac{\pi}{3})) - (0+0)\} = \frac{9}{2}\{\tfrac{\pi}{6} + \tfrac{\sqrt{3}}{4}\}$$

Example 42: Evaluate $\int_0^1 \sqrt{16-4x^2}\, dx$.

SOLUTION

Changing the limits
$x = 2\sin u$
$x = 0 \Rightarrow u = 0$
$x = 1 \Rightarrow u = \frac{\pi}{6}$

$$\mathrm{I} = \int_0^1 \sqrt{16-4x^2}\, dx = 2\int_0^1 \sqrt{4-x^2}\, dx$$

Let $x = 2\sin u \Rightarrow dx = 2\cos u\, du$

$$\mathrm{I} = 4\int_0^{\frac{\pi}{6}} \sqrt{4-4\sin^2 u}\cos u\, du = 8\int_0^{\frac{\pi}{6}} \cos^2 u\, du = 4\int_0^{\frac{\pi}{6}} (1+\cos 2u)$$

$$= 4[u + \tfrac{\sin 2u}{2}]_0^{\frac{\pi}{6}} = 4(\tfrac{\pi}{6} + \tfrac{1}{2}\tfrac{\sqrt{3}}{2}) = \tfrac{2\pi}{3} + \sqrt{3}$$

Exercise 5 (Answers: page **416**)

(Answers: page **416**)

Specials

1. **Inverse Quadratics**

(a) $\int_0^2 \frac{dx}{x^2+4}$

(b) $\int_0^4 \frac{dx}{16+x^2}$

(c) $\int_0^{\frac{1}{2}} \frac{dx}{16x^2+4}$

(d) $\int_0^4 \frac{dx}{2x^2+32}$

(e) $\int_0^{\frac{1}{\sqrt{2}}} \frac{dx}{1+2x^2}$

(f) $\int_{-1}^1 \frac{dx}{x^2+2x+5}$

(g) $\int_1^4 \frac{dx}{x^2-2x+10}$

(h) $\int_{-2}^0 \frac{dx}{x^2+4x+8}$

2. **Inverse Square roots of Quadratics**

(a) $\int_0^{\frac{1}{2}} \frac{dx}{\sqrt{1-x^2}}$

(b) $\int_0^2 \frac{dx}{\sqrt{16-x^2}}$

(c) $\int_0^{\frac{3}{2}} \frac{dx}{\sqrt{9-4x^2}}$

(d) $\int_0^{\frac{1}{3}} \frac{dx}{\sqrt{1-9x^2}}$

(e) $\int_{\frac{7}{2}}^5 \frac{dx}{\sqrt{5-x^2+4x}}$

(f) $\int_1^2 \frac{dx}{\sqrt{3+2x-x^2}}$

(g) $\int_{\frac{7}{2}}^4 \frac{dx}{\sqrt{6x-x^2-8}}$

3. **Square roots of Quadratics (Lousers)**

(a) $\int_0^1 \sqrt{1-x^2}\, dx$

(b) $\int_0^2 \sqrt{4-x^2}\, dx$

(c) $\int_0^{\frac{2}{3}} \sqrt{9-4x^2}\, dx$

(d) $\int_0^{\frac{2}{3}} \sqrt{4-9x^2}\, dx$

(e) $\int_0^{\frac{3\sqrt{3}}{2}} \sqrt{9-x^2}\, dx$

And finally, some tough questions where you have to work backwards.

TYPE 1: Given the first derivative of a function you can find the function by integrating once.

Example 43: If $\frac{dy}{dx}=x-\frac{1}{x}$ find y in terms of x if $y=\frac{1}{2}$ when $x=1$.

SOLUTION

$$\frac{dy}{dx}=x-\frac{1}{x}\Rightarrow\int dy=\int\left(x-\frac{1}{x}\right)dx$$

$$\Rightarrow y=\tfrac{x^2}{2}-\ln x+c$$

$$y=\tfrac{1}{2}\text{ when }x=1\Rightarrow\tfrac{1}{2}=\tfrac{1}{2}-0+c\Rightarrow c=0$$

$$\therefore y=\tfrac{x^2}{2}-\ln x$$

TYPE 2: Given the second derivative of a function, you can find the function by integrating twice.

Example 44: If $\frac{d^2y}{dx^2}=3x-1$ find y if $\frac{dy}{dx}=0$ when $x=2$ and $y=1$ when $x=0$.

SOLUTION

$$\frac{d^2y}{dx^2}=3x-1\Rightarrow\frac{dy}{dx}=\int(3x-1)\,dx=\frac{3x^2}{2}-x+c$$

$$\frac{dy}{dx}=0\text{ when }x=2\Rightarrow 0=6-2+c\Rightarrow c=-4$$

$$\therefore\frac{dy}{dx}=3x^2-x-4\Rightarrow y=\int(3x^2-x-4)\,dx=x^3-\frac{x^2}{2}-4x+d$$

$$y=1\text{ when }x=0\Rightarrow 1=d$$

$$\therefore y=x^3-\tfrac{x^2}{2}-4x+1$$

Exercise 6 (Answers: page **416**)

(Answers: page 416)

Mixture of Integrals

I. Integrate the following:

1. $\displaystyle\int_0^1 t^{\frac{2}{3}}(t^{\frac{5}{3}}+1)^{\frac{2}{3}}\, dt$

2. $\displaystyle\int_{\frac{\pi^2}{16}}^{\frac{\pi^2}{4}} \frac{\cos\sqrt{x}}{\sqrt{x}}\, dx$

3. $\displaystyle\int_1^{32} \frac{dx}{x^{\frac{1}{5}}\sqrt{1+x^{\frac{4}{5}}}}$

4. $\displaystyle\int_{-\frac{1}{2}}^{0} x\sqrt{2x+1}\, dx$

5. $\displaystyle\int_{-3}^{2} \frac{dx}{\sqrt{16-x^2-6x}}$

6. $\displaystyle\int_{-\frac{\pi}{4}}^{0} \frac{\sin 2x}{(1+\cos 2x)^3}\, dx$

7. $\displaystyle\int_0^1 \frac{x^2-4}{x+2}\, dx$

8. $\displaystyle\int_0^{\frac{\pi}{4}} \frac{\sec^2 x}{(2+\tan x)^2}\, dx$

9. $\displaystyle\int_1^2 ye^{y^2}\, dy$

10. $\displaystyle\int_0^1 \frac{2x+5}{x^2+5x+7}\, dx$

11. $\displaystyle\int_7^8 \frac{x}{(9-x)^4}\, dx$

12. $\displaystyle\int_2^3 \frac{dx}{x^2-4x+5}$

13. $\displaystyle\int_0^1 \frac{dx}{\sqrt{4-x^2}}$

14. $\displaystyle\int_{-\frac{4}{3}}^{0} e^{3x+4}\, dx$

15. $\displaystyle\int_0^{\frac{\pi}{4}} \cos 2x \sin 4x\, dx$

16. $\displaystyle\int_{-4}^{-1} \frac{dx}{x^2+8x+25}$

17. $\displaystyle\int_0^2 \frac{dy}{\sqrt{25-4y^2}}$

18. $\displaystyle\int_0^{\ln 2} \frac{e^x(e^x-1)}{e^{2x}-2e^x+3}\, dx$

19. $\displaystyle\int_0^1 \frac{x^2}{1+x^3}\, dx$

20. $\displaystyle\int_{\tan^{-1}2}^{\tan^{-1}5} \frac{dx}{\cos^2 x\sqrt{\tan x-1}}$

21. $\displaystyle\int_{-1}^{0} \frac{dx}{x^2+2(x+1)}$

22. $\displaystyle\int_{3}^{4} \frac{(x-2)\,dx}{x^2-4x+4}$

23. $\displaystyle\int_{1}^{2} \frac{x+1}{(x^2+2x-3)^{\frac{2}{3}}}\,dx$

24. $\displaystyle\int_{0}^{\frac{\pi}{2}} \sin^2 5x\,dx$

25. $\displaystyle\int_{1}^{4} \frac{dx}{\sqrt{x}+x}$

26. $\displaystyle\int_{0}^{1} \frac{x^3+1}{x+1}\,dx$

27. $\displaystyle\int_{1}^{4} e^{-\ln x}\,dx$

28. $\displaystyle\int_{0}^{\frac{\pi}{2}} \sin 2x(1+\sin^2 x)\,dx$

29. $\displaystyle\int_{0}^{1} \frac{dt}{t+1}$

30. $\displaystyle\int_{0}^{1} \frac{x\,dx}{4-x^2}$

31. $\displaystyle\int_{2}^{3} \frac{x}{x-1}\,dx$

II. Unusual integral questions

1. Find a if $\displaystyle\int_{1}^{a} (x+\tfrac{1}{2})\,dx = 2\int_{0}^{\frac{\pi}{4}} \sec^2 x\,dx$, $a>0$

2. Find c if $\displaystyle\int_{0}^{c} (x-1)(x-3)\,dx = 0$

3. If $y=x^3$ evaluate $\displaystyle\int_{0}^{4} y\,dx + \int_{0}^{64} x\,dy$.

III. Weirdos

1. In each of the following write s as a function of t given that $v = \frac{ds}{dt}$:

(a) $v = 3t^2$ with $s = 0$ at $t = 0$,

(b) $v = 2t + 1$ with $s = 3$ at $t = 0$,

(c) $v = u + at$ with $s = 0$ at $t = 0$,

(d) $v = t^2 + 2t + 1$ with $s = 2$ at $t = 0$.

2. (a) If $\frac{dy}{dx} = 9x^2 - 4x + 5$ find y if $x = 1$ when $y = 1$,

(b) If $\frac{dy}{dx} = \frac{x^2 + 1}{x^2}$ find y if $x = 1$ when $y = 1$,

(c) If $\frac{d^2y}{dx^2} = 1 - x$ find y if $\frac{dy}{dx} = 0$ and $y = 0$ when $x = 0$,

(d) Solve $\frac{d^2y}{dx^2} = x(1 - x)$ when $y = 0$ at $x = 0$ and $x = 1$,

(e) If $\frac{dy}{dx} = ax + 2$ where a is a constant, express y as a function

of x given that $\frac{d^2y}{dx^2} = 6$ and that $y = 4$ when $x = 0$.

3. (a) The slope of a curve at any point is given by $\frac{dy}{dx} = 2x - 1$.
If the curve passes through the point (1, 1) find the equation of the curve.

(b) Find the equation of the curve whose slope at any point is $1 - 2x^2$ and which passes through (0, 1).

(c) A particle starts from rest with acceleration $(30 - 6t)$ m/s^2 at time t. When and where will it come to rest again?

4. AREAS AND VOLUMES

4.1 AREA

[A] **The Idea**: This process finds the Area under a curve.

1. X-axis

Strips onto the X-axis

TRICK

The area under the curve $y = f(x)$ and between the lines $x = a, x = b$ and the X-axis is given by:

$$A = \int_a^b y\,dx$$

Example 1: Find the area under the curve $y = x^3$ and between the lines $x = 2$, $x = 3$ and the X-axis.

SOLUTION

$$A = \int_2^3 y\,dx = \int_2^3 x^3\,dx = \tfrac{1}{4}[x^4]_2^3 = \tfrac{1}{4}(81-16) = \tfrac{65}{4}$$

2. Y-axis

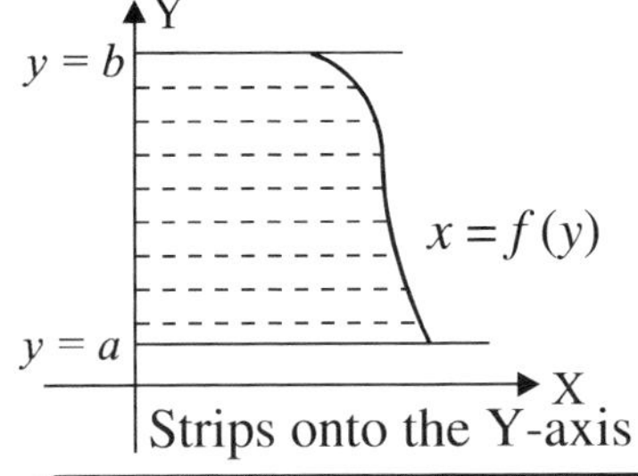

Strips onto the Y-axis

TRICK

The area under the curve $x = f(y)$ and between the lines $y = a, y = b$ and the Y-axis is given by:

$$A = \int_a^b x\,dy$$

Example 2: Find the area under the curve $y = x^3$ and between the lines $y = 1$, $y = 8$ and the Y-axis.

SOLUTION

$$y = x^3 \Rightarrow y^{\frac{1}{3}} = x$$

$$A = \int_1^8 x\,dy = \int_1^8 y^{\frac{1}{3}}\,dy = \tfrac{3}{4}[y^{\frac{4}{3}}]_1^8 = \tfrac{3}{4}(16-1) = \tfrac{45}{4}$$

NOTES

1. Strips onto X-axis $\Rightarrow A = \int y\,dx$

   Strips onto Y-axis $\Rightarrow A = \int x\,dy$

2. If strips are above X-axis

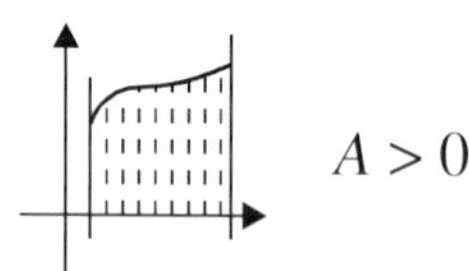

$A > 0$

If strips are below X-axis: Take $|A|$

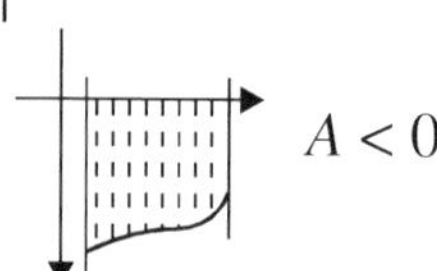

$A < 0$

3. If strips are to the right of the Y-axis

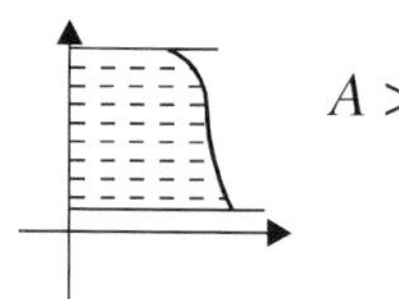

$A > 0$

If strips are to the left of the Y-axis: Take $|A|$

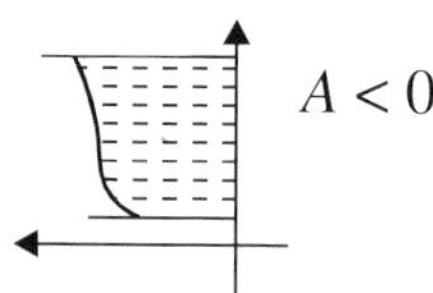

$A < 0$

Example 3: Find the area under the curve $y = x^3$ between the lines $x = 0$, $x = -1$ and the X-axis.

SOLUTION

$$\Rightarrow |A| = \left|\int_{-1}^{0} y\,dx\right| = \left|\int_{-1}^{0} x^3\,dx\right|$$

$$= \left|\left[\frac{x^4}{4}\right]_{-1}^{0}\right| = \left|0 - \frac{1}{4}\right| = \tfrac{1}{4}$$

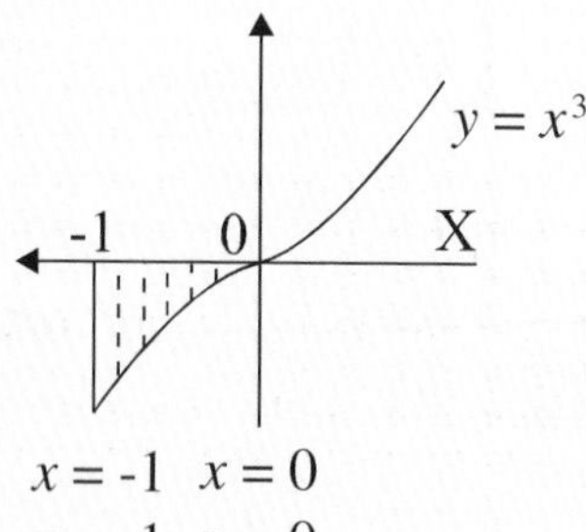

$x = -1 \quad x = 0$

$y = -1 \quad y = 0$

TRICK

Always write limits of integration $\int_a^b$ from left (a) to right (b) on the X-axis and from down (a) to up (b) on the Y-axis.

Example: $A = \int_{-2}^{3} x\,dy$

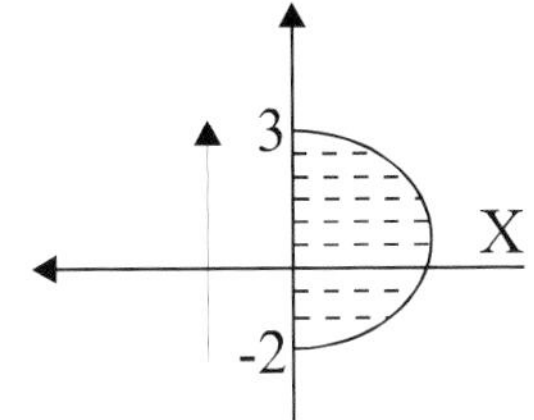

[B] **One Curve Problems**

STEPS

1. Check if curve crosses X or Y axis between the limits of integration.
2. If it doesn't cross integrate out and take modulus if negative.
3. If it does cross, find the point c where it crosses the axis and do 2 separate integrals.

$$A_1 = \int_a^c y\,dx > 0$$

$$|A_2| = \left|\int_c^b y\,dx\right| > 0$$

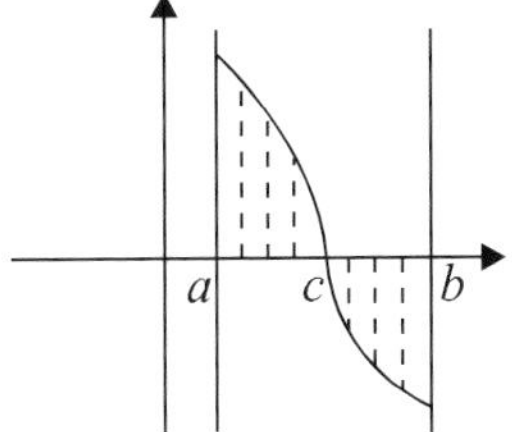

$\therefore A = A_1 + |A_2|$

4. If no limits of integration are given find the points where it crosses the given axis.

Example 4: Find the area enclosed by the curve $y = x^2 - 4$, the X-axis and the lines $x = 0$, $x = 1$.

SOLUTION

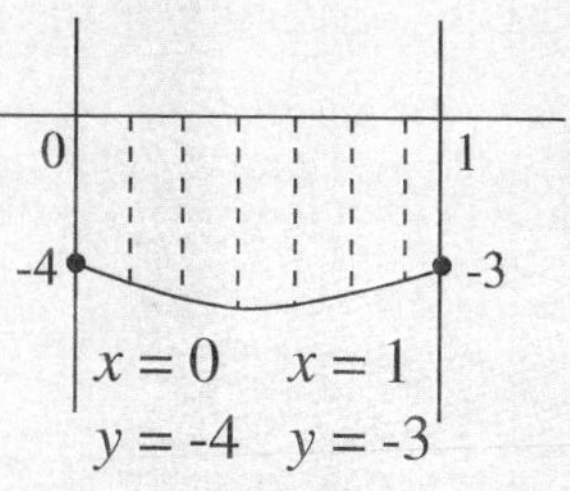

Crosses X-axis ($y = 0$): $x^2 - 4 = 0$

$\Rightarrow x = \pm 2$

Therefore, the curve doesn't cross between 0 and 1.

$$\therefore A = \int_0^1 y\,dx = \int_0^1 (x^2 - 4)\,dx = [\tfrac{x^3}{3} - 4x]_0^1 = (\tfrac{1}{3} - 4) = -\tfrac{11}{3}$$

$$\therefore \text{Area} = |A| = \tfrac{11}{3}$$

Example 5: Find the area enclosed by the curve $y = x^2 - x - 2$, the X-axis and the lines $x = 0$ and $x = 3$.

SOLUTION

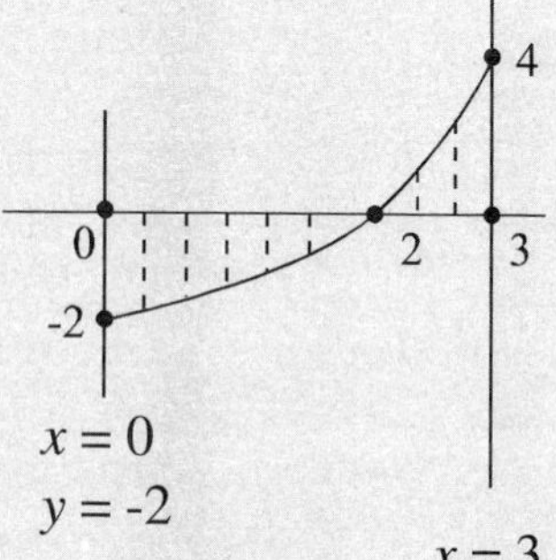

Crosses X-axis ($y = 0$): $x^2 - x - 2 = 0$

$\Rightarrow (x + 1)(x - 2) = 0 \Rightarrow x = -1, 2.$

Therefore, only the number 2 is between 0 and 3.

$$\therefore A_1 = \int_0^2 y\,dx = \int_0^2 (x^2 - x - 2)\,dx$$

$$= \left[\frac{x^3}{3} - \frac{x^2}{2} - 2x\right]_0^2 = \tfrac{8}{3} - 2 - 4 = -\tfrac{10}{3}$$

$$\therefore \text{Area} = |A_1| = \tfrac{10}{3}$$

$$\therefore A_2 = \int_2^3 y\,dx = \int_2^3 (x^2 - x - 2)\,dx = \left[\frac{x^3}{3} - \frac{x^2}{2} - 2x\right]_2^3$$

$$= (9 - \tfrac{9}{2} - 6) - (\tfrac{8}{3} - 2 - 4) = -\tfrac{3}{2} + \tfrac{10}{3} = \tfrac{11}{6}$$

$$\therefore \text{Total Area} = |A_1| + A_2 = \tfrac{10}{3} + \tfrac{11}{6} = \tfrac{31}{6}$$

Example 6: Find the area enclosed by the curve $y = x^3 - 3x^2 + 2x$ and the X-axis.

SOLUTION

Crosses X-axis ($y = 0$): $x^3 - 3x^2 + 2x = 0 \Rightarrow x(x^2 - 3x + 2) = 0$

$\Rightarrow x(x - 1)(x - 2) = 0 \Rightarrow x = 0, 1, 2$

$$A_1 = \int_0^1 y\,dx = \int_0^1 (x^3 - 3x^2 + 2x)\,dx$$

$x = \frac{1}{2}$, $y = \frac{3}{8}$ $\quad$ $x = \frac{3}{2}$, $y = -\frac{3}{8}$

$$= \left[\frac{x^4}{4} - x^3 + x^2\right]_0^1 = \tfrac{1}{4} - 1 + 1 = \tfrac{1}{4}$$

$$A_2 = \int_1^2 y\,dx = \int_1^2 (x^3 - 3x^2 + 2x)\,dx = \left[\frac{x^4}{4} - x^3 + x^2\right]_1^2$$

$$= (4 - 8 + 4) - (\tfrac{1}{4} - 1 + 1) = -\tfrac{1}{4} \quad \therefore |A_2| = \tfrac{1}{4}$$

Area $A_1 + |A_2| = \frac{1}{4} + \frac{1}{4} = \frac{1}{2}$

Example 7: Find the area between the curve $y = \dfrac{4x}{x^2 + 4}$ and the lines $x = 1$, $x = 2$ and the X-axis.

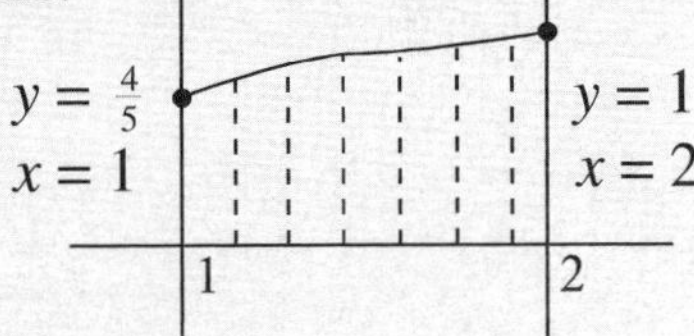

SOLUTION

Crosses the X-axis:

$$y = \frac{4x}{x^2 + 4} = 0 \Rightarrow x = 0$$

Therefore, it does not cross the X-axis between 1 and 2.

$$\therefore A = \int_1^2 y\,dx = \int_1^2 \frac{4x}{x^2 + 4}\,dx$$

Let $u = x^2 + 4 \Rightarrow du = 2x\,dx \;\therefore \tfrac{1}{2}du = x\,dx$

New Limits

$x = 1 \Rightarrow u = 5$

$x = 2 \Rightarrow u = 8$

$$\Rightarrow A = \tfrac{4}{2}\int_5^8 \frac{1}{u}\,du = 2[\ln u]_5^8 = 2\ln(\tfrac{8}{5})$$

Example 8: Find the area of the circle $x^2 + y^2 = r^2$ by integration.
(*This is an important question. It uses the louser integral.*)

SOLUTION

$x^2 + y^2 = r^2$ is a circle, centre (0, 0) and radius r.

$$y^2 = r^2 - x^2$$

$$\Rightarrow y = \sqrt{r^2 - x^2}$$

$$A = 4\int_0^r y\,dx = 4\int_0^r \sqrt{r^2 - x^2}\,dx$$

(**Note**: 4 is put in front of the integral sign because there are 4 quadrants)

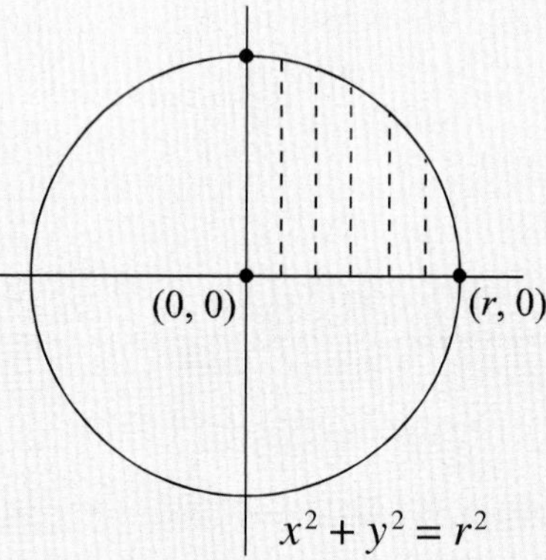

Let $x = r\sin u \Rightarrow dx = r\cos u\, du$

New Limits

$x = 0 \Rightarrow r\sin u = 0$

$\Rightarrow \sin u = 0 \Rightarrow u = 0$

$x = r \Rightarrow r\sin u = r$

$\Rightarrow \sin u = 1 \Rightarrow u = \frac{\pi}{2}$

$$\therefore A = 4r\int_0^{\frac{\pi}{2}} \sqrt{r^2 - r^2\sin^2 u}\cos du$$

$$= 4r^2\int_0^{\frac{\pi}{2}} \cos^2 u\, du$$

$\cos^2 u = \frac{1}{2}(1 + \cos 2u)$

$$= \frac{4r^2}{2}\int_0^{\frac{\pi}{2}} (1 + \cos 2u)\,du = 2r^2[u + \tfrac{1}{2}\sin 2u]_0^{\frac{\pi}{2}}$$

$$= 2r^2\{(\tfrac{\pi}{2} + \tfrac{1}{2}\sin\pi) - (0 + 0)\} = \pi r^2$$

[C] **2 Curve Problems**

STEPS

1. Find the points of intersection of the curves by solving simultaneously.
2. Shade in the specified area.

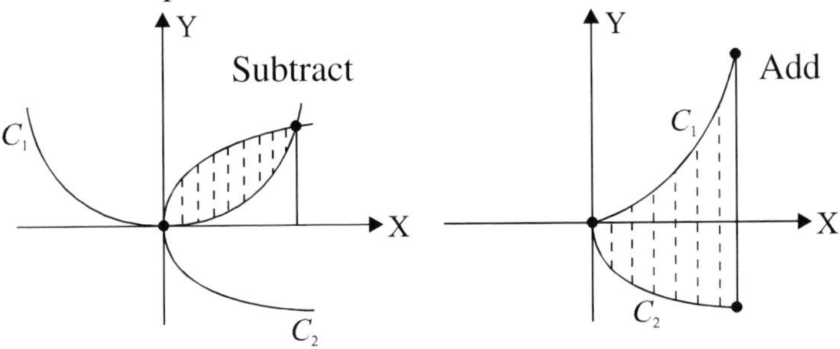

3. Draw line(s) from the point(s) of intersection onto X or Y-axis.
4. Add or subtract $\int ydx$ for each curve *OR* $\int xdy$ for each curve.
5. Look out for rectangles and triangles.

Example 9: Find the area enclosed by the curves C_1: $y^2 = 4x$ and C_2: $x^2 = 4y$.

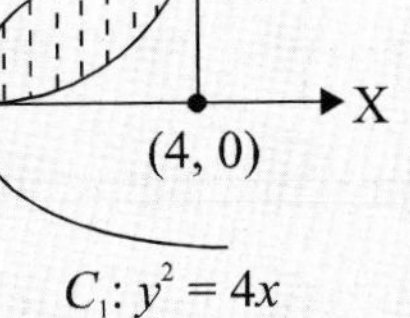

SOLUTION

$C_1 \cap C_2$

C_2: $y = \frac{x^2}{4}$

C_1: $\frac{x^4}{16} = 4x \Rightarrow x^4 - 64x = 0$

$\Rightarrow x(x^3 - 64) = 0$

$\therefore x = 0 \Rightarrow y = 0$ (0, 0) and $x = 4 \Rightarrow y = 4$ (4, 4)

Cont...

A = Area under C_1 - Area under C_2

$$\int_0^4 y\,dx_{C_1} - \int_0^4 y\,dx_{C_2} = \int_0^4 2x^{\frac{1}{2}}\,dx - \tfrac{1}{4}\int_0^4 x^2\,dx$$

$$= 2(\tfrac{2}{3})[x^{\frac{3}{2}}]_0^4 - \tfrac{1}{4}[\tfrac{x^3}{3}]_0^4 = \tfrac{4}{3}(8) - \tfrac{1}{4}(\tfrac{64}{3}) = \tfrac{16}{3}$$

Example 10: Find the area enclosed by the curve
$C: y = x^2 - 2x + 2 = 0$ and the line $L: y = 4 - x$

SOLUTION

$C \cap L$

$L: y = (4 - x)$

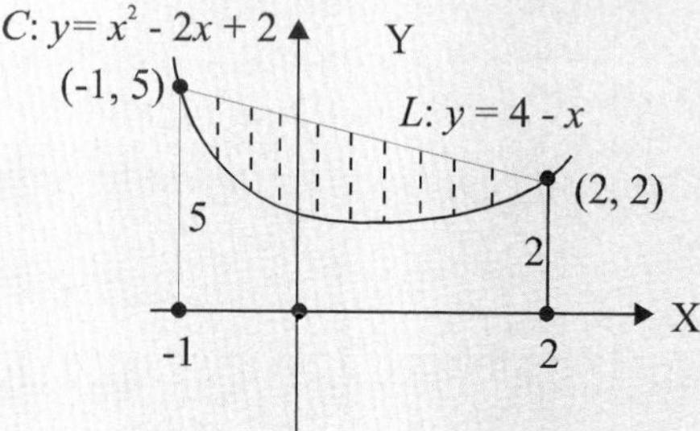

$C :\Rightarrow 4 - x = x^2 - 2x + 2$

$\Rightarrow x^2 - x - 2 = 0$

$\Rightarrow (x+1)(x-2) = 0$

$\Rightarrow x = -1, x = 2$

$\Rightarrow y = 5, y = 2$

$a(-1, 5), b(2, 2)$

L is easy to plot. C goes through a and b. We must check if it crosses the X-axis.

$y = 0 \Rightarrow x^2 - x + 2 = 0$ (No solutions - therefore it does not cross).

$x = 0 \Rightarrow y = 2$

$$\text{Area} = \int_{-1}^2 y\,dx_{L} - \int_{-1}^2 y\,dx_{C}$$

$$\int_{-1}^2 (4-x)\,dx - \int_{-1}^2 (x^2 - 2x + 2)\,dx = [4x - \tfrac{x^2}{2}]_{-1}^2 - [\tfrac{x^3}{3} - x^2 + 2x]_{-1}^2$$

$$= (6 + \tfrac{9}{2}) - (\tfrac{8}{3} + \tfrac{10}{3}) = \tfrac{9}{2}$$

Example 11: A line L meets the curve $y^2 = x$ at (0, 0) and at a point whose x co-ordinate is t. If the enclosed shaded area is $\frac{\sqrt{3}}{2}$ find t.

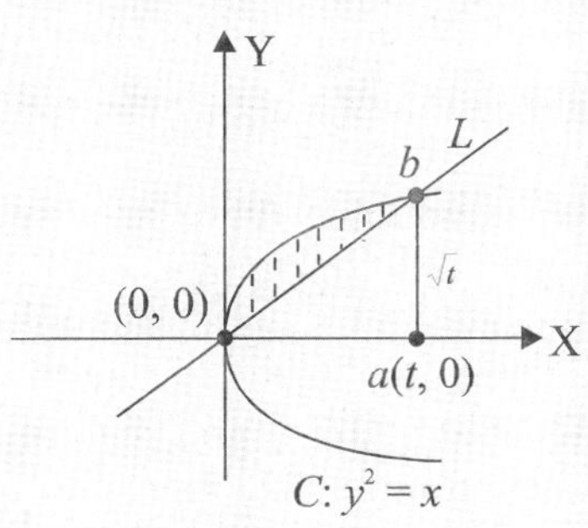

SOLUTION

$C: y^2 = x$

$x = t \Rightarrow y^2 = t \Rightarrow \; y = \sqrt{t}$

$\therefore \; b(t, \sqrt{t}\,)$

$$A = \int_0^t y\,dx - \text{Area}\,\Delta oab$$

$$\Rightarrow \tfrac{\sqrt{3}}{2} = \int_0^t x^{\frac{1}{2}}\,dx - \tfrac{1}{2}t\sqrt{t} \Rightarrow \tfrac{\sqrt{3}}{2} = \tfrac{2}{3}[x^{\frac{3}{2}}]_0^t - \tfrac{1}{2}t^{\frac{3}{2}}$$

$$\Rightarrow \tfrac{\sqrt{3}}{2} = \tfrac{2}{3}t^{\frac{3}{2}} - \tfrac{1}{2}t^{\frac{3}{2}} \Rightarrow 3\sqrt{3} = 4t^{\frac{3}{2}} - 3t^{\frac{3}{2}} = t^{\frac{3}{2}} \Rightarrow 27 = t^3 \Rightarrow 3 = t$$

Exercise 7 (Answers: page **417**)

Area

1. Find the area bounded by the X-axis, the given curve and the given lines:

(a) $y = 9 - x^2$, $x = 0$, $x = 3$

(b) $xy = c^2$, $x = a$, $x = b$

(c) $y = 2x + \frac{1}{x^2}$, $x = 1$, $x = 4$

(d) $x = 3 - y^2$, $x = 2$, $x = 3$, $y > 0$

(e) $y = 4x - x^2$, $x = 1$, $x = 3$.

2. Find the area bounded by the Y-axis, the given curve and the given lines:

(a) $y = -x^2 + 9$, $y = 0$, $y = 8$, $x > 0$

(b) $xy = 8$, $y = 1$, $y = 4$

(c) $y = x^2$, $y = 1$, $y = 4$

(d) $y = \frac{4}{x^2}$, $y = 16$, $y = 25$, $x > 0$

3. Find the area enclosed by the curve $y = x^2$ and the line $y = x + 6$.

4. Show by integration that the area enclosed by the circle $x^2 + y^2 = 9$ is 9π.

5. Find the area enclosed by the curve $y = \frac{1}{x}$, the X-axis and the lines $x = 1$ and $x = a$.

6. The area bounded by the curve $y = x^2$ and the line $y = 4$ is divided into 2 equal parts by the line $y = a$. Show that $a^3 = 16$.

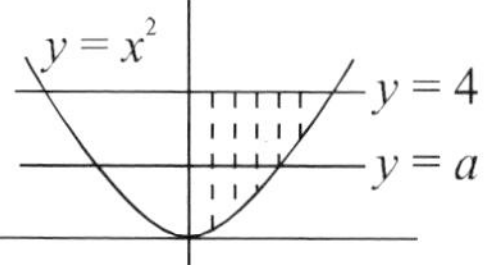

7. A curve, C, passes through (1, 1) and its slope at any point is $3x - 5$. Find the equation of the curve and the area enclosed by it and the line $5x - 2y - 3 = 0$.

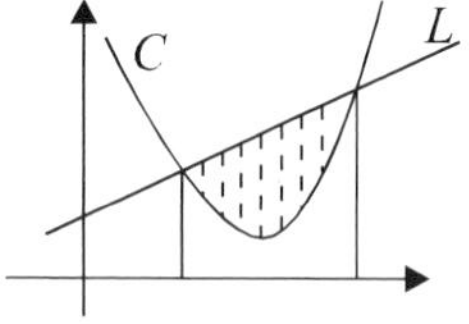

8. Find the area enclosed by $y = \frac{4}{4 + x^2}$, the X-axis and the lines $x = -2$, $x = 2$.

9. Find the points of intersection of the curves C_1: $y = x^2$ and C_2: $y = 8 - x^2$. Find the area enclosed by them.

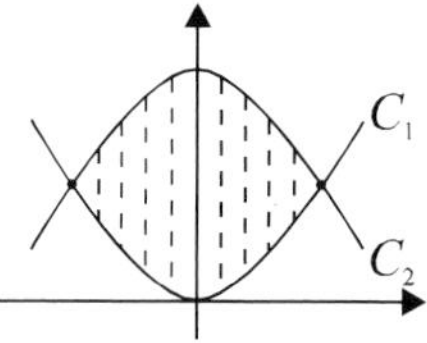

10. Show that the area enclosed by $y = x^n$ and $y = x^{\frac{1}{n}}$ is $\frac{n-1}{n+1}$.

11. Calculate the area between the X-axis and the curve $y = x(x - 4)$.

12. The equation of a curve is of the form $y = ax^2 + bx + c$. It meets the X-axis at $x = -1$ and $x = 3$. Also $y = 12$ when $x = 1$. Find the equation of the curve and the area between it and the X-axis.

13. The diagram shows a sketch of the graph of $y=(x+1)(x-1)^2$. Find the co-ordinates of *a*, *b*, *c* and *d*. Prove that *oc* divides the area between the curve and the line *ab* in the ratio 11:5,

i.e. $\dfrac{\text{Area } adc}{\text{Area } ocb}=\dfrac{11}{5}$

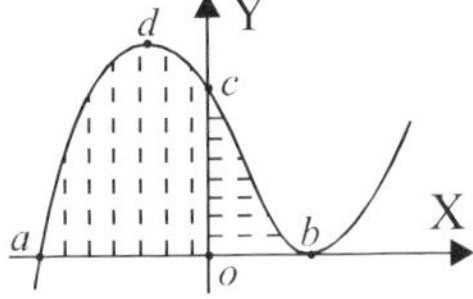

14. Find the area enclosed by the line L: $y = x + 3$ and the curve C: $y=5x-x^2$.

15. Find, by integration, the area enclosed by the circle $x^2+y^2=1$.

16. Find the area enclosed by $y=4-x^2$, the Y-axis, $y=0$, $y=3$, $x>0$.

17. Find the area enclosed by $y=\dfrac{2x}{x^2+1}$, the X-axis and the lines $x=0$, $x=1$.

18. Find the area enclosed by the curve $y = (x - 1)(x - 2)(x - 3)$ and the X-axis.

19. Find the area enclosed by $y=\cos^2 x$, $0\le x\le 2\pi$, and the X-axis.

20. Find, by integration, the area enclosed by the circle $x^2+y^2=25$.

21. Find the shaded area.

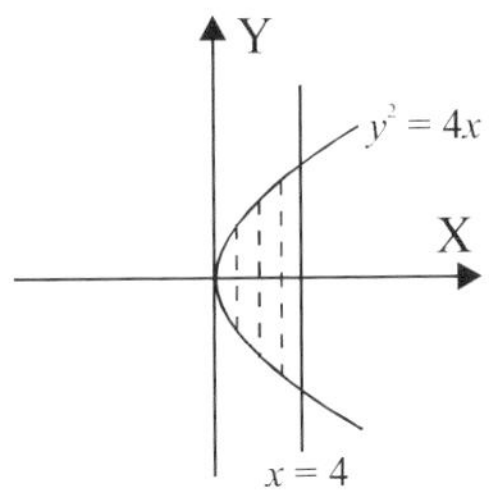

22. Find the area bounded by the lines L: $y = 2x - 1$, $x = 4$ and the curve C: $y=\frac{1}{x}$, $x>0$.

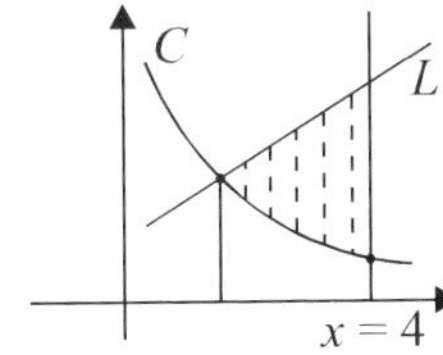

4.2 Volumes of Rotation

[A] The Idea

1. The volume obtained by rotating the curve $y = f(x)$ between the lines $x = a$, $x = b$ and the X-axis is given by:

$$V = \pi \int_a^b y^2 \, dx \, .$$

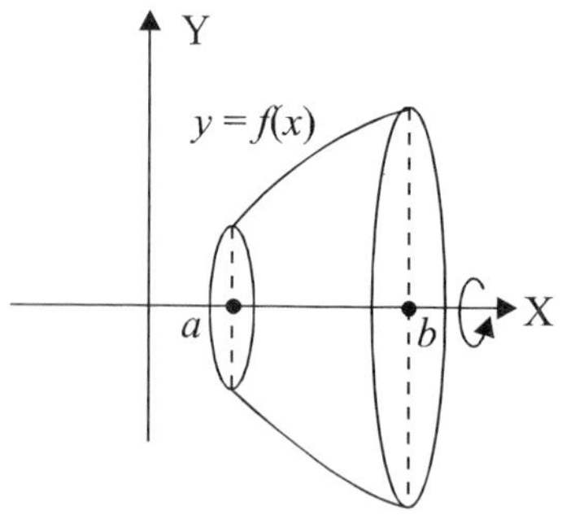

2. The volume obtained by rotating the curve $x = f(y)$ between the lines $y = a$, $y = b$ and the Y-axis is given by:

$$V = \pi \int_a^b x^2 \, dy$$

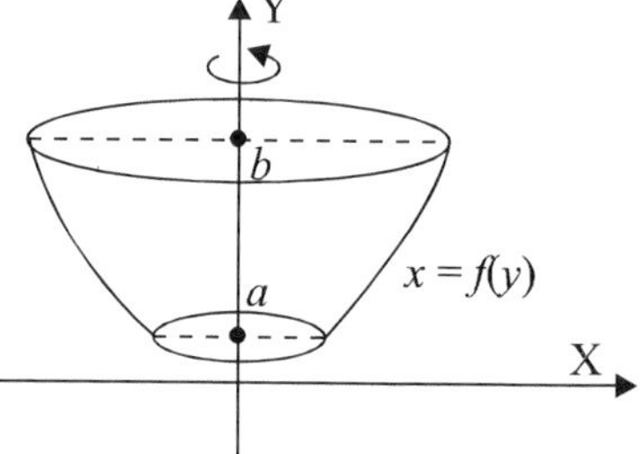

[B] Rotating Lines

Trick: Lines → Cones *or* frustrums of cones.

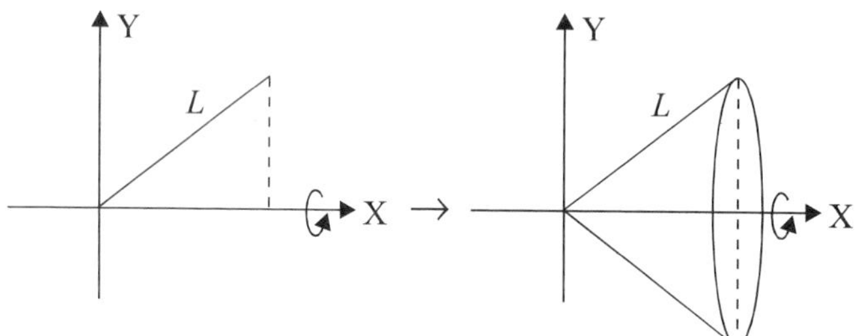

Steps

1. Find the equation of the line.
2. Find where it crosses the given axis to get limits.
3. Use $V = \pi \int_a^b y^2 \, dx$ or $V = \pi \int_a^b x^2 \, dy$

Example 12: Find the volume of the cone obtained by rotating the line $y = 2x$ about the X-axis between $x = 0$ and $x = 4$.

SOLUTION

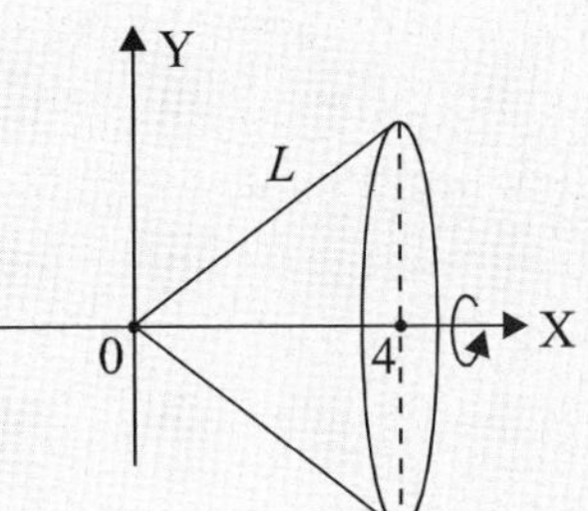

Equation $y = 2x$

$$V = \pi\int_0^4 y^2\,dx = \pi\int_0^4 4x^2\,dx$$

$$= \tfrac{4\pi}{3}[x^3]_0^4 = \tfrac{4\pi}{3}.64 = \tfrac{256\pi}{3}$$

Example 13: Find the volume of the frustrum of the cone obtained by rotating the line L about the X-axis between $x = a$ and $x = b$.

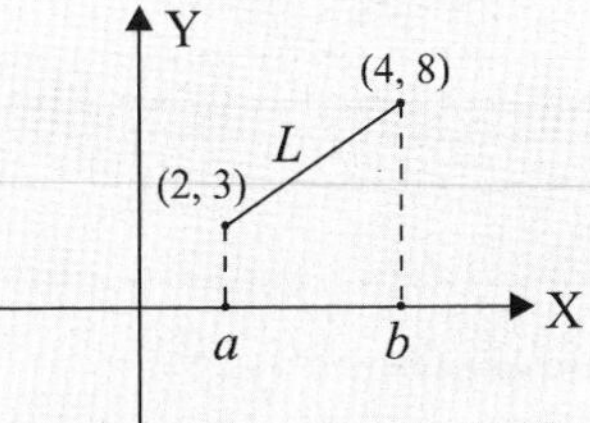

SOLUTION

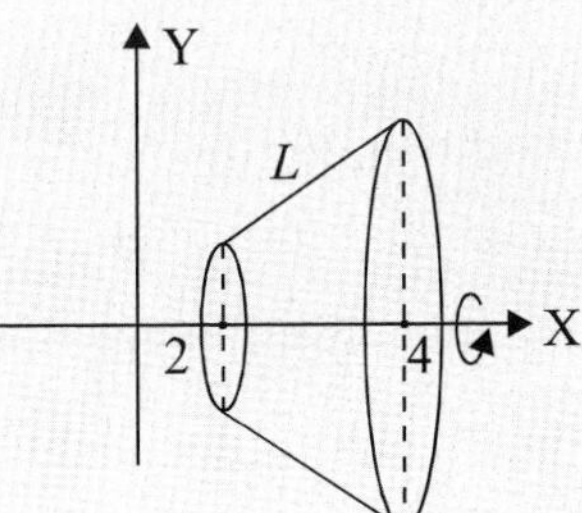

Equation of ab: Slope = $\tfrac{5}{2}$

L: $5x - 2y + k = 0$

(2, 3): $10 - 6 + k = 0 \Rightarrow k = -4$

$\therefore 5x - 2y - 4 = 0$

$\therefore \tfrac{(5x-4)}{2} = y$

$$V = \pi\int_2^4 y^2\,dx = \tfrac{\pi}{4}\int_2^4 (5x-4)^2\,dx = \tfrac{\pi}{4}\int_2^4 (25x^2 - 40x + 16)\,dx$$

$$= \tfrac{\pi}{4}[\tfrac{25x^3}{3} - 20x^2 + 16x]_2^4 = \tfrac{\pi}{4}\{(\tfrac{1600}{3} - 320 + 64) - (\tfrac{200}{3} - 80 + 32)\}$$

$$= 64\tfrac{2}{3}\pi$$

Example 14: Show by integration that the volume of a cone is given by $V = \frac{1}{3}\pi r^2 h$.

Trick: Rotate L about the X-axis.

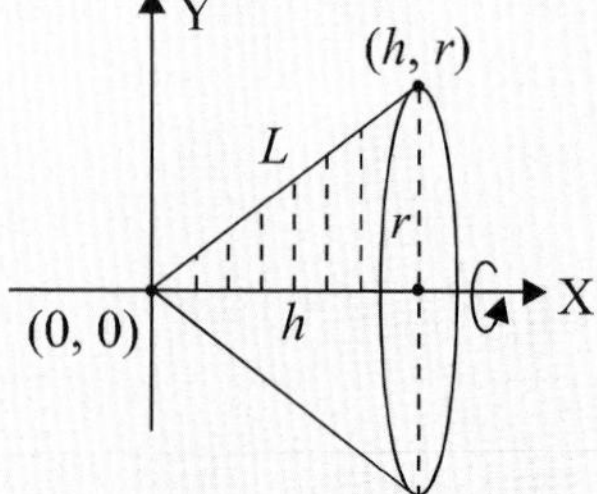

Equation of L:

Slope = $\frac{r}{h}$

L: $rx - hy = 0$

$\therefore y = \frac{r}{h}x$

$$V = \pi\int_0^h y^2 dx = \pi\int_0^h \frac{r^2}{h^2}x^2\, dx = \frac{\pi r^2}{h^2}\left[\frac{x^3}{3}\right]_0^h = \frac{\pi r^2}{h^2}\frac{h^3}{3}$$

$= \frac{1}{3}\pi r^2 h$

[C] **Rotating Circles**

Trick: Circles $\rightarrow$ Spheres

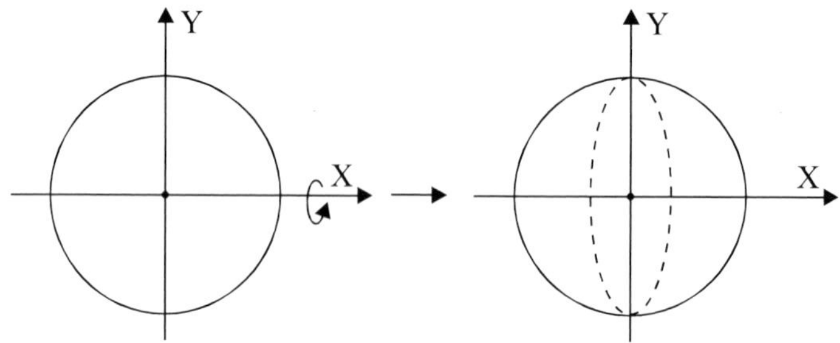

STEPS

1. Find the equation of the circle.
2. Find where it crosses the given axis to get limits.
3. Use $V = \pi\int_a^b y^2\, dx$ or $V = \pi\int_a^b x^2\, dy$.

Example 15: Find the volume obtained by rotating the circle $x^2 + y^2 = 25$ about the X-axis.

SOLUTION

$x^2 + y^2 = 25$

Crosses the X-axis at $x = \pm 5$

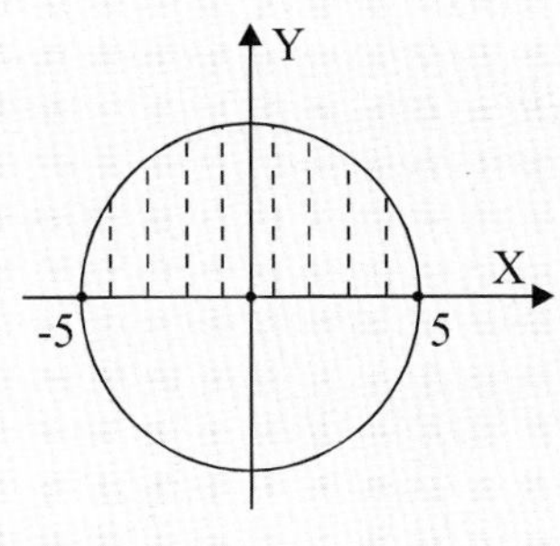

$$V = \pi\int_{-5}^{5} y^2\, dx = \pi\int_{-5}^{5} (25 - x^2)\, dx$$

$$= \pi\left[25x - \frac{x^3}{3}\right]_{-5}^{5}$$

$$= \pi\{(125 - \tfrac{125}{3}) - (-125 + \tfrac{125}{3})\} = \pi\{250 - \tfrac{250}{3}\} = \tfrac{500\pi}{3}$$

Example 16: Show by integration that the volume of a sphere is given by $V = \frac{4}{3}\pi r^3$

Trick: Rotate the circle $x^2 + y^2 = r^2$ about the X-axis.

SOLUTION

$x^2 + y^2 = r^2$

Crosses the X-axis at $x = \pm r$

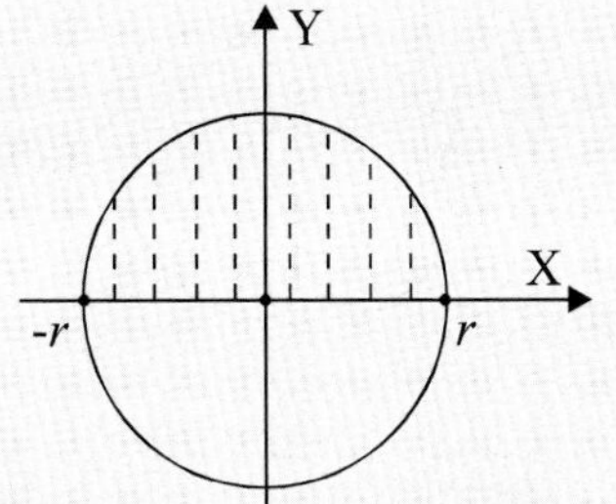

$$V = \pi\int_{-r}^{r} y^2\, dx = \pi\int_{-r}^{r} (r^2 - x^2)\, dx$$

$$= \pi\left[r^2 x - \frac{x^3}{3}\right]_{-r}^{r} = \pi\{(r^3 - \tfrac{r^3}{3}) - (-r^3 + \tfrac{r^3}{3})\} = \tfrac{4}{3}\pi r^3$$

Example 17: Find the volume of the section of the sphere.

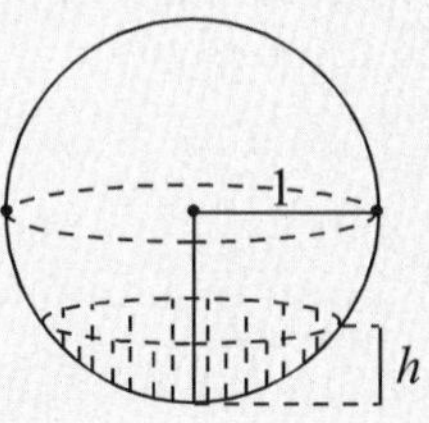

SOLUTION

Rotate the circle $x^2 + y^2 = 1$ from $y = -1$ to $y = -1 + h$.

$$V = \pi \int_{-1}^{-1+h} x^2 \, dy = \pi \int_{-1}^{-1+h} x^2 \, dy = \int_{-1}^{-1+h} (1 - y^2) \, dy$$

$$= \left[y - \frac{y^3}{3} \right]_{-1}^{h-1} = \left((h-1) - \frac{(h-1)^3}{3} \right) - \left(-1 + \frac{1}{3} \right)$$

$$= h - 1 - \frac{(h^3 - 3h^2 + 3h - 1)}{3} + \frac{2}{3}$$

$$= h - 1 - \tfrac{h^3}{3} + h^2 - h + \tfrac{1}{3} + \tfrac{2}{3} = h^2 (1 - \tfrac{h}{3})$$

[D] **Rotations involving 2 Curves**

STEPS

1. Find points of intersection.
2. Draw lines onto axis to get limits for each part of the volume.
3. Do 2 separate volume integrals for each curve.

1. **Line $\cap$ Circle**

Example 18: Find the volume obtained by rotating the area between the circle $x^2 + y^2 = 25$, the line $y = 2x$ and the X-axis in the first quadrant about the X-axis.

SOLUTION

$S \cap L: y = 2x$

$\Rightarrow x^2 + 4x^2 = 25 \Rightarrow 5x^2 = 25$

$\Rightarrow x^2 = 5 \Rightarrow x = \sqrt{5}$

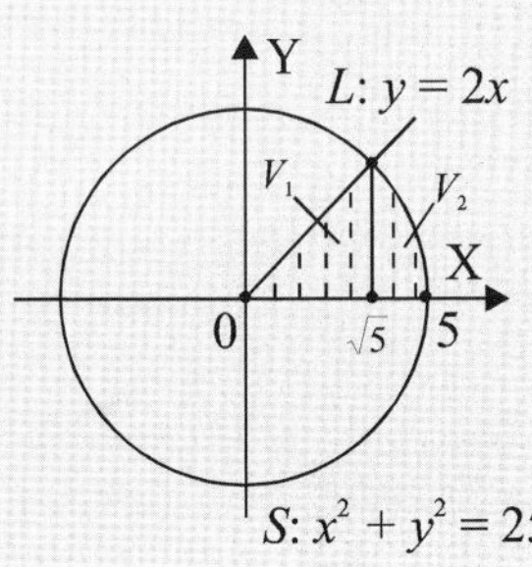

$$V = \pi \int_0^{\sqrt{5}} 4x^2\, dx + \pi \int_{\sqrt{5}}^{5} (25 - x^2)\, dx$$

$$= \frac{4\pi}{3}[x^3]_0^{\sqrt{5}} + \pi\left[25x - \frac{x^3}{3}\right]_{\sqrt{5}}^{5}$$

$$= \tfrac{20\pi}{3}\sqrt{5} + \pi\{(125 - \tfrac{125}{3}) - (25\sqrt{5} - \tfrac{5\sqrt{5}}{3})\}$$

$$= \tfrac{250\pi}{3} - \tfrac{50\sqrt{5}\pi}{3} = \tfrac{50\pi}{3}(5 - \sqrt{5})$$

2. **Circle $\cap$ Circle**

Example 19: The area enclosed by circles

S_1: $x^2 + y^2 = 1$

S_2: $(x-1)^2 + y^2 = 1$

is rotated about the X-axis. Find the volume obtained.

SOLUTION

$S_1 \cap S_2$

$\Rightarrow (x-1)^2 + 1 - x^2 = 1 \Rightarrow x^2 - 2x + 1 + 1 - x^2 = 1$

$\therefore x = \frac{1}{2}$

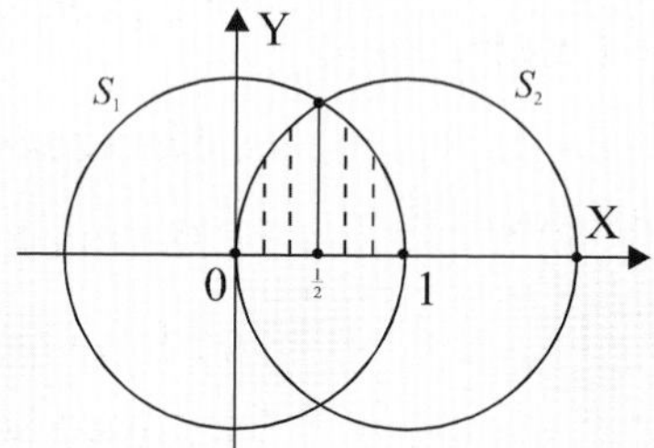

$$V = \pi \int_0^{\frac{1}{2}} \underset{S_2}{y^2}\, dx + \pi \int_{\frac{1}{2}}^1 \underset{S_1}{y^2}\, dx = \pi \int_0^{\frac{1}{2}} (2x - x^2)\, dx + \pi \int_{\frac{1}{2}}^1 (1 - x^2)\, dx$$

$$= \pi \left[x^2 - \frac{x^3}{3} \right]_0^{\frac{1}{2}} + \pi \left[x - \frac{x^3}{3} \right]_{\frac{1}{2}}^1 = \pi\{(\tfrac{1}{4} - \tfrac{1}{24})\} + \pi\{(\tfrac{2}{3}) - (\tfrac{1}{2} - \tfrac{1}{24})\}$$

$$= \pi\{\tfrac{2}{3} - \tfrac{1}{4}\} = \tfrac{5\pi}{12}$$

Exercise 8 (Answers: page **418**)

Volume

1. Find the volume obtained by rotating the following circles:

(a) $x^2 + y^2 = r^2$ about X-axis,

(b) $x^2 + y^2 = 4$ about X-axis,

(c) $x^2 + y^2 = 9$ about Y-axis,

(d) $y = \sqrt{25 - x^2}$ about X-axis,

(e) $(x-2)^2 + y^2 = 4$ about X-axis,

(f) $x^2 + (y-1)^2 = 9$ about Y-axis.

2. Find the volume obtained by rotating:
(a) the line $y = 3x$ between $x = 0$, $x = 1$ about X-axis,
(b) the line $x = 2y$ between $x = 0$, $x = 2$ about X-axis,
(c) the line $y = 2x$ between $y = 0$, $y = -1$ about Y-axis,
(d) the line $y = mx$ between $x = 0$, $x = 1$ about X-axis.

3. Find the equation of line L and the volume obtained by rotating it about the X-axis.

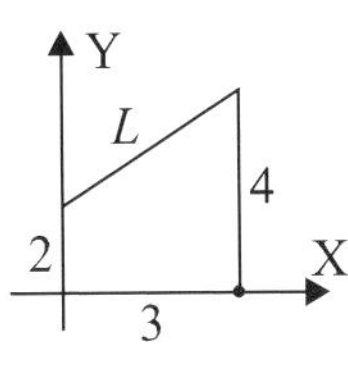

4. Find the volume obtained by rotating the circle $x^2 + y^2 = 16$ between $x = 2$, $x = 4$ about the X-axis.

5. Find the volume obtained by rotating the circle $x^2 + y^2 = 25$ between $y = 3$, $y = 5$ about the Y-axis.

6. The shaded area enclosed by the circles $S_1: x^2 + y^2 = 9$ and $S_2: (x-3)^2 + y^2 = 9$ in the first quadrant is rotated about the X-axis. Find the volume.

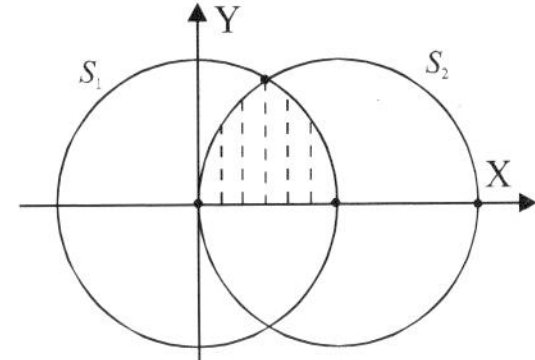

7. Find the volume obtained by rotating the shaded area enclosed by the line $L: 2x - y = 0$ and the circle $S: x^2 + y^2 = 25$ and the Y-axis about the Y-axis.

INTEGRATION REVISION QUESTIONS

These 3 part questions are similar to the questions on the LC paper. The answers to these questions and hints to help you solve them are available on our website:
www.studentxpress.ie

1. (a) Evaluate $\int_0^{\frac{\pi}{2}} \cos(\frac{1}{2}x + \frac{3}{4}\pi)\,dx$.

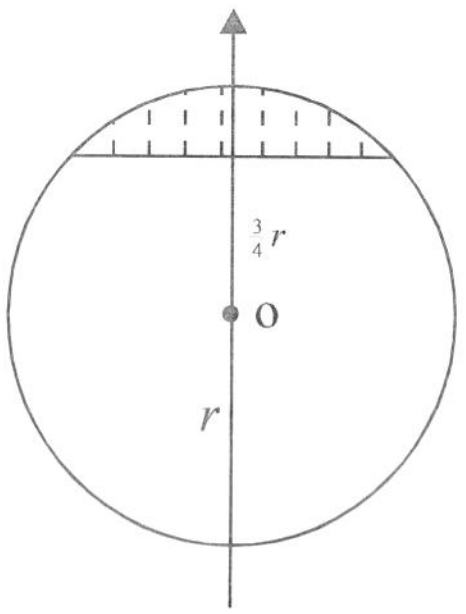

(b) Evaluate $\int_0^{\ln 2} \frac{e^x\,dx}{e^{2x}+1}$ by letting $u = e^x$.

(c) Find the volume of rotation of the circle $x^2 + y^2 = r^2$ from $\frac{3}{4}r$ to r about the Y-axis.

$\frac{3}{4}r$
o
r

2. (a) Evaluate $\int \frac{x^2 - 1}{x^3 - 3x + 1}\,dx$.

(b) The slope of the tangent to a curve which passes through (3, 0) is given by $\frac{dy}{dx} = x^2 - 4x + 3$. Find the equation of the curve and the area enclosed by the curve, the lines $x = 0$, $x = 3$ and the X-axis.

(c) Verify $(1, \sqrt{3})$ is common to the 2 circles $x^2 + y^2 = 4$ and $(x-2)^2 + y^2 = 4$. Find the volume generated by rotating the common area about the X-axis.

3. (a) Evaluate $\int_{\frac{\pi}{3}}^{\frac{\pi}{2}} \cos^2 x\,dx$.

(b) Find the volume obtained by rotating $y = x(3 - x)$ between $x = 1$ and $x = 5$ about the X-axis.

(c) Evaluate (i) $\int_0^{\ln 2} \frac{e^x(e^x-1)}{e^x+1}\,dx$, (ii) $\int_{-2}^{0} \frac{dx}{\sqrt{(5+x)(1-x)}}$.

4. (a) Evaluate (i) $\int_0^1 \frac{x}{x+1}\,dx$, (ii) $\int_1^2 \frac{x+1}{x}\,dx$.

(b) Evaluate (i) $\int \frac{x\,dx}{\sqrt{x-1}}$, (ii) $\int_0^1 \frac{\sqrt{x}\,dx}{e^{\sqrt{x}}x}$.

(c) The area between the curve $xy = 4$, the X-axis and the lines $x = 1$, $x = 2$ is the same as the area between the curve, the X-axis and the lines $x = t$, $x = 1$ where $0 < t < 1$. Find the value of t.

5. (a) Evaluate $\int_0^{\frac{\pi}{4}} \cos^2\theta\,d\theta - \int_0^{\frac{\pi}{4}} \sin^2\theta\,d\theta$.

(b) Evaluate (i) $\int_1^5 \frac{x\,dx}{x^4+10x^2+25}$, (ii) $\int_0^{\frac{\pi}{4}} e^{1+\ln(\cos x)}\,dx$.

(c) Evaluate $\int_0^{\frac{\pi}{3}} \frac{\sin^3 x\,dx}{1+\cos 2x}$.

6. (a) Evaluate $\int_1^2 \frac{x^4+2x^2+1}{x^2}\,dx$.

(b) (i) $\int_0^{\frac{\pi}{4}} \tan x\sec^2 x\,dx$, (ii) $\int_0^1 xe^{-x^2}\,dx$.

(c) Show by integration that the volume of a sphere of radius r is $\frac{4}{3}\pi r^3$.

7. (a) A tangent is drawn to the graph $y = f(x)$. The slope of this tangent is $6x^2 - 2x + 3$. If the graph contains the point (-1, -6), find $f(x)$.

(b) Evaluate (i) $\int_0^1 (1+x^2)^2 dx$, (ii) $\int_0^{\frac{\pi}{2}} \sin x(1+\cos^2 x)\, dx$.

(c) Evaluate $\int_1^4 \frac{dx}{(\sqrt{x}+4)\sqrt{x}}$.

8. (a) Evaluate $\int_1^2 (x+\frac{1}{x})^2 dx$.

(b) Evaluate (i) $\int_0^1 \frac{x^3+8}{x+2} dx$, (ii) $\int_0^{\frac{\pi}{6}} \sin 2x \sin 4x\, dx$.

(c) Show that the function $f(x) = x^3 - x^2 - x$ has a local max. at $(-\frac{1}{3}, \frac{5}{27})$ and a local min. at (1, -1). Show that the area enclosed by the curve, the X-axis and the line $x = 1$ is $\frac{7}{12}$.

9. (a) Evaluate $\int_0^{\frac{\pi}{6}} \cos x \cos 3x\, dx$.

(b) Show that for $x \in R$, $\frac{1}{(e^x+1)^2} = 1 - \frac{e^x}{e^x+1} - \frac{e^x}{(e^x+1)^2}$ and hence evaluate $\int \frac{dx}{(e^x+1)^2}$.

(c) If $I_n = \int_0^1 x^n \sqrt{1-x^2}\, dx$, evaluate I_0 and I_3.

10. (a) By factorising the numerator find $\int_1^2 \frac{x^3+x^2+x+1}{x^2+1}\,dx$.

(b) (i) Evaluate (i) $\int_0^{\frac{\pi}{2}} \cos x \cos 2x\,dx$, (ii) $\int_{-1}^{1} \frac{x}{x^2+1}\,dx$.

(c) Show that the area enclosed between the 2 curves is $\frac{2}{3}$.

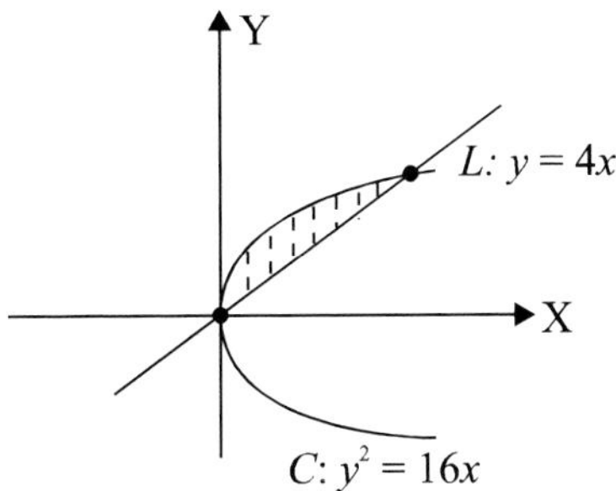

11. (a) Evaluate (i) $\int_1^2 \frac{1+x^2}{x^2}\,dx$, (ii) $\int_0^1 \frac{x^2}{1+x^2}\,dx$.

(b) Evaluate (i) $\int_{-2}^{0} (x+1)e^{x(x+2)}\,dx$, (ii) $\int_0^{\frac{\pi}{4}} (\tan x + \tan^3 x)\,dx$.

(c) The diagram shows a sketch of the function $f(x) = (3x-4)(3x+4)$. Find the co-ordinates of the point c such that Area of oab = Area of bcd.

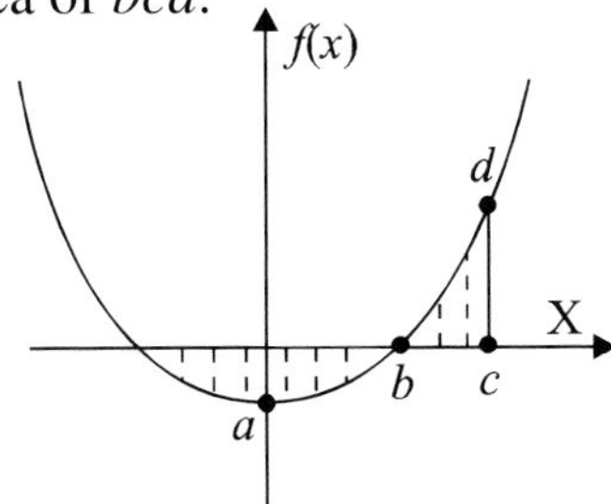

Answers and hints to Integration Revision Questions available on: **www.studentxpress.ie**

ANSWERS

Exercise 1 [*Algebraic Integration* (page **364**)]

I. 1. 30 2. 2 3. $\frac{8}{81}$

4. 16 5. $\frac{2}{21}p^{\frac{3}{2}}(7-3p^2)+c$ 6. $-2\theta-\frac{1}{\theta}-\frac{1}{2\theta^2}+c$

7. $\frac{62a}{5}+\frac{14b}{3}+2c$ 8. $\frac{ax^2}{2}+\frac{bx^3}{3}+\frac{cx^4}{4}+c$ 9. $\frac{\phi^3}{3}-\frac{4}{3}\phi^{\frac{3}{2}}-\ln\phi+c$

10. $\frac{2}{5}x^{\frac{5}{2}}+\frac{3}{2}x^2+\frac{4}{3}x^{\frac{3}{2}}+6x+c$ 11. $\frac{83}{3}$

12. $\frac{20}{3}$ 13. $\ln x-\frac{2}{x}-\frac{1}{2x^2}+c$ 14. $\frac{4}{3}x^3+\frac{9}{x}+c$

15. $-\frac{1}{6}$ 16. $\frac{17}{15}k$ 17. 2

18. 0 19. $\frac{x^2}{2}+\frac{5}{x}+c$ 20. $-\frac{1}{x}-\frac{1}{2x^2}-\ln x+c$

II. 1. $\frac{3}{4}$ 2. $\frac{61}{3}$ 3. 6

4. $\frac{7936}{5}$ 5. $\frac{13}{8}$ 6. $\frac{4}{9}(x+\frac{1}{x})^{\frac{9}{4}}+c$

7. $\frac{1}{9}(2x-5)^9+\frac{13}{16}(2x-5)^8+c$ 8. $\frac{1}{100}$

9. $\frac{9}{16}(2^{\frac{8}{3}}-1)$ 10. $\frac{85}{4}$ 11. $\frac{1}{2}\ln(\frac{12}{5})$

12. $\frac{1}{2}\ln 49$ 13. $\frac{4}{3}$ 14. $\frac{7}{2}+\ln 2$

15. 1 16. 2 17. $1-\ln(\frac{5}{4})$

18. $-\frac{1}{182}$ 19. $\frac{3}{2}-\ln 2$ 20. $\frac{1}{3}\ln(\frac{59}{3})$

Exercise 2 [*Exponential Integration* (page **370**)]

I. 1. $(1-\frac{1}{e})$ 2. $\frac{1}{3}(e^3-1)$ 3. $\frac{e}{4}(e^4-1)$

4. $\frac{e^3}{2}(e^2-1)$ 5. $e^3(e^2-1)$ 6. $\frac{e^4}{2}(e^2-1)$

7. $3(2^{\frac{1}{3}}-1)$ 8. $\frac{5(e^3-1)}{3e^6}$ 9. $\frac{e^2}{2}-\frac{1}{2e^2}+2$

10. $\frac{37}{12}-8\ln 2$ 11. $\frac{3}{4}(e-1)$ 12. $\frac{3}{5}e^6(e^5-1)+7$

II. 1. $\frac{1}{4}(e-1)$ 2. e^2-1 3. $2e(e^2-1)$

4. $\sqrt{e}(\sqrt{e}-1)$ 5. $\frac{3}{2}(e^4-1)$ 6. $2\sqrt{e}(\sqrt{e}-1)$

7. e^2-1 8. $e(e-1)$ 9. $4e^8(e-1)$

10. $e-1$

III. 1. $\frac{17}{81\times128}$ 2. $\ln(\frac{5}{4})$ 3. $\frac{2}{3}(\sqrt{19}-2)$

4. $\ln(\frac{5}{4})$ 5. $\frac{1}{12}$

Exercise 3 [*Log Integration* (page **373**)]

1. $\ln 2$ 2. $\frac{1}{3}\ln(\frac{13}{4})$ 3. $\ln 3$

4. $2\ln 3$ 5. $\frac{1}{2}\ln 3$ 6. $-2\ln 3$

7. 12 8. 3 9. $\frac{19}{3}$

10. $x\ln 7+\frac{x^p}{p+1}+c$ 11. $\frac{3}{2}$

12. $\frac{26}{3}$ 13. $\frac{14}{3}$ 14. $e^2\ln 4$

Exercise 4 [*Trigonometric Integration* (page **380**)]

1. (a) $\frac{1}{2}$ (b) 2 (c) $-\frac{1}{7}$

(d) $\frac{1}{2}(1-\cos 3)$ (e) $\frac{1}{5}\sin(5x-7)+c$ (f) $-2\left\{\cos\frac{11}{2}-\cos 5\right\}$

(g) $\frac{1}{3}\sin(3x-1)+c$ (h) $2\sin(\frac{x}{2}+5)+c$

2. (a) $\frac{14}{5}$ (b) $-\frac{1}{2}$

(c) $\frac{1}{2}\left\{\frac{\cos(m-n)x}{m-n}-\frac{\cos(m+n)x}{m+n}\right\}+c$

(d) $-\frac{2}{7}$ (e) $-\frac{5}{3}$ (f) $-\frac{\cos 2nx}{4n}+c$

3. (a) 1 (b) $\frac{4}{3}$ (c) $\ln(\frac{8}{7})$

(d) $\frac{1}{2}$ (e) -2

4. (a) $\frac{1}{3}$ (b) $\frac{1}{7}$ (c) $\frac{1}{3}$

(d) $\frac{2}{15}$ (e) $\frac{x}{16}$ (f) $\frac{1}{6}$

(g) $\frac{3\pi-2}{24}$

Exercise 5 [*Specials* (page **386**)]

1. (a) $\frac{\pi}{8}$ (b) $\frac{\pi}{16}$ (c) $\frac{\pi}{24}$

   (d) $\frac{\pi}{32}$ (e) $\frac{\pi\sqrt{2}}{8}$ (f) $\frac{\pi}{8}$

   (g) $\frac{\pi}{12}$ (h) $\frac{\pi}{8}$

2. (a) $\frac{\pi}{6}$ (b) $\frac{\pi}{6}$ (c) $\frac{\pi}{4}$

   (d) $\frac{\pi}{6}$ (e) $\frac{\pi}{3}$ (f) $\frac{\pi}{6}$

   (g) $\frac{\pi}{3}$

3. (a) $\frac{\pi}{4}$ (b) π (c) $\frac{9\pi}{8}$

   (d) $\frac{\pi}{3}$ (e) $\frac{9}{2}(\frac{\pi}{3}+\frac{\sqrt{3}}{4})$

Exercise 6 [*Mixture of Integrals* (page **388**)]

I. 1. $\frac{9}{25}(2^{\frac{5}{3}}-1)$ 2. $2-\sqrt{2}$ 3. $\frac{5}{2}(\sqrt{17}-\sqrt{2})$

4. $-\frac{1}{15}$ 5. $\frac{\pi}{2}$ 6. $-\frac{3}{16}$

7. $-\frac{3}{2}$ 8. $\frac{1}{6}$ 9. $\frac{1}{2}e(e^3-1)$

10. $\ln(\frac{13}{7})$ 11. $\frac{9}{4}$ 12. $\frac{\pi}{4}$

13. $\frac{\pi}{6}$ 14. $\frac{1}{3}(e^4-1)$ 15. $\frac{1}{3}$

16. $\frac{\pi}{12}$ 17. $\frac{1}{2}\sin^{-1}(\frac{4}{5})$ 18. $\frac{1}{2}\ln(\frac{3}{2})$

19. $\frac{1}{3}\ln 2$ 20. 2 21. $\frac{\pi}{4}$

22. $\ln 2$ 23. $\frac{3}{2}(5^{\frac{1}{3}})$ 24. $\frac{\pi}{4}$

25. $2\ln(\frac{3}{2})$ 26. $\frac{5}{6}$ 27. $\ln 4$

28. $\frac{3}{2}$ 29. $\ln 2$ 30. $\frac{1}{2}\ln(\frac{4}{3})$

31. $1 + \ln 2$

II. 1. -3, 2   2. 0, $\frac{15 \pm \sqrt{33}}{4}$ 3. 256

III. 1. (a) $s = t^3$ (b) $s = t^2 + t + 3$ (c) $s = ut + \frac{1}{2}at^2$

(d) $s = \frac{t^3}{3} + t^2 + t + 2$

2. (a) $y = 3x^3 - 2x^2 + 5x - 5$ (b) $y = x - \frac{1}{x} + 1$

(c) $y = \frac{x^2}{6}(3 - x)$ (d) $y = \frac{x}{12}(2x^2 - x^3 - 1)$

(e) $y = 3x^2 + 2x + 4$

3. (a) $y = x^2 - x + 1$ (b) $y = x - \frac{2x^2}{3} + 1$ (c) $t = 10$ s, $s = 500$ m

Exercise 7 [*Area* (page **399**)]

1. (a) 18   (b) $c^2 \ln(\frac{b}{a})$ (c) $\frac{63}{4}$

(d) $\frac{2}{3}$ (e) $\frac{22}{3}$

2. (a) $\frac{52}{3}$ (b) 8 ln 4   (c) $\frac{14}{3}$

(d) 4

3. $\frac{125}{6}$ 5. $\ln |a|$

7. $2y = 3x^2 - 10x + 9$, $\frac{27}{4}$ 8. π

9. (2, 4), (-2, 4), $\frac{64}{3}$ 11. $\frac{32}{3}$

12. $y = 9 + 6x - 3x^2$, 32

13. (-1, 0), (1, 0), (0, 1)   14. $\frac{4}{3}$ 15. π

16. $\frac{14}{3}$ 17. ln 2

18. $\frac{1}{2}$ 19. π 20. 25π

21. $\frac{64}{3}$ 22. 12 - ln 4

Exercise 8 [*Volumes* (page **409**)]

1. (a) $\frac{4}{3}\pi r^3$ (b) $\frac{32}{3}\pi$ (c) 36π

   (d) $\frac{500}{3}\pi$ (e) $\frac{32}{3}\pi$ (f) 36π

2. (a) 3π (b) $\frac{2}{3}\pi$ (c) $\frac{\pi}{12}$

   (d) $\frac{\pi m^2}{3}$

3. $2x - 3y + 6 = 0,\ 28\pi$

4. $\frac{40}{3}\pi$

5. $\frac{52}{3}\pi$

6. $\frac{10}{3}\pi$

7. $\frac{50\pi}{3}(5-2\sqrt{5})$

Proofs

1. FACTOR THEOREM

You can be asked to prove the **Factor Theorem** in Questions 2 and 3 (Algebra).

STATEMENT OF THE FACTOR THEOREM (FOR A CUBIC)
If $f(x) = ax^3 + bx^2 + cx + d$ and if $f(k) = 0$ then $(x - k)$ is a factor of $f(x)$ and vice versa.

PROOF

$f(x) = ax^3 + bx^2 + cx + d$

$f(k) = ak^3 + bk^2 + ck + d$

$\therefore f(x) - f(k) = a(x^3 - k^3) + b(x^2 - k^2) + c(x - k)$

$= (x - k)\{ax^2 + akx + ak^2 + bx + bk + c\}$

$= (x - k)\, g(x)$

$\therefore f(x) = f(k) + (x - k)g(x)$

(i) $f(k) = 0 \Rightarrow f(x) = (x - k)g(x)$

$\therefore x - k$ is a factor.

(ii) $x - k$ is a factor $\Rightarrow f(k) = 0$

Can you prove the Factor Theorem for a quadratic:
$f(x) = ax^2 + bx + c$?

2. DIFFERENTIATION RULES

You can be asked to prove certain **differentiation rules** in Questions 6 and 7 (Differentiation).

2.1 THE SUM RULE

STATEMENT OF THE SUM RULE

If $y = u + v$ then $\dfrac{dy}{dx} = \dfrac{du}{dx} + \dfrac{dv}{dx}$

PROOF

$y = u + v$

$$\begin{array}{lcl} y + \Delta y & = & (u + \Delta u) + (v + \Delta v) \\ y & = & u + v \\ \hline \Delta y & = & \Delta u + \Delta v \end{array}$$

$$\therefore \frac{\Delta y}{\Delta x} = \frac{\Delta u}{\Delta x} + \frac{\Delta v}{\Delta x}$$

$$\therefore \lim_{\Delta x \to 0} \frac{\Delta y}{\Delta x} = \frac{dy}{dx} = \frac{du}{dx} + \frac{dv}{dx}$$

2.2 THE PRODUCT RULE

STATEMENT OF THE PRODUCT RULE

If $y = u.v$ then $\frac{dy}{dx} = u\frac{dv}{dx} + v\frac{du}{dx}$

PROOF

$y = uv$

$$\begin{array}{ll} y + \Delta y & = (u + \Delta u)(v + \Delta v) = uv + u\Delta v + v\Delta u + \Delta u.\Delta v \\ y & = uv \\ \hline \Delta y & = u\Delta v + v\Delta u + \Delta u.\Delta v \end{array}$$

$$\therefore \frac{\Delta y}{\Delta x} = u\frac{\Delta v}{\Delta x} + v\frac{\Delta u}{\Delta x} + \frac{\Delta u}{\Delta x}\Delta v$$

$$\therefore \lim_{\Delta x \to 0} \frac{\Delta y}{\Delta x} = \frac{dy}{dx} = u\frac{dv}{dx} + v\frac{du}{dx}$$

2.3 THE QUOTIENT RULE

STATEMENT OF THE QUOTIENT RULE

If $y = \frac{u}{v}$ then $\dfrac{dy}{dx} = \dfrac{v\dfrac{du}{dx} - u\dfrac{dv}{dx}}{v^2}$

PROOF

$$y = \frac{u}{v}$$

$$y + \Delta y = \frac{u + \Delta u}{v + \Delta v}$$

$$y = \frac{u}{v}$$

$$\Delta y = \frac{u + \Delta u}{v + \Delta v} - \frac{u}{v} = \frac{uv + v\Delta u - uv - u\Delta v}{(v + \Delta v)v}$$

$$\therefore \Delta y = \frac{v\Delta u - u\Delta v}{(v + \Delta v)v}$$

$$\therefore \frac{\Delta y}{\Delta x} = \frac{v\dfrac{\Delta u}{\Delta x} - u\dfrac{\Delta v}{\Delta x}}{(v + \Delta v)v}$$

$$\therefore \lim_{\Delta x \to 0} \frac{\Delta y}{\Delta x} = \frac{dy}{dx} = \frac{v\dfrac{du}{dx} - u\dfrac{dv}{dx}}{v^2}$$

3. PROOF BY INDUCTION

This is a domino/chain reaction proof.

| | | | | | | | |

1 $\quad\quad\quad\quad$ k $\quad$ $k+1$

If you can show 2 things then the whole bunch will fall.
(i) The first one falls,

(ii) If the kth falls so does $(k+1)^{\text{st}}$.

Then 1 falls → 2 falls → 3 falls etc...

STEPS

1. Prove result is true for some starting value of $n \in N_0$.
2. Assuming result is true for $n = k$.
3. Prove result is true for $n = (k+1)$.

Induction can prove these types:

3.1 De Moivre's Theorem
3.2 Summations
3.3 Divisibilities
3.4 Inequalities
3.5 Differentiation

3.1 DE MOIVRE'S THEOREM

You can be asked to prove **De Moivre's Theorem** in Question 3 (Complex Numbers) or Questions 4 and 5 (Sequences and Series).

STATEMENT OF DE MOIVRE'S THEOREM

$(\cos A + i\sin A)^n = \cos nA + i\sin nA$ for all $n \in N_0$.

PROOF

STEP 1

For $n = 1$: Prove $(\cos A + i\sin A)^1 = \cos 1A + i\sin 1A$
i.e. $\cos A + i\sin A = \cos A + i\sin A$
This is obviously true.

STEP 2

For $n = k$: Assume $(\cos A + i\sin A)^k = \cos kA + i\sin kA$

STEP 3

For $n = k + 1$:
Prove $(\cos A + i\sin A)^{k+1} = \cos (k + 1)A + i\sin (k + 1)A$
Proof: $(\cos A + i\sin A)^{k+1} = (\cos A + i\sin A)^k(\cos A + i\sin A)$
$= (\cos kA + i\sin kA)(\cos A + i\sin A)$ using **STEP 2**
$= (\cos kA\cos A - \sin kA\sin A) + i(\sin kA\cos A + \cos kA\sin A)$
$= \cos (k + 1)A + i\sin (k + 1)A$
$\therefore$ true for $n = k \Rightarrow$ true for $n = k + 1$.
So true for $n = 1$ and true for $n = k \Rightarrow$ true for $n = k + 1 \Rightarrow$ true for all $n \in N_0$.

3.2 SUMMATIONS

You can be asked to prove **Summations** in Questions 4 and 5 (Sequences and Series).

Trick: Write out sums as follows:

1. $\displaystyle\sum_{r=1}^{k} f(r) = \{f(1) + f(2) + ... + f(k)\}$

2. $\sum_{r=1}^{k+1} f(r) = \{f(1)+f(2)+......+f(k)\}+f(k+1)$

Example 1: Prove $\sum_{r=1}^{n} r^2 = \frac{n}{6}(n+1)(2n+1)$ for all $n \in N_0$.

SOLUTION

STEP 1. For $n = 1$: Prove $\sum_{r=1}^{1} r^2 = \frac{1}{6}(1+1)(2+1)$

i.e $1^2 = \frac{1}{6}(2)(3) = 1$ (True)

STEP 2. For $n = k$: Assume $\sum_{r=1}^{k} r^2 = \frac{k}{6}(k+1)(2k+1)$

Trick: Assume $\{1^2+2^2+.....+k^2\} = \frac{k}{6}(k+1)(2k+1)$

STEP 3. For $n = k + 1$: Prove $\sum_{r=1}^{k+1} r^2 = \frac{(k+1)}{6}(k+2)(2k+3)$

PROOF: Trick $\sum_{r=1}^{k+1} r^2 = \{1^2+2^2+.....+k^2\}+(k+1)^2$

$= \frac{k}{6}(k+1)(2k+1)+(k+1)^2 = (k+1)\left[\frac{k(2k+1)}{6}+(k+1)\right]$

$= (k+1)\left[\frac{2k^2+k+6k+6}{6}\right] = (k+1)\frac{[2k^2+7k+6]}{6}$

$= \frac{(k+1)(k+2)(2k+3)}{6}$

$\therefore$ true for $n = k \Rightarrow$ true for $n = k + 1$

So true for $n = 1$ and true for $n = k \Rightarrow$ true for $n = k + 1 \Rightarrow$ true for all $n \in N_0$.

Example 2: Prove $\sum_{r=1}^{n} x^r = \frac{x(1-x^n)}{1-x}$ for all $n \in N_0$.

SOLUTION

STEP 1. For $n = 1$: Prove $\sum_{r=1}^{1} x^r = \frac{x(1-x^1)}{1-x}$, i.e. $x^1 = x$ (True)

STEP 2. For $n = k$: Assume $\sum_{r=1}^{k} x^r = \frac{x(1-x^k)}{1-x}$

Trick: $\{x^1 + x^2 + ... + x^k\} = \frac{x(1-x^k)}{1-x}$

STEP 3. For $n = k + 1$: Prove $\sum_{r=1}^{k+1} x^r = \frac{x(1-x^{k+1})}{1-x}$

PROOF: Trick $\sum_{r=1}^{k+1} x^r = \{x^1 + x^2 + ... + x^k\} + x^{k+1}$

$$= \frac{x(1-x^k)}{1-x} + x^{k+1} = \frac{x - x^{k+1} + x^{k+1} - x^{k+2}}{1-x}$$

$$= \frac{x(1-x^{k+1})}{1-x}$$

$\therefore$ true for $n = k \Rightarrow$ true for $n = k + 1$

So true for $n = 1$ and true for $n = k \Rightarrow$ true for $n = k + 1 \Rightarrow$ true for all $n \in N_0$.

3.3 DIVISIBILITIES

You can be asked to prove **Divisibilities** in Questions 4 and 5 (Sequences and Series).

TRICK

$7^n - 3^n$ divisible by 4 $\Rightarrow 7^n - 3^n$ = multiple of 4 = $4m$, $m \in N_0$.

Example 3: Show $7^{2n+1} + 1$ is divisible by 8 for all $n \in N_0$.

SOLUTION

STEP 1. For $n = 1$: Prove $7^{2+1} + 1$ is divisible by 8.
i.e. 344 is divisible by 8

$\frac{344}{8} = 43$ (True)

STEP 2. For $n = k$: Assume $7^{2k+1} + 1$ is divisible by 8.
Trick: $7^{2k+1} + 1 = 8m$

STEP 3. For $n = k + 1$: Prove $7^{2k+3} + 1$ is divisible by 8.

PROOF: $7^{2k+3} + 1 = 7^2.7^{2k+1} + 1 = 7^2(8m - 1) + 1$
$= 49(8m - 1) + 1 = 392m - 48 = 8(49m - 6) = 8a, a \in N_0$.
$\therefore$ true for $n = k \Rightarrow$ true for $n = k + 1$
So true for $n = 1$ and true for $n = k \Rightarrow$ true for $n = k + 1 \Rightarrow$ true for all $n \in N_0$.

Example 4: Show $x^n - y^n$ is divisible by $x - y$ for all $n \in N_0$, x, y whole numbers with $x > y$.

SOLUTION

STEP 1. For $n = 1$: Prove $x^1 - y^1$ is divisible by $x - y$

$$\frac{x-y}{x-y} = 1 \text{ (True)}$$

STEP 2. For $n = k$: Assume $x^k - y^k$ is divisible by $x - y$
Trick: $x^k - y^k = m(x - y)$

Cont...

STEP 3. For $n = k + 1$: Prove $x^{k+1} - y^{k+1}$ is divisible by $x - y$

PROOF: $x^{k+1} - y^{k+1} = x.x^k - y^{k+1}$
$= x\{y^k + m(x - y)\} - y^{k+1} = xy^k + xm(x - y) - y^{k+1}$
$= y^k(x - y) + xm(x - y) = (x - y)(y^k + xm) = a(x - y)$
$\therefore$ true for $n = k \Rightarrow$ true for $n = k + 1$
So true for $n = 1$ and true for $n = k \Rightarrow$ true for $n = k + 1 \Rightarrow$ true for all $n \in N_0$.

Example 5: Prove $n^3 + 6n^2 + 8n$ is divisible by 3 for all $n \in N_0$.

SOLUTION

STEP 1. For $n = 1$: Prove $1^3 + 6.1^2 + 8.1$ is divisible by 3
i.e. 15 is divisible by 3
$\frac{15}{3} = 5$ (True)

STEP 2. For $n = k$: Assume $k^3 + 6k^2 + 8k$ is divisible by 3
Trick: $k^3 + 6k^2 + 8k = 3m$

STEP 3. For $n = k + 1$: Prove $(k + 1)^3 + 6(k + 1)^2 + 8(k + 1)$ is divisible by 3.

PROOF: $(k + 1)^3 + 6(k + 1)^2 + 8(k + 1)$
$= k^3 + 3k^2 + 3k + 1 + 6k^2 + 12k + 6 + 8k + 8$
$= k^3 + 9k^2 + 23k + 15$
$= 3m - 6k^2 - 8k + 9k^2 + 23k + 15$ (Trick)
$= 3m + 3k^2 + 15k + 15 = 3(m + k^2 + 5k + 5)$
$= 3a$
$\therefore$ true for $n = k \Rightarrow$ true for $n = k + 1$
So true for $n = 1$ and true for $n = k \Rightarrow$ true for $n = k + 1 \Rightarrow$ true for all $n \in N_0$.

3.4 INEQUALITIES

You can be asked to prove **Inequalities** in Questions 4 and 5 (Sequences and Series).

Example 6: Prove $7! > 3^7$ for all $n \geq 7, n \in N_0$.

SOLUTION

TRICK

Factorials Trick
Break up:
$(k+1)! = (k+1)k!$

STEP 1. $n = 7$: Prove $7! > 3^7$
i.e. $5040 > 2187$ (True)

STEP 2. $n = k$: Assume $k! > 3^k$

STEP 3. $n = k + 1$: Prove $(k+1)! > 3^{k+1}$

PROOF: $(k+1)! = (k+1)k!$

$\Rightarrow (k+1)! > 3.3^k$ because $k+1 \geq 8 > 3$
$\Rightarrow (k+1)! > 3^{k+1}$
$\therefore$ true for $n = k \Rightarrow$ true for $n = k + 1$
So true for $n = 7$ and true for $n = k \Rightarrow$ true for $n = k + 1 \Rightarrow$ true for all $n \geq 7, n \in N_0$.

Example 7: Prove $n^2 < 2^n$ for all $n \geq 5, n \in N_0$.

SOLUTION

TRICK

Break up by taking out a suitable factor:
$(k+1)^2 = k^2(1+\frac{1}{k})^2$

STEP 1. For $n = 5$: Prove $5^2 < 2^5$
i.e. $25 < 32$ (True)

STEP 2. For $n = k$: assume $k^2 < 2^k$

STEP 3. For $n = k + 1$: Prove $(k+1)^2 < 2k + 1$

PROOF: $(k+1)^2 = k^2(1+\frac{1}{k})^2$

$\Rightarrow (k+1)^2 < 2^k(1+\frac{1}{k^2})$

$k \geq 5 \Rightarrow k^2 \geq 25$
$\Rightarrow \frac{1}{k^2} \leq \frac{1}{25}$
$\Rightarrow 1+\frac{1}{k^2} \leq \frac{26}{25} < 2$

$(k+1)^2 < 2^k.2$
$\Rightarrow (k+1)^2 < 2^{k+1}$
$\therefore$ true for $n = k \Rightarrow$ true for $n = k + 1$
So true for $n = 5$ and true for $n = k \Rightarrow$ true for $n = k + 1 \Rightarrow$ true for all $n \geq 5, n \in N_0$.

3.5 DIFFERENTIATION

You can be asked to prove certain **differentiation rules** in Questions 6 and 7 (Differentiation).Other proofs are given in the Differentiation section.

Example 8: If $y = x^n$ prove $\frac{dy}{dx} = nx^{n-1}$ for all $n \in N_0$.

SOLUTION

STEP 1. For $n = 1$: Prove $y = x^1 \Rightarrow \frac{dy}{dx} = 1$

$y = x$
$y + \Delta y = x + \Delta x$

$\Delta y = \Delta x$

Trick: This requires a first principles proof.

$\therefore \frac{\Delta y}{\Delta x} = 1$

$\therefore \lim_{\Delta x \to 0} \frac{\Delta y}{\Delta x} = \frac{dy}{dx} = 1$

STEP 2. $n = k$: Assume $y = x^k \Rightarrow \frac{dy}{dx} = kx^{k-1}$

STEP 3. $n = k + 1$: Prove $y = x^{k+1} \Rightarrow \frac{dy}{dx} = (k+1)x^k$

PROOF: $y = x^{k+1} = x^k.x \Rightarrow \frac{dy}{dx} = x^k.1 + x.kx^{k-1}$ (Product Rule)

$= x^k + kx^k = x^k(k+1)$

$\therefore$ true for $n = k \Rightarrow$ true for $n = k + 1$

So true for $n = 1$and true for $n = k \Rightarrow$ true for $n = k + 1 \Rightarrow$ true for all $n \in N_0$.

Exercise 1

$N_0 = \{1, 2, 3, 4, ...\}$

1. Prove by induction

(a) $\sum_{r=1}^{n} r = \frac{n}{2}(n+1)$ for all $n \in N_0$.

(b) $\sum_{r=1}^{n} r^3 = [\frac{n}{2}(n+1)]^2$ for all $n \in N_0$.

(c) $\sum_{r=1}^{n} \frac{1}{r(r+1)} = \frac{n}{n+1}$ for all $n \in N_0$.

(d) $\sum_{r=1}^{n} ax^{r-1} = \frac{a(1-x^n)}{1-x}$ for all $n \in N_0$.

2. **Divisibilities**

Prove by Induction

(a) $n^2 + n$ is divisible by 2 for all for all $n \in N_0$.

(b) $11^{n+2} + 12^{2n+1}$ is divisible by 133 for all for all $n \in N_0$.

(c) $10^{n+1} + 3.10^n + 5$ is divisible by 9 for all for all $n \in N_0$.

(d) $7^n - 4^n$ is divisible by 3 for all for all $n \in N_0$.

3. **Inequalities**

Prove by induction

(a) $n^3 < 3^n$ for all $n \geq 4$, $n \in N_0$.

(b) $n < 2^n$ for all $n \geq 4$, $n \in N_0$.

(c) $\frac{1}{n!} < \frac{1}{2^n}$ for all $n \geq 4$, $n \in N_0$.

(d) $(1 + a)^n > 1 + na$ for all $n \geq 2$, $n \in N_0$, $a > 0$.